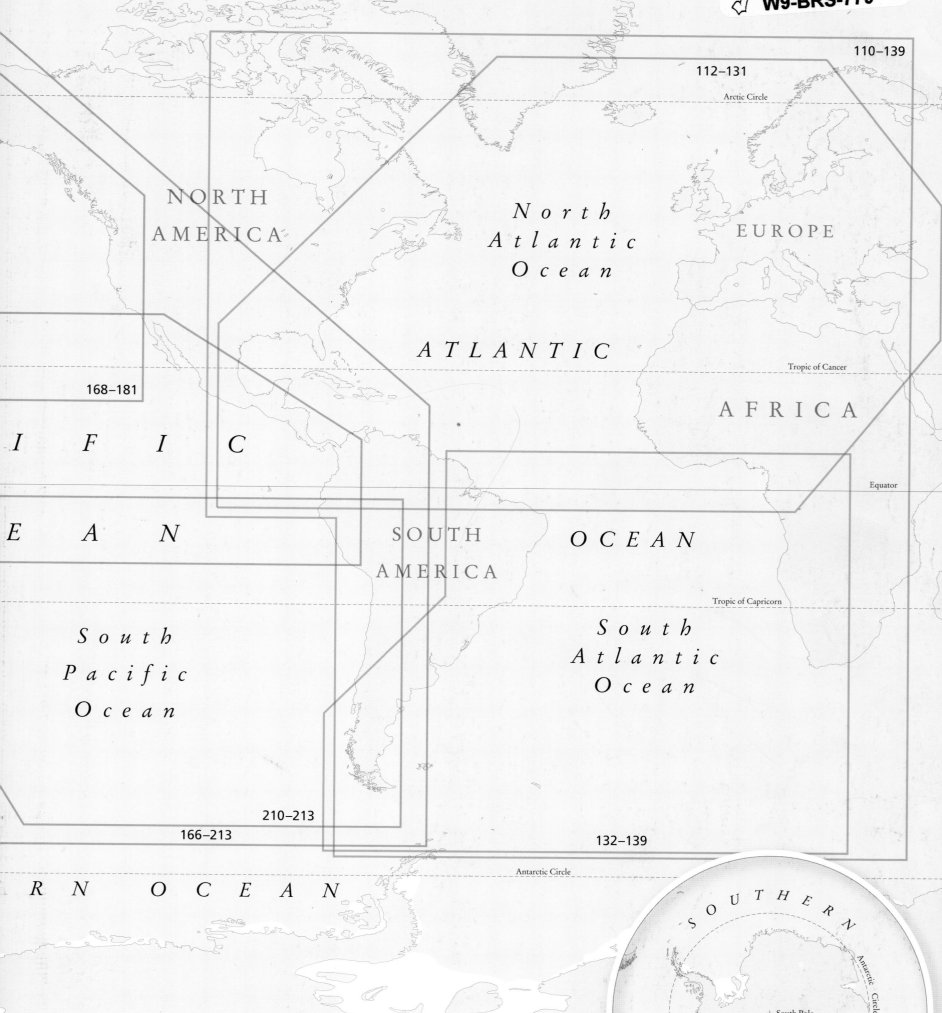

110–139

112–131

Arctic Circle

NORTH
AMERICA

*North
Atlantic
Ocean*

EUROPE

ATLANTIC

Tropic of Cancer

168–181

AFRICA

I F I C

Equator

E A N

SOUTH
AMERICA

OCEAN

*South
Pacific
Ocean*

Tropic of Capricorn

*South
Atlantic
Ocean*

210–213

166–213

132–139

Antarctic Circle

RN OCEAN

SOUTHERN

Antarctic Circle

+ South Pole

ANTARCTICA

102–107

OCEAN

the **illustrated**
ATLAS OF THE SEA

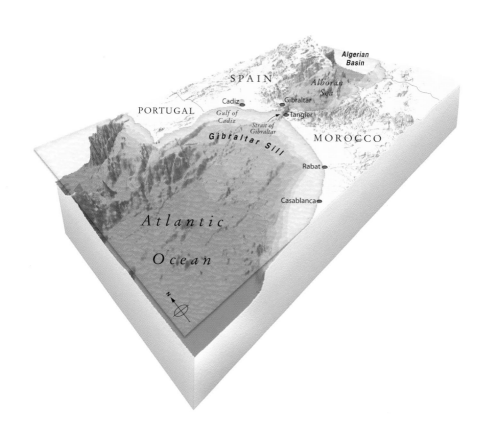

the **illustrated**
ATLAS OF THE SEA

WELDON OWEN

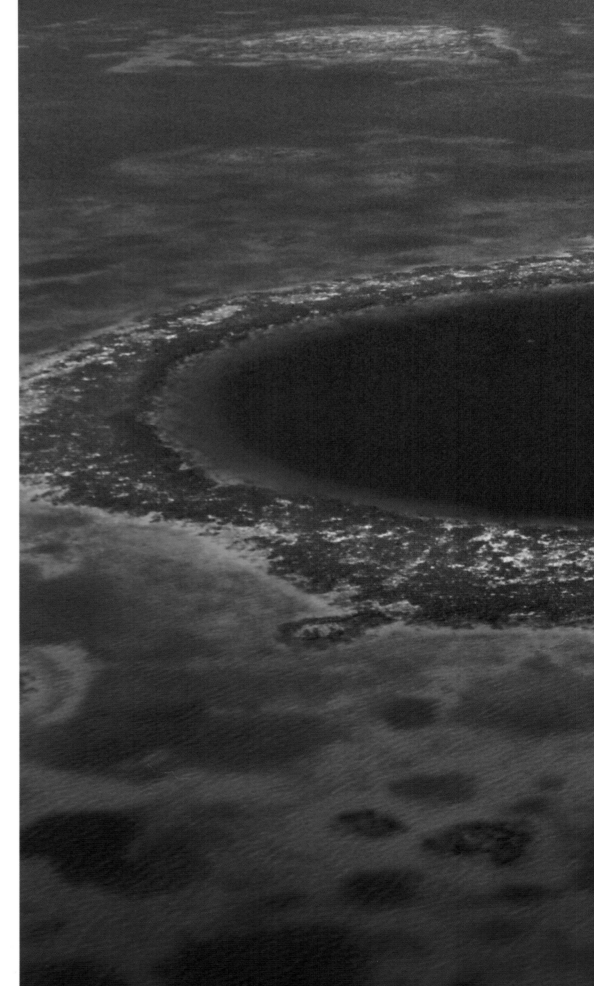

Conceived and produced by Weldon Owen Pty Ltd
59–61 Victoria Street, McMahons Point
Sydney NSW 2060 Australia
www.weldonowen.com

WELDON OWEN PTY LTD
Chief Executive Officer Sheena Coupe
Creative Director Sue Burk
Publisher Corinne Roberts
Art Manager Trucie Henderson
Senior Vice President, International Sales Stuart Laurence
Sales Manager, North America Ellen Towell
Vice President Sales: Asia and Latin America Dawn L. Owen
Administration Manager, International Sales Kristine Ravn
Production Director Todd Rechner
Production Controller Lisa Conway
Production Coordinator Mike Crowton
Production Assistant Nathan Grice

Managing Editor Jennifer Taylor
Project Editors Averil Moffat, Jasmine Parker
Editorial Assistant Natalie Ryan
Picture Researcher Jo Collard
Series Designer John Bull, The Book Design Company
Designers John Bull, The Book Design Company, Gabrielle Green
Cartographers Will Pringle/mapgraphx, Laurie Whiddon/Map
Illustrations
Information Graphics Andrew Davies/Creative Communication
Index Jo Rudd

ISBN: 978-1-921530-86-9

10 9 8 7 6 5 4 3 2 1

Color reproduction by Chroma Graphics (Overseas) Pte Ltd
Printed by Tien Wah Press
Manufactured in Singapore

A WELDON OWEN PRODUCTION

Tiger sharks (previous page)
In temperate and tropical seas tiger sharks
(Galeocerdo cuvier) range over the continental
shelf and around islands. These active hunters
feed on a variety of other fishes as well as sea
turtles and trash from vessels. They can grow
to about 16 feet (5 m), although such large
specimens are increasingly rare.

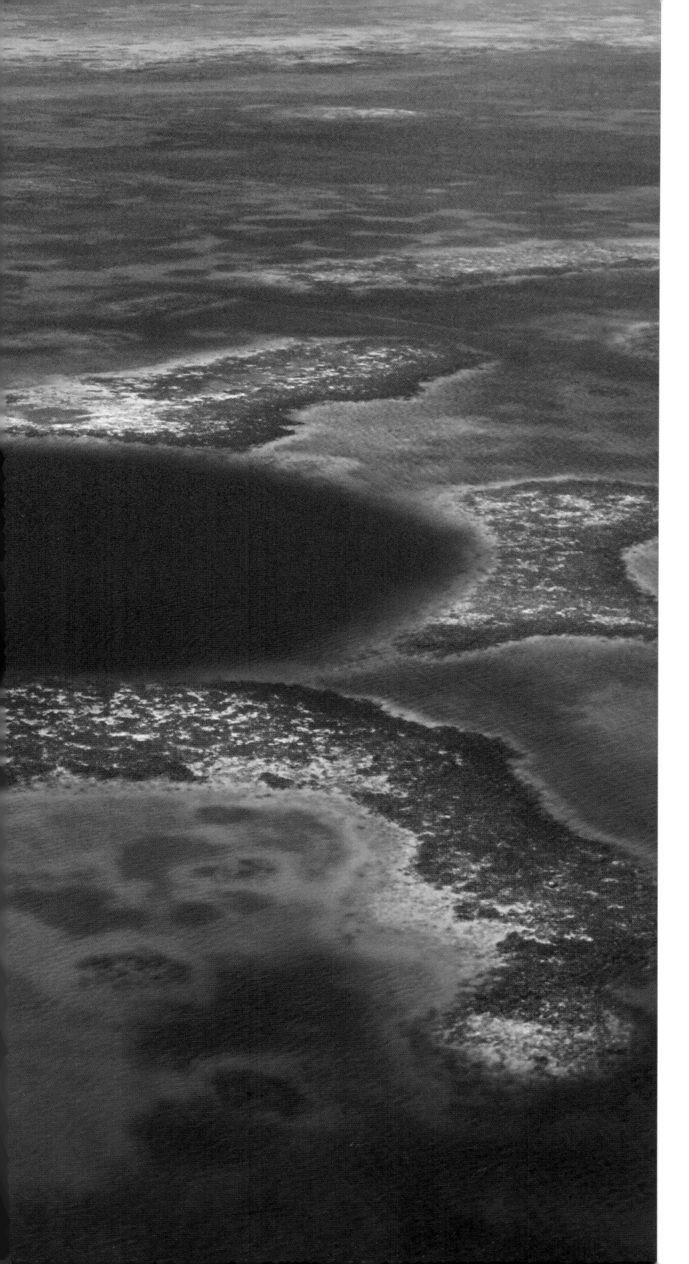

Authors and Consultants

Dr Stephen Hutchinson
Senior Research Fellow
National Oceanography Centre
Southampton, UK

Professor Johann R. E. Lutjeharms
Department of Oceanography
University of Cape Town, South Africa

Beverly McMillan
Science writer and author
Virginia, USA

Dr John Musick
Marshall Acuff Professor Emeritus in Marine Science
Virginia Institute of Marine Science
College of William and Mary
Virginia, USA

Dr Bernard Stonehouse
Emeritus Associate
Scott Polar Research Institute
University of Cambridge, UK
Honorary Research Fellow
Maritime Historical Studies Centre
University of Hull, UK

Dr Matthias Tomczak
Emeritus Professor of Oceanography
Flinders University
South Australia

Blue hole
Forming an almost perfect circle a quarter-mile
(0.4 km) in diameter, the Great Blue Hole of
Lighthouse Reef in Belize is one of the most
dramatic diving destinations in the world.
Several such sinkholes exist, all in coastal areas
where rising seas flooded a limestone cave
system and caused the roof to collapse.

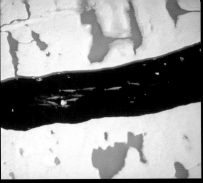

 **Hawaiian monk seal (below left)**
The shy, critically endangered Hawaiian monk seal
(*Monachus schauinslandi*) is native to the tropical
waters of the northwestern Hawaiian islands. Its
numbers have declined dramatically due to several
factors including coastal development encroaching
on its habitat.

Great Barrier Reef (below)
This is the world's largest coral reef system and
possibly the largest single structure made by living
organisms. It is made up of some 3,000 individual
reefs and 900 tropical islands. It lies off northeast
Australia and supports a great diversity of flora
and fauna.

Day octopus (above)
The day octopus (*Octopus cyanea*),
so-called because it hunts during
daylight hours, uses its blue-tinged
legs to dig holes in the sandy Indo-
Pacific reef habitats where its feeds
on small fish, crabs, and other prey.

White-maned anemonefish (left)
The white-maned anemonefish
(*Amphiprion perideraion*) spends
much of its life amid the protective
tentacles of an equally colorful sea
anemone in the tropical waters off
Palau in Micronesia. Its food
includes algae and plankton.

FOREWORD

Producing an atlas is a daunting undertaking that requires an incredible breadth of knowledge, great attention to detail, creative skill in illustrative design and, of course, an ability to convey essential information with a well-written narrative. Indeed, producing an atlas of the oceans creates additional challenges in that the topography of the seafloor and of the ocean surface must be sensed remotely, and the marine life that inhabits the waters can be understood only from painstaking scientific research, much of which may not be widely available to the general public. Not only are the waters, the ocean floor, and the marine life complex and varied, but together they represent a coupled system with threads of connections that run throughout both time and space.

The *Illustrated Atlas of the Sea* is an amazing publication. It is more than an atlas in a traditional sense; it has nuggets of recent scientific research, ranging in scale from global to molecular that are embedded within the chapters. It contains stunning photographs to illustrate the diversity of marine environments and marine life and it offers much that is relevant in our lives through the inclusion of forays into climate change, pollution, natural resources, hurricanes, tsunamis, threatened sea life, and conservation. It is also more than a standard atlas in that it is comprehensive, easy-to-read, and offers an introduction to the casual scientist—yet contains much of interest to the more sophisticated scientific adventurer.

The *Illustrated Atlas of the Sea* is divided into nine chapters, the first four of which provide an overview of the water, its composition, circulation, and never-ending motion from waves and tides; its physical environments extending from the dynamic coastlines to the frigid dark plains of the deep sea; and its marine habitats, forms of life, and rich natural resources. The next four chapters, written by experts in their respective fields, are structured around the four ocean regions: Polar, Atlantic, Indian, and Pacific. It is here that the maps of the oceans can be found with color-coded bathymetric depths that are superimposed with hundreds of geographic names to depict the shoals, plateaus, ridges, basins, trenches, and other features that together make up 70 percent of Earth's surface. Each of these chapters is presented in a similar format that also includes, interspersed throughout the pages, dozens of helpful insets to convey ocean basin statistics, patterns of ocean currents, and the distribution of natural resources within the basins. A final reference chapter provides an encyclopedic fact file, glossary, and gazetteer. The large-format layout allows an ideal balance between maps, photographs, illustrations, and text.

Humans have always had a fascination for the oceans, and you will surely enjoy reading about them in this compelling reference atlas. It brings together in one volume all of the attributes that provide this fascination, ranging from the intensity of the ocean's physical processes, to the incredible diversity of marine life that lives in the waters, to the shape and structure of the basins that hold both the waters and the life. The *Illustrated Atlas of the Sea* will surely be a lasting contribution.

Dr John T. Wells
Dean and Director, Virginia Institute of Marine Science.

How to Use this Atlas

This atlas is arranged in two main sections. The first section provides a historical and physical overview of the global sea. Photographs, diagrams, and mapping illustrate information about different marine environments and species. The second section is a chapter-by-chapter cartographic survey of the world's major oceans and the sea divisions they encompass.

It includes details of seafloor topography, maps that show the key currents, and photographs and information about animal life and human activity in the region. A reference section completes the book and consists of a detailed fact file on the oceans and their subdivisions, a glossary, a gazetteer, and an index.

Thematic pages
The thematic pages include detailed world maps accompanied by illustrations, diagrams, charts, graphs, and photographs. They cover topics as diverse as the origins of water on Earth, exploration of the seas, ocean ecosystems, and conservation.

Thematic map key

Informative photography
Current photographs about the sea, marine life, and resources are included with captions.

Thematic maps
Thematic maps show a range of data from wildlife distribution, physical features, and sea depth.

Scale
The scale of the main map, plus a scale bar and projection information are included here.

Introduction
This text gives a clear, concise overview of the most salient facts about the featured topic or sea.

Pie charts, tables, and graphs
Additional details about regions, or the animal life found there, is provided in the form of tables, charts, or graphs. This at-a-glance information adds to captions and photographs.

Diagrams and illustrations
These highlight relevant topics such as geological processes, ecosystems, wildlife, and oceanographic research equipment.

THEMATIC MAPPING

Marine life maps
Maps display marine life topics such as wildlife species range, migratory paths, and coral distribution.

Physical geography maps
Geographical features such as hot spots, ice extent, and continental margins are shown on thematic maps.

NASA and NOAA maps
Maps display data and information gathered using the latest satellite and sonar technology.

Feature box
Special-interest subjects are shown in a feature box, with their own introduction and selected photographs or illustrations.

Locator map
This map indicates the location of the sea within its ocean.

The Facts
Charts detail the dimensions of the seas and oceans.

NASA imagery
Satellite photography provides up-to-date visual information.

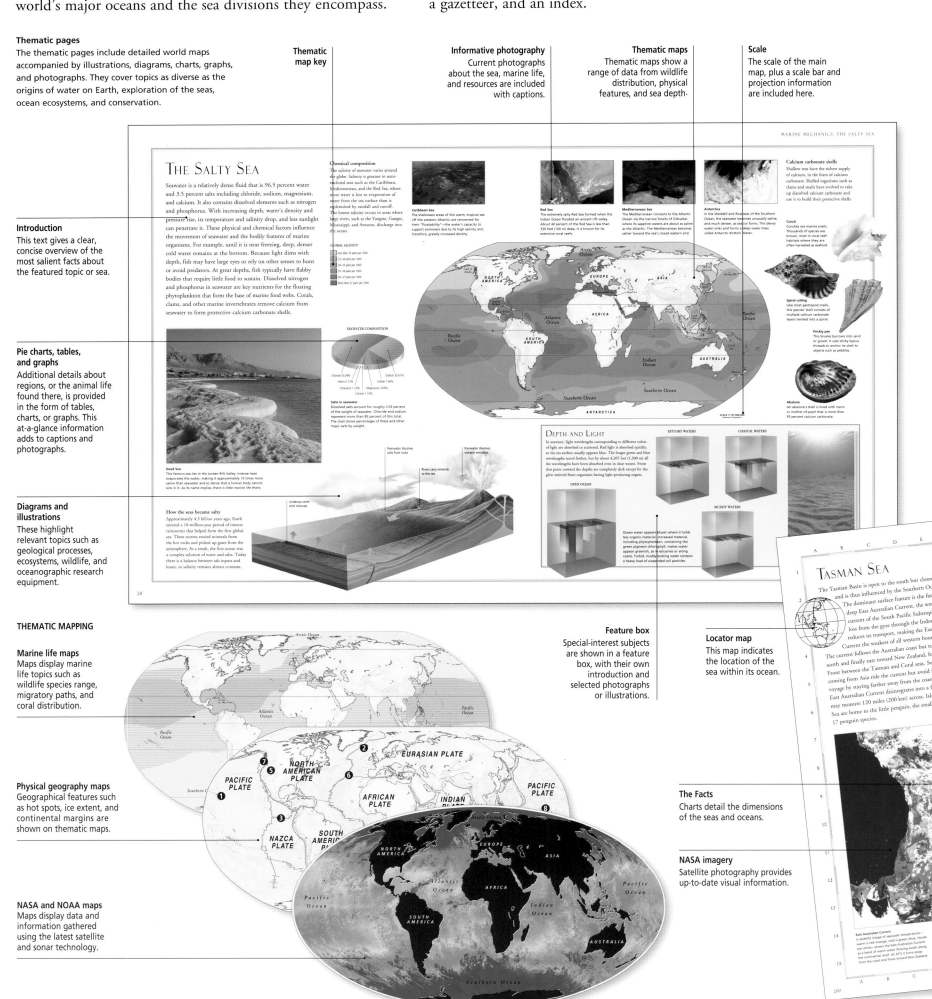

Cartographic pages
These pages show detailed maps of the world's oceans and seas, accompanied by illustrations, diagrams, charts, graphs, and photographs. The text describes the nature of each sea and its major currents and climatic influences.

Oceans
The introduction page for each chapter displays a large map of the entire ocean and provides an overview of natural resources, statistical information, and typical ecosystems.

Locator map
This map indicates the location of the ocean.

Pie chart
Facts about each ocean are presented in a pie-chart.

Cartographic map
Each map shows details of the seafloor including variations in depth, topography, and named features.

Natural resources
A small map carries icons to denote the natural resources to be found in each ocean area.

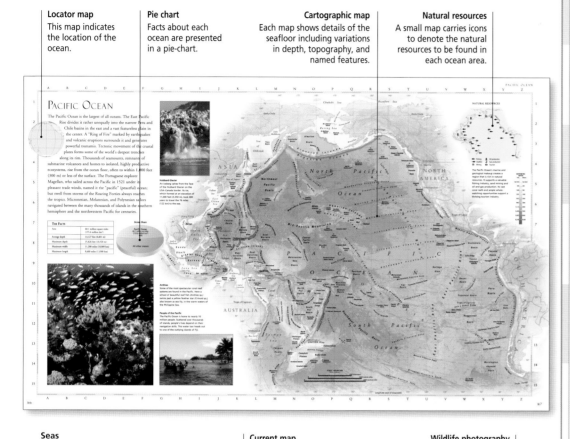

Seas
These pages take a close-focus look at a particular sea; a large-scale map shows the seafloor features in detail. Smaller supporting maps and images show key currents, natural resources, wildlife, and human activity.

Current map
A diagrammatic map shows the prevailing surface currents in the area.

Wildlife photography
Photographs from wildlife and undersea specialists show the animal life in the region.

Three-dimensional view of seafloor
A computer-generated map reveals details of ridges, canyons, and other seafloor features.

Bathymetric depth scale

VISUAL KEYS

Conservation icons
The conservation status of endangered and critically endangered animals, as determined by the IUCN Red List of Threatened Species, is indicated by a red or yellow icon.

- 🔴 Critically endangered
- 🟡 Endangered

CARTOGRAPHIC MAPS

Map legend
The maps in this atlas contain a variety of labels, symbols, and other graphic devices to provide detailed information such as ocean floor depth and topography, and the location of undersea mountains, trenches, and volcanoes, rivers, cities, and country borders.

BATHYMETRIC DEPTHS

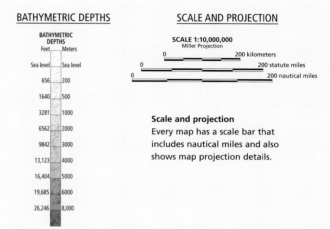

Feet	Meters
Sea level	Sea level
656	200
1640	500
3281	1000
6562	2000
9842	3000
13,123	4000
16,404	5000
19,685	6000
26,246	8,000

SCALE AND PROJECTION

SCALE 1:10,000,000
Miller Projection

0 — 200 kilometers
0 — 200 statute miles
0 — 200 nautical miles

Scale and projection
Every map has a scale bar that includes nautical miles and also shows map projection details.

WATER FEATURES

Ocean	*PACIFIC OCEAN*
Sea	*Bering Sea*
Bay/gulf	*Gulf of Alaska*
Channel/strait	*Bering Strait*
Lakes	*Lake Nasser*
Rivers	*Nile*
Canal	*Suez Canal*
Seamount	▲ *Zheng He Seamount* 6,263ft (1,909m)
Bathymetric feature	*Madagascar Basin*

PHYSICAL FEATURES

Geographic feature	*Baja California*
Peninsula	*Cape York Peninsula*
Cape/point	*Beachy Head*
Island group	*Solomon Islands*
Island	*Isla Santa Maria*
Pole	North Pole

PLACE NAMES

Country names	F R A N C E

City symbols

■ **Los Angeles**	Over 5 million	◼ **Bangkok**	National Capital
● **Houston**	1 million to 5 million	◆ **Hanoi**	National Capital
○ Miami	100,000 to 1 million	✳ Riga	National Capital

A sculpted and eroding rocky shore hints at the changeable physical features of the undersea world beyond. Like ecosystems on land, the marine environment is dynamic and varied. It encompasses an array of geological forms as well as changing physical and chemical conditions that establish the wide array of habitats where communities of marine life may survive.

WATER ON EARTH

THE GLOBAL SEA

Liquid water covers more than 70 percent of the world's surface and is the defining feature of planet Earth. Salt water makes up 97 percent of this watery domain, forming a global sea that is subdivided into five named oceans. These interconnected marine regions are the vast Atlantic and Pacific oceans; the Indian Ocean, which stretches between eastern Africa and Australia; the Southern Ocean that encircles Antarctica; and the small, polar Arctic Ocean ringed by the northern fringes of North America and Eurasia. For much of recorded history this global sea has been a fascinating enigma. Its currents and weather patterns have challenged seafarers for centuries, while its undersea landscape and abundant marine life have largely been hidden beneath the waves. Only within the last two centuries have mariners and scientists begun to uncover the mysteries of Earth's oceans, providing an ever-deeper understanding of the global sea and the forces that have shaped it—and continue to do so today.

The marine map

A map of the global sea recognizes the five oceans and a wide array of subdivisions. Although the boundaries between these features may be rather arbitrary, geography and size are key factors in defining them. To geographers a "sea" is a large area of ocean that is partly enclosed by land. It may include a smaller arm called a gulf. Bays are smaller still.

Salty and fresh water
Seawater makes up about 97 percent of Earth's water. The remainder is fresh water in lakes, rivers, groundwater, land ice, and water vapor.

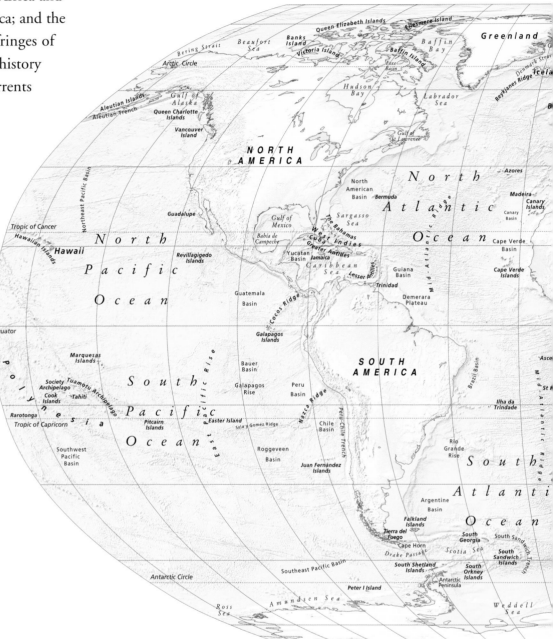

Earth from space
Orbiting astronauts called Earth "the big blue marble," noting the sapphire color of the global sea. Continents appear as patches of green and tan. Wisps of white are clouds formed when seawater evaporates.

GLOBAL SEA FACTS

Total area	139 million square miles (361 million km²)
Total volume	310,000,000 cubic miles (1,347,000,000 km³)
Average depth	12,230 feet (3,730 m)
Greatest depth	35,840 feet (10,900 m)
Mean ocean crust thickness	4.04 miles (6.5 km)
Longest mountain range	10,000 miles (16,000 km)

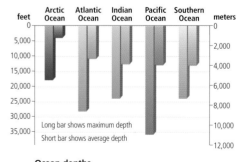

OCEAN DEPTHS

Ocean depths
For each ocean basin, the long colored bar shows maximum depth. The shorter bar indicates the basin's average depth.

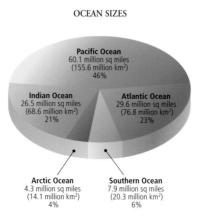

OCEAN SIZES

Pacific Ocean
60.1 million sq miles
(155.6 million km²)
46%

Indian Ocean
26.5 million sq miles
(68.6 million km²)
21%

Atlantic Ocean
29.6 million sq miles
(76.8 million km²)
23%

Arctic Ocean
4.3 million sq miles
(14.1 million km²)
4%

Southern Ocean
7.9 million sq miles
(20.3 million km²)
6%

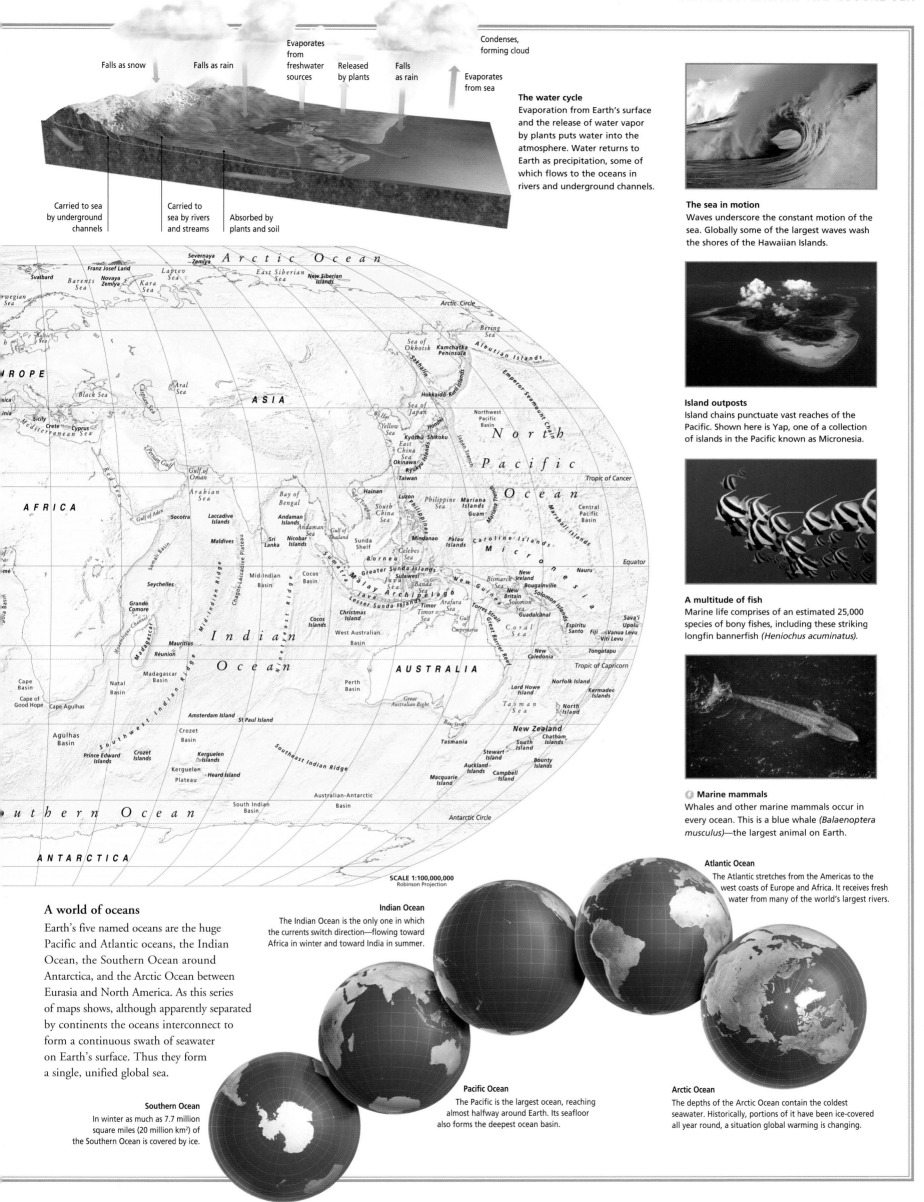

The water cycle
Evaporation from Earth's surface and the release of water vapor by plants puts water into the atmosphere. Water returns to Earth as precipitation, some of which flows to the oceans in rivers and underground channels.

Falls as snow
Falls as rain
Evaporates from freshwater sources
Released by plants
Falls as rain
Condenses, forming cloud
Evaporates from sea

Carried to sea by underground channels
Carried to sea by rivers and streams
Absorbed by plants and soil

The sea in motion
Waves underscore the constant motion of the sea. Globally some of the largest waves wash the shores of the Hawaiian Islands.

Island outposts
Island chains punctuate vast reaches of the Pacific. Shown here is Yap, one of a collection of islands in the Pacific known as Micronesia.

A multitude of fish
Marine life comprises of an estimated 25,000 species of bony fishes, including these striking longfin bannerfish (*Heniochus acuminatus*).

Marine mammals
Whales and other marine mammals occur in every ocean. This is a blue whale (*Balaenoptera musculus*)—the largest animal on Earth.

SCALE 1:100,000,000
Robinson Projection

A world of oceans

Earth's five named oceans are the huge Pacific and Atlantic oceans, the Indian Ocean, the Southern Ocean around Antarctica, and the Arctic Ocean between Eurasia and North America. As this series of maps shows, although apparently separated by continents the oceans interconnect to form a continuous swath of seawater on Earth's surface. Thus they form a single, unified global sea.

Southern Ocean
In winter as much as 7.7 million square miles (20 million km²) of the Southern Ocean is covered by ice.

Indian Ocean
The Indian Ocean is the only one in which the currents switch direction—flowing toward Africa in winter and toward India in summer.

Pacific Ocean
The Pacific is the largest ocean, reaching almost halfway around Earth. Its seafloor also forms the deepest ocean basin.

Atlantic Ocean
The Atlantic stretches from the Americas to the west coasts of Europe and Africa. It receives fresh water from many of the world's largest rivers.

Arctic Ocean
The depths of the Arctic Ocean contain the coldest seawater. Historically, portions of it have been ice-covered all year round, a situation global warming is changing.

ORIGIN OF A WATERY WORLD

The newly formed Earth was a turbulent, volcanic planet. No liquid water—and no life—could exist on its searing surface, but gases vented from volcanoes included water vapor that accumulated in dense, hot clouds. More steam rose from ice evaporating from comets that bombarded Earth's surface. As early Earth rapidly cooled, however, the clouds of steam began to condense into rain—the source of the first liquid water on the planet's surface. Water's chemical properties were crucial in the evolution of the seas and eventually of life itself. One is a high heat capacity, the ability to absorb a great deal of heat before water warms appreciably. As a result, temperatures in watery environments, including oceans and the bodies of organisms, remain remarkably stable. Water also dissolves many other substances, and it has surface tension—the cohesiveness that keeps individual molecules connected to one another in raindrops, rivers, and in the vast global sea.

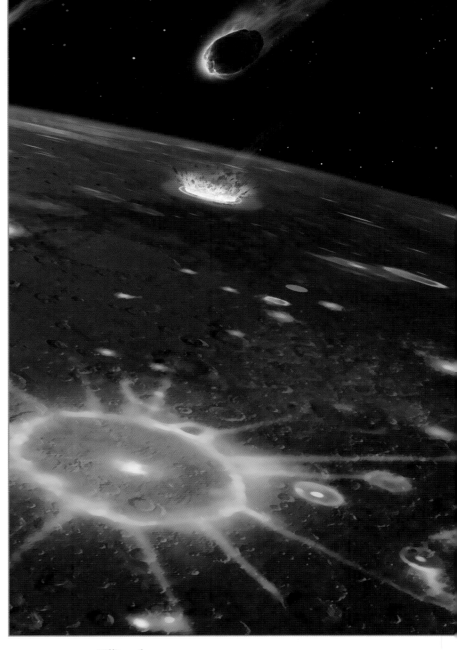

EVIDENCE FOR EARLY BEGINNINGS

Zircon crystals from ancient streambeds, such as Jack Hills in Western Australia shown below, form when water is present around melting granite. Dated to about 4.4 million years ago, zircons are remnants of Earth's first rocky crust, which was later destroyed by meteorite impacts. Their age strongly implies that conditions required for life—including liquid water—may have developed much earlier and faster than once thought.

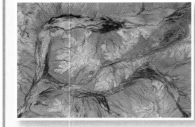

This enlarged image shows an ancient zircon crystal formed when searing heat, possibly from the impact of an ancient meteorite, melted granite in early Earth's crust.

Filling the oceans

Earth's first water supply probably was vaporizing ice from comets and asteroids that struck the hot planet over billions of years. As Earth cooled, water vapor condensed and fell. Erosion of volcanoes began and the ocean basins slowly filled with water and sediment.

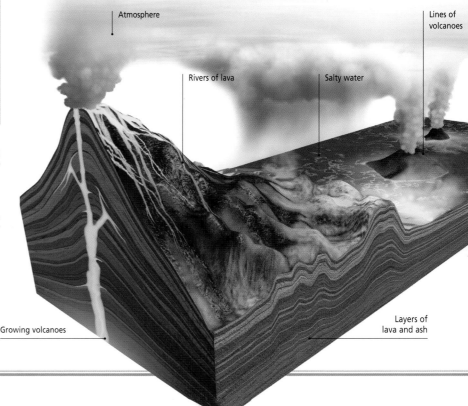

Atmosphere

Lines of volcanoes

Rivers of lava

Salty water

Growing volcanoes

Layers of lava and ash

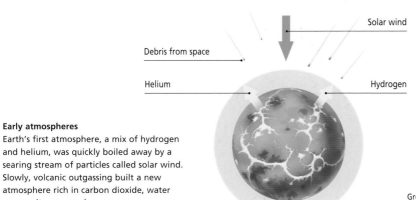

Solar wind

Debris from space

Helium

Hydrogen

Early atmospheres

Earth's first atmosphere, a mix of hydrogen and helium, was quickly boiled away by a searing stream of particles called solar wind. Slowly, volcanic outgassing built a new atmosphere rich in carbon dioxide, water vapor, nitrogen, and ozone.

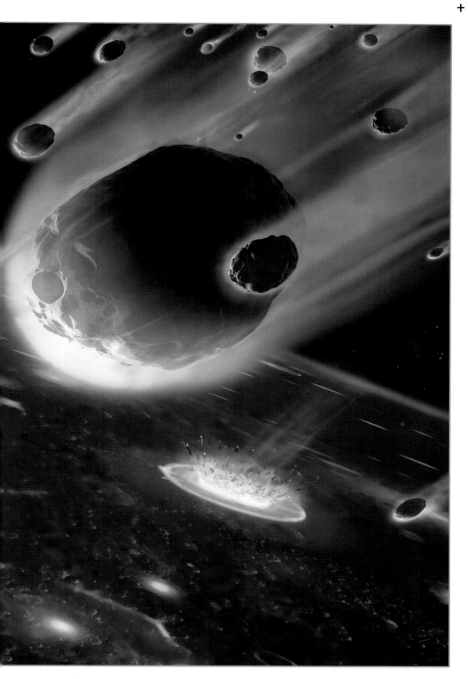

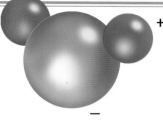

Making a water molecule
A water molecule has an oxygen atom sandwiched between two hydrogen atoms, giving the molecule two arms with opposite electrical charges. This difference spurs the formation of hydrogen bonds that give water unique properties.

Properties of water
Water's properties make it one of the most extraordinary substances on Earth. Links between water molecules called hydrogen bonds cause water to lose or gain heat slowly, so temperatures in watery environments are quite stable. Water also is relatively dense, providing physical support for floating and swimming organisms. Yet water's solid form, ice, is less dense than liquid water, so ice floats—allowing aquatic life to survive beneath it.

SOLID

Solid water
Below 32°F (0°C), bonds between water molecules form a rigid, open lattice, which makes ice less dense than liquid water.

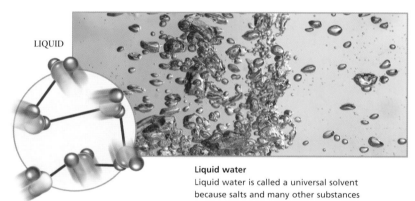

LIQUID

Liquid water
Liquid water is called a universal solvent because salts and many other substances can readily dissolve in it.

GAS

Gas
Water vapor is the gaseous phase of water. Water is the only substance on Earth that naturally exists as a solid, liquid, and gas.

Water from Earth or space?
At one time most scientists believed that Earth's first liquid water condensed from water vapor spewed by volcanoes along with other gases. Further study has supported the "heavy bombardment" theory that over billions of years ice-rich comets and asteroids brought water with them when they collided with Earth's atmosphere. Quite possibly, some combination of processes generated the planet's water supply.

Land and seas
Rain, formed by condensing water vapor, fed the oceans. The emerging waters lapped the volcanic granite that formed the first continents.

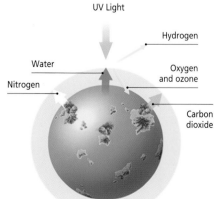

UV Light

Hydrogen

Water

Oxygen and ozone

Nitrogen

Carbon dioxide

Earth's first ozone layer
Intense sunlight interacted with oxygen in the early atmosphere. This chemical reaction formed an ozone layer that protected Earth's surface from further harmful solar radiation. The ozone barrier paved the way for the evolution of more complex life.

The Water Table	
Boiling point	212°F (100°C)
Freezing point, pure water	32°F (0°C)
Freezing point, seawater	around 28.6°F (-1.9°C)
Weight of one gallon (2.2 L) at 68°F (20°C)	8.3 pounds (3.8 kg)
Seawater salt content	average 3.5%
Fresh water salt content	less than 0.1%
Pressure increase with depth	14.7 pounds (6.7 kg) per each 33 feet (10 m)
Average speed of sound in water at 46°F (8°C)	4,721 feet (1,439 m) per second
Greatest supply of fresh water	Antarctic ice (90%+)

THE EVOLVING SEA

As Earth cooled, a crust formed over its molten interior. This rocky skin's features included both highlands and basin-like depressions. As water vapor in the atmosphere condensed into droplets, torrential rains began to fill what would become ocean basins. Runoff from land areas contained eroded minerals, the beginnings of the salty global sea and a seafloor blanketed by layers of sediments. Geological evidence suggests that several times during Earth's early history the heat from massive asteroid impacts boiled away the oceans and any life they may have contained. By about 3.8 billion years ago, however, primitive cells became established, and over geologic time the evolution of animals and other major groups would be well underway. Meanwhile, climatic changes coincided with rising and falling sea levels, and shifts in Earth's crust were rearranging landmasses and ocean basins. By 200 million years ago, a vast global sea teeming with life washed the shores of a single huge continent, now called Pangea.

Millennia of change and loss

Over the ages Earth's ecosystems and the types of organisms in them have changed dramatically as climate shifts correlated with ice ages and fluctuating sea levels. Different factors have also triggered at least five mass extinction episodes, in which more than half of animal species were lost. Many ecologists today fear that a sixth mass extinction is underway due to unrestrained development and other human activities.

— Temperature
— Sea level (present at 0)
— Extinction rate
● Mass extinction event

A 444 mya
Ordovician extinction
Possible causes of this mass extinction include prolonged global glaciation and irradiation from an exploding star.

B 359 mya
Devonian extinction
A long series of smaller extinctions destroyed 70 percent of all species.

Millions of years ago

■ **Cambrian period**
542 mya Animals with shells and jawless fish (first vertebrates) evolve

Trilobites resembled bugs, but some grew more than 2 feet (60 cm) long.

■ **Ordovician period**
490 mya Jawless fish diversify and jawed sharks evolve

Sharks with jaws may have evolved from the jawless thelodonts.

■ **Silurian period**
435 mya Fish diversify; the first insects and amphibians appear

Life blossomed on land, as bony fish such as spiny *Nostolepis* swam with sharks.

■ **Devonian period**
408 mya First bony fish and first land plants and animals appear

Some modern sharks have spines in front of their dorsal fins, like *Ctenacanthus* did.

■ **Carboniferous period**
360 mya Golden Age of Sharks; the first reptiles appear

No one knows how the scissor-tooth shark used its weird whorls of teeth.

Evolving life

Bacteria were among the first lifeforms to evolve in early Earth's shallow seas. Some of these single-celled species, called cyanobacteria, carried out photosynthesis as plants do, using sunlight to manufacture their own food. Over time they formed domed mats—known today as stromatolites—that hardened into limestone as sediments and minerals accumulated in them. Fossil stromatolites have been dated radiometrically to about 3.5 billion years old. Shark Bay, shown left, in Western Australia is home to Earth's only living stromatolites. These specimens may be up to 1,000 years old.

Stromatolite structure

Growth The mat of bacteria grows, mounding above the accumulating sediment.

Mineralization The bacteria secrete calcium carbonate, or limestone. The mineral secretions trap sediments that form darker layers.

Interior The interior of the stromatolite reveals concentric layers formed during previous growth.

Base The base of the stromatolite is firmly attached to the surface upon which the mound was originally established.

ICY TIMES

During an ice age, extensive ice sheets develop in certain regions, as in Antarctica and Greenland. By this measure, Earth is still in an ice age that began 2.6 million years ago. Sea level falls as large amounts of water become locked up in ice. The process continues during colder ice-age periods when glaciers advance. Sea level rises when glaciers retreat, a trend that accelerates as the overall ice age wanes.

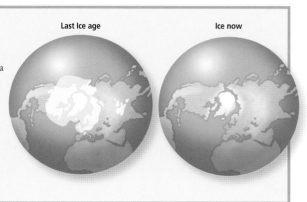

Last Ice age

Ice now

The supercontinent Pangea
About 260 million years ago a single supercontinent called Pangea was essentially a gigantic island surrounded by sea. The geologic changes that created Pangea would later break it apart, forming the modern position of continents and seas.

C **251 mya**
Permian extinction
Loss of 96 percent of marine species followed global warming caused by volcanism and shifts in sea chemistry.

D **208 mya**
Triassic extinction
About 20 percent of major marine groups and the last large amphibians vanished at this time.

E **65 mya**
Cretaceous extinction
An asteroid impact and massive volcanism plunged Earth into years of "impact winter," killed off the non-avian dinosaurs and half of marine species.

Seal level (ft/m)

980/300

660/200

330/100

0

−330/−100

−660/−200

Last ice age

Pangea

Triassic

Jurassic

Cretaceous

Tertiary

Quaternary

250

200

150

100

50

0

Permian period

286 mya Mass extinctions occurred both on land and in the seas

Permian rivers were home to eel-like sharks such as *Xenacanthus*.

Triassic period

248 mya Early dinosaurs, mammals, and marine reptiles appear

Nothosaurus was a reptile with webbed toes and needle-like teeth.

Jurassic period

208 mya First modern sharks and rays; mass extinctions in seas

Protospinax was an ancient relative of angel sharks and saw sharks.

Cretaceous period

144 mya Sand tigers and some other modern shark lineages; first birds, dinosaurs

Top ocean predators included *Cretoxyrhina*—a relative of the great white.

Tertiary period

65 mya to today Mammals, birds, and flowering plants diversify

Gigantic Megalodon ruled the oceans. On land, ancestors of modern humans evolved.

Into the future: Possible sixth mass extinction

A dramatic increase in species extinctions began in the Quaternary around 1.8 million years ago. These human-caused losses continue today.

EARTH'S DYNAMIC CRUST

Earth's crust is divided into about a dozen sections or plates that move in different ways atop semi-fluid material underneath. Some contain all or part of the modern-day continents, while others, such as the Pacific Plate, lie entirely beneath the sea. By way of the process once called continental drift and now known as plate tectonics, plate movements slowly reposition continents, push up mountains, and recycle the crust of ocean basins. Such changes have been reshaping the seas for more than half a billion years. As ancient continents moved, the lifeforms on them were carried along, and researchers have been able to use fossil discoveries and the global distribution patterns of living species to help confirm hypotheses about continental movements. Today's continents have occupied the same general positions for about 10 million years. Even so, they are still on the move—on average, about 2 inches (5 cm) a year—as the age-old shifting of Earth's crustal plates continues.

Making ocean basins

Ocean basins form over millions of years as magma upwelling from Earth's interior gradually splits continental crust, creating an opening into which water can flood. About 150 million years ago, the Atlantic, Indian, and other modern ocean basins began to form as the supercontinent Pangea started to break apart. The same process is occurring today in parts of eastern Africa.

MOVING CONTINENTS

Earth's crust is divided into movable rocky sections called tectonic plates that essentially float on the upper mantle. Over geologic time, moving plates have carried continental landmasses along with them in a process known as plate tectonics. When continents separate, the populations of species inhabiting them also may be separated, a phenomenon that helps explain the global distribution of certain plants and animals.

Today, the unusual plants called cycads occur on several continents. This ancient group first arose on Pangea and evidently cycads were carried around the globe as the supercontinent broke up.

200 million years ago

90 million years ago

Present day

60 million years from now

Birth of a rift valley
As a landmass begins to split apart, the land tilts and begins to subside, creating a wide valley.

Flooding the new ocean basin
When the valley floor subsides below sea level, seawater fills the depression. The formation of seafloor pushes the landmasses further apart.

Seafloor spreading
The ocean widens as spreading continues. As the seafloor moves outward it settles and sinks, leaving a ridge on either side of the rift.

Geological features

Earth's constantly moving tectonic plates are responsible for many of the planet's large-scale geological features, including those all or partly submerged under the sea.

Undersea collision
Arcs of volcanic islands occur where two ocean plates collide and one slides beneath the other.

Mid-ocean ridge
Where plates meet at mid-ocean ridges, new seafloor forms as crust material wells up from the mantle underneath.

Hot-spot volcanoes
Areas of unusually hot mantle beneath the interiors of crustal plates give rise to hot-spot volcanoes.

Coastal collision
Arcs of volcanic mountains occur where an oceanic plate collides with a continent and subducts beneath it.

Sliding plates
Transform faults occur where plates move past each other. Earthquakes occur where fault zones intermittently lock up, then release.

Continental rift
The tectonic splittin of a continent form deep valley. If the v floor continues to th seafloor spreading a new ocean basin.

Plate boundaries

Heat rising by convection from Earth's mantle drives the movement of crustal plates. The plates may slide past each other, spread apart, or collide, forming three general types of plate junctions—transform fault, divergent, and convergent boundaries. Volcanism and mountain building are common where plates collide. Examples are the volcano-dotted Andes, Cascades and other great mountain ranges along the coasts of continents.

Convergent boundary
When plates collide, the heavier one often is subducted into the mantle, slipping under the lighter one.

Divergent boundary
When plates move apart, new seafloor forms at oceanic spreading centers, or rifts, in continental crust.

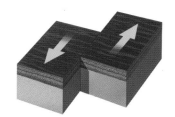

Transform fault boundary
Where crustal plates mainly slide past each other, they form a transform fault boundary.

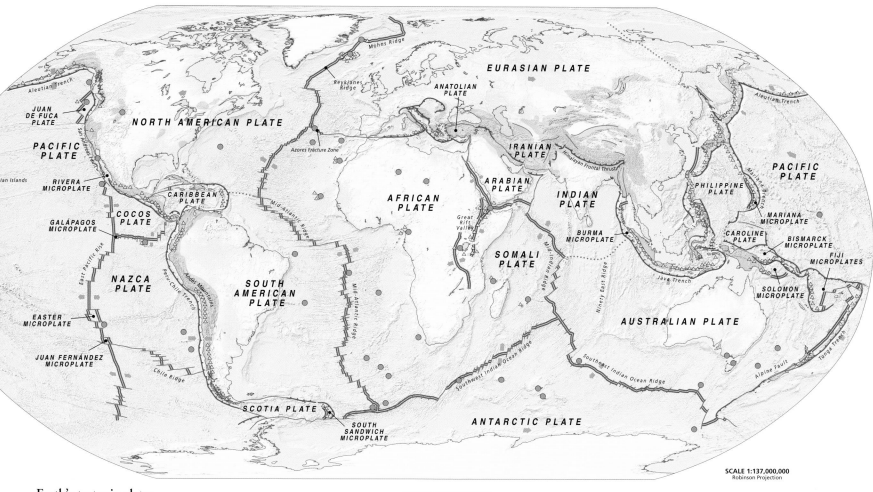

SCALE 1:137,000,000
Robinson Projection

Earth's tectonic plates

This map shows the present-day configuration of Earth's crustal plates. The red lines mark actively spreading ridges, features that occur in most ocean basins. Orange dots mark the major hot spots that have been active during the past 1 million years. Earthquake-prone areas correlate with subduction zones—for example, along the west coast of South America where the Nazca plate is sliding under and pushing up the South American plate.

TECTONIC FEATURES

- Earthquake zone
- △ Volcanic zone
- ● Prominent hotspot
- ▲ Convergent margin
- ═ Divergent margin
- — Transform fault
- ···· Diffuse or uncertain
- ➡ Direction of movement

Folding crust
Colliding continental plates cause the crust to thicken and crumple, which produces high mountains.

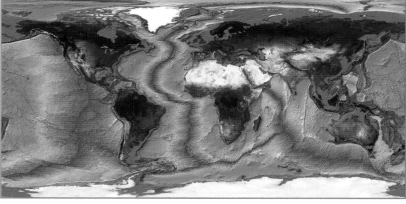

Age of the ocean floor
This computer-generated image shows the relative ages of seafloor areas, with the youngest (red) clearly aligned along mid-ocean spreading centers.

Million years
0 20 40 60 80 100 120 140 160 180 200 220 240 260 280

Pillow lava
As lava flows undersea, it quickly cools and forms a skin. As pressure builds within, new "pillows" burst through the skin.

SEA HIGHWAYS

Humans have taken to the waves for thousands of years, seeking food, commerce, new lands, treasure, and scientific understanding. The first intrepid mariners included Polynesians in dugout canoes and Egyptian traders in simple watercraft fashioned from bundles of reeds. Initially employing oars and sails, and later increasingly sophisticated engines, shipbuilding knowledge and technology advanced steadily over the centuries. Likewise, navigation tools evolved from devices such as the cross staff and astrolabe to the finely tuned chronometers developed by European watchmakers. By the 1400s, larger, sturdier vessels were expanding the range of ocean travel, transforming the seas into highways that could carry seafarers across whole oceans. Some coastal nations created navies that could extend their military might and support voyages of conquest. Eventually nearly every corner of the globe became accessible to those with the vision, vessels, and stamina to explore it.

Historic sea routes

Early records describe the intrepid journeys of an Egyptian explorer who sailed to Arabia in 2750 BC. Polynesians used outrigger canoes and celestial navigation to reach Tonga and Samoa in 1000 BC. Later, European, Chinese, and Muslim mariners all helped chart the oceans. By the 18th century, only the inhospitable seas of Antarctica remained unknown.

→ Polynesian expeditions
→ Viking expeditions
→ Chinese expeditions
→ Spanish expeditions
→ Portuguese expeditions
→ English expeditions
→ French expeditions
→ Dutch expeditions

SCALE 1:119,100,000
Robinson Projection

→ **Viking mariners**
Ancient Vikings braved the North Atlantic in sleek ships powered by oars and a sail. Archeological discoveries reveal that they reached North America more than 1,000 years ago, long before Columbus arrived.

→ **Columbus and the *Santa Maria* 1492**
The *Santa Maria*, a bulky cargo ship, was the flagship of Columbus's fleet during his voyage across the Atlantic, from Spain to North America. The ill-fated ship foundered off Haiti on Christmas Day, 1492.

FINDING THE NORTHWEST PASSAGE

The search for a Northwest Passage from the Atlantic to the Pacific beckoned a long line of explorers willing to challenge the harrowing conditions of the Arctic. Vitus Bering, James Cook, and Sir John Franklin all mounted unsuccessful expeditions, Franklin's ending in catastrophe. Eventually it was the savvy and meticulously prepared Norwegian explorer Roald Amundsen who discovered a route through the Arctic Ocean in 1906, after a four-year effort.

THE NORTHWEST PASSAGE, THE ARCTIC

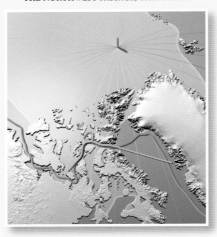

▭ **Franklin's route**
Sir John Franklin and his crew were last seen in Lancaster Sound in July 1845. Expedition remains were found on Beechey Island five years later.

▭ **Amundsen's route**
Initially following Franklin's route, Amundsen had the good fortune to attempt the Passage when conditions in the Arctic were more favorable.

Vessels equipped to plow through ice and withstand its pressure have been essential to travel and exploration in polar seas. Early icebreakers were wooden sailing ships with an iron-sheathed hull. A modern icebreaker's hull is broad for added stability and its steel bow is reinforced. Rather than ramming through ice, the heavy bow slides up over and crushes it.

Finding the way

Mariners of old navigated by the sun and stars. Early celestial navigation tools such as the cross staff, astrolabe, and sextant measured latitude, a ship's location north or south of the equator. A later invention, the chronometer—essentially a seagoing clock—measured longitude, a ship's location east or west of a starting point. By combining latitude and longitude a seafarer could accurately plot a ship's position and progress.

Cross staff

Sextant

Astrolabe

Chronometer

Map labels

Cook's third voyage 1776-79
New
Baba
Cuba
Hispa
Hawaiian Islands (Sandwich Islands)
Acapulco
Drake 1577-80
Pana
600
200-0 BC
Magellan-Del Cano 1519-22
Li
Tahiti
Pitcairn Is. 700
Rapa Nui (Easter Island)
Cook's second voyage 1772-75
Cook's first voyage 1768-71
Cook's second voyage 1772-75

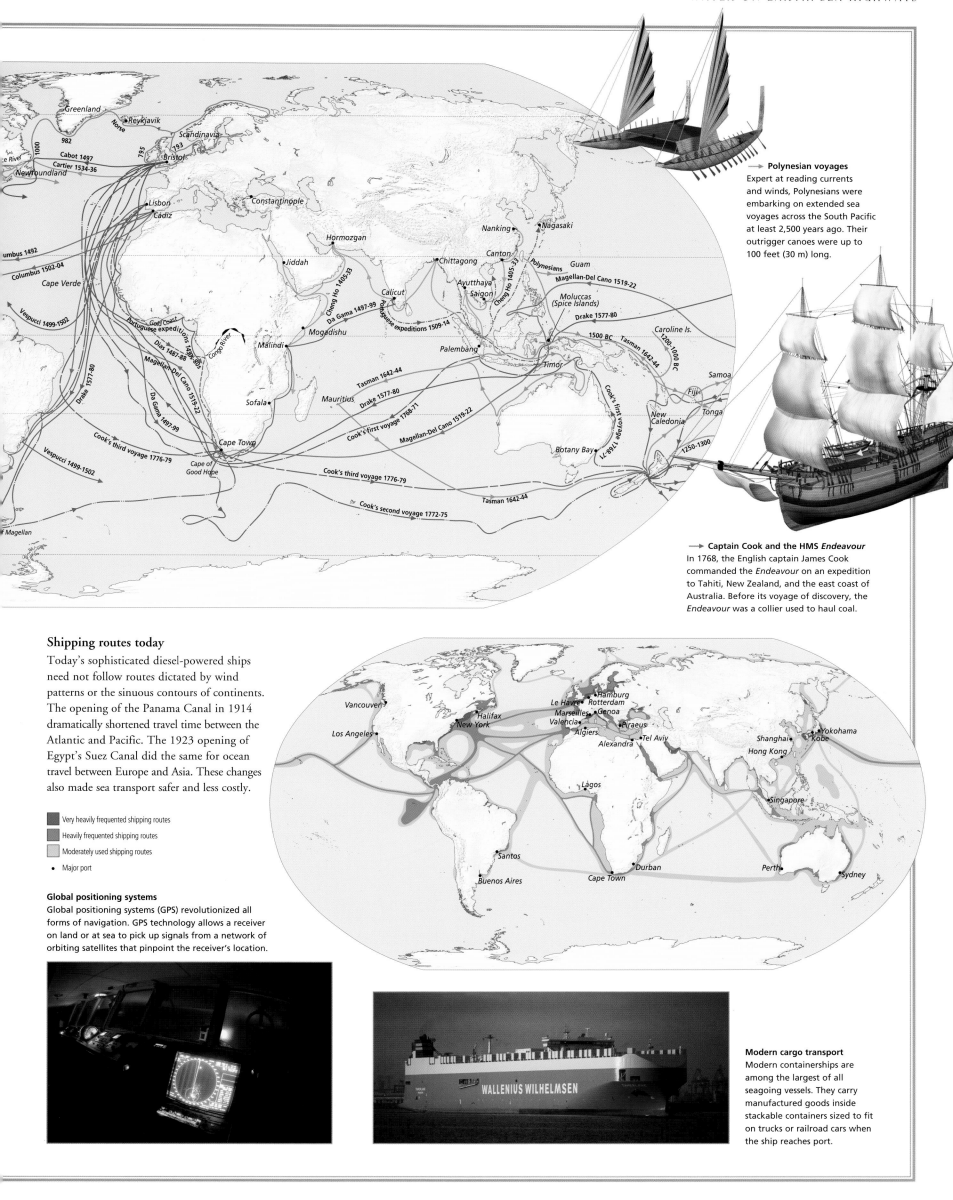

Greenland
Reykjavik
Norse
Scandinavia
982
795
793
1000
Bristol
Cabot 1497
Cartier 1534-36
Newfoundland
e River

Constantinople

Lisbon
Cádiz

umbus 1492
Columbus 1502-04
Cape Verde

Vespucci 1499-1502

Hormozgan

Jiddah

Nanking
Nagasaki
Canton
Chittagong
Ayutthaya
Saigon

Polynesians
Guam
Magellan-Del Cano 1519-22

Cheng Ho 1405-33

Calicut
Da Gama 1497-99
Portuguese expeditions 1509-14
Cheng Ho 1405-33
Moluccas
(Spice Islands)

Portuguese expeditions
Gold Coast
1480s-90s
Dias 1487-88
Da Gama 1497-99
Magellan-Del Cano 1519-22
Congo River
Mogadishu
Malindi

Palembang

Drake 1577-80

1500 BC
Tasman 1642-44
Caroline Is.
1200-1000 BC
Samoa
Fiji
Tonga

Sofala
Mauritius
Drake 1577-80
Tasman 1642-44
Timor
New
Caledonia

Drake 1577-80

Cook's first voyage 1768-71
Magellan-Del Cano 1519-22
Cook's first voyage 1768-71

Cape Town
Cook's third voyage 1776-79
Botany Bay
1250-1300

Vespucci 1499-1502
Cape of
Good Hope
Cook's third voyage 1776-79
Tasman 1642-44

Magellan

Cook's second voyage 1772-75

→ **Polynesian voyages**
Expert at reading currents
and winds, Polynesians were
embarking on extended sea
voyages across the South Pacific
at least 2,500 years ago. Their
outrigger canoes were up to
100 feet (30 m) long.

→ **Captain Cook and the HMS *Endeavour***
In 1768, the English captain James Cook
commanded the *Endeavour* on an expedition
to Tahiti, New Zealand, and the east coast of
Australia. Before its voyage of discovery, the
Endeavour was a collier used to haul coal.

Shipping routes today

Today's sophisticated diesel-powered ships
need not follow routes dictated by wind
patterns or the sinuous contours of continents.
The opening of the Panama Canal in 1914
dramatically shortened travel time between the
Atlantic and Pacific. The 1923 opening of
Egypt's Suez Canal did the same for ocean
travel between Europe and Asia. These changes
also made sea transport safer and less costly.

■ Very heavily frequented shipping routes
■ Heavily frequented shipping routes
■ Moderately used shipping routes
• Major port

Vancouver
Halifax
Le Havre
Hamburg
Rotterdam
Marseilles
Genoa
Valencia
Algiers
Piraeus
Shanghai
Yokohama
Kobe
Los Angeles
New York
Alexandra
Tel Aviv
Hong Kong

Lagos
Singapore

Santos
Perth
Buenos Aires
Cape Town
Durban
Sydney

Global positioning systems
Global positioning systems (GPS) revolutionized all
forms of navigation. GPS technology allows a receiver
on land or at sea to pick up signals from a network of
orbiting satellites that pinpoint the receiver's location.

WALLENIUS WILHELMSEN

→ **Modern cargo transport**
Modern containerships are
among the largest of all
seagoing vessels. They carry
manufactured goods inside
stackable containers sized to fit
on trucks or railroad cars when
the ship reaches port.

Surveying the Seas

People have long been drawn to explore remote mountains and jungles, study the heavens, and travel across the sea's surface, but for most of human history the ocean depths remained inaccessible. This changed in the 1800s with the advent of motorized winches and strong steel cables which enabled deep-sea sampling, and of diving gear that allowed humans to spend extended periods underwater. Today, underwater cameras and sophisticated sonar and sampling tools are transforming current scientific understanding of the dynamic marine landscape and its lifeforms. From space, satellites gather data about seasonal changes in ocean temperatures. Studies of Earth's shifting magnetic field and changes in ocean basins have helped confirm the effects of plate tectonics. Some of the most exciting discoveries have come from expeditions using remotely operated vehicles, which have revealed caches of vital mineral resources, bizarre communities at undersea vents, and details of the deep abyss.

GYRE, JAPAN

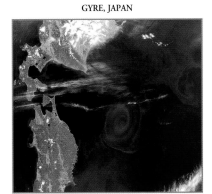

Mapping the sea surface

Satellites allow scientists to observe and compare ocean conditions on a global scale. Using advanced sensing technology, satellites relay data that is converted into computerized images. Among other benefits, the vivid map-like images provide previously unavailable information about shifts in ocean currents that affect climate. They also allow monitoring of ocean chemistry and phytoplankton—the foundation for sea food webs.

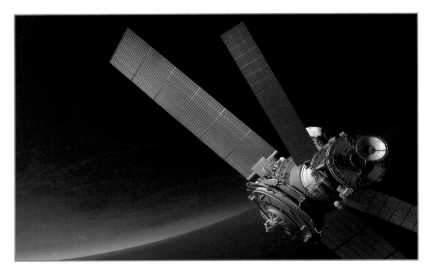

Historical Study

Long before oceanography was a recognized science, scholar-naturalists surveyed marine life and deepened understanding of currents and ocean basin features. The American Benjamin Franklin published a chart of the Gulf Stream in 1777. Later, Matthew Fontaine Maury did extensive research on currents and winds. Other 19th-century scientists probed the physical conditions and distribution of life in the oceans.

In 1873, scientists aboard the British vessel *Challenger* launched the first major voyage to study marine life and the seas. Traveling more than 79,000 miles (127,000 km) over three years, the expedition covered large areas of the Atlantic and Pacific oceans.

Sir John Murray was a driving force in interpreting the masses of data collected by the *Challenger* expedition.

HMS *Challenger* was the first ship used to study the deep sea. Scientists on board discovered the Mariana Trench, the deepest point in the ocean.

SEAFLOOR OFF LOS ANGELES

Mapping the seafloor

Ship-based sonar devices allow scientists to map the seafloor. Pulses of sound waves directed at some part of the seafloor bounce off submerged objects and surfaces. Aboard ship, instruments convert these echoes into an image of the undersea landscape and objects, such as sunken ships, that might be there. In seismic surveying, sound waves directed into the seabed yield computer-generated images of the seafloor interior.

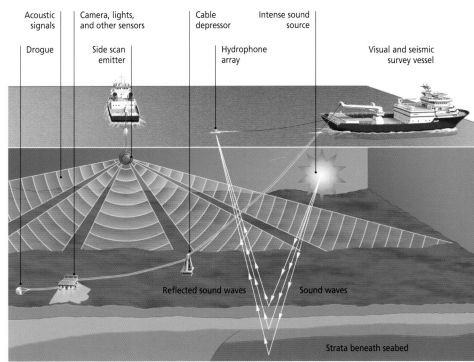

Acoustic signals

Camera, lights, and other sensors

Cable depressor

Intense sound source

Drogue

Side scan emitter

Hydrophone array

Visual and seismic survey vessel

Reflected sound waves

Sound waves

Strata beneath seabed

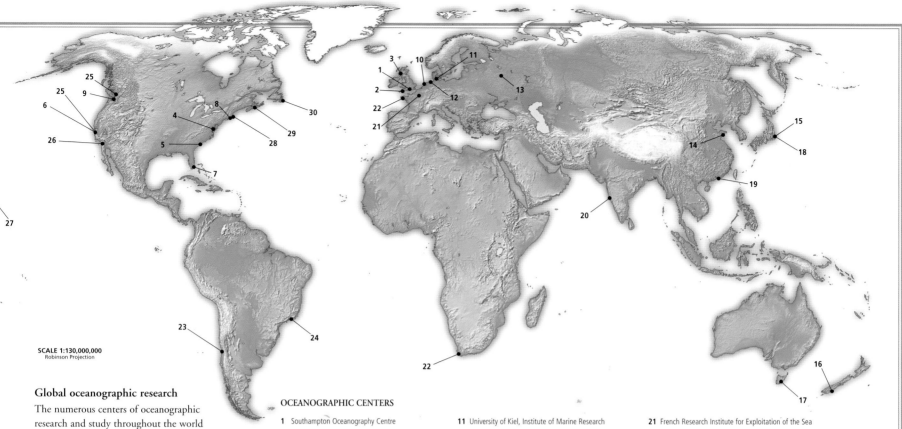

SCALE 1:130,000,000
Robinson Projection

Global oceanographic research

The numerous centers of oceanographic research and study throughout the world attest to the importance of the sea in human affairs. Governments continue to invest in new centers, equipped with the latest research facilities and vessels. Their discoveries have applications not only for improving basic understanding of the marine world, but also for naval operations and locating potential mineral resources such as oil and gas reserves.

OCEANOGRAPHIC CENTERS

1 Southampton Oceanography Centre
2 Plymouth Marine Laboratory
3 Dunstuffnage Marine Laboratory
4 Virginia Institute of Marine Science
5 Duke Marine Laboratory
6 Moss Landing Marine Laboratories
7 Rosenstiel School of Marine Science
8 University of Rhode Island School of Marine Science
9 University of Washington School of Marine Science
10 Netherlands Institute for Sea Research

11 University of Kiel, Institute of Marine Research
12 Alfred Wegener Institute for Polar and Marine Research
13 Shirshov Institute of Oceanology
14 Ocean University of Qingdao
15 Japan Agency for Marine-Earth Science and Technology
16 University of Otago, Department of Marine Science
17 CSIRO Marine Laboratories
18 University of Tokyo, Ocean Research Institute
19 University of Hong Kong, Swire Institute of Marine Science
20 University of Cape Town, Center for Marine Studies

21 French Research Institute for Exploitation of the Sea
22 Université de Bretagne Occidentale, Institut Universitaire Européen de la Mer
23 Universidad Catolica de Valparaiso, Escuela de Ciencias del Mar
24 University of São Paulo, Oceanographic Institute
25 Monterey Bay Aquarium Research Institute
26 University of California, Scripps Institution of Oceanography
27 University of Hawaii, School of Ocean and Earth Science and Technology
28 Woods Hole Oceanographic Institution
29 Bedford Institute of Oceanography, Ocean Sciences Division
30 Memorial University of Newfoundland, Ocean Sciences Center

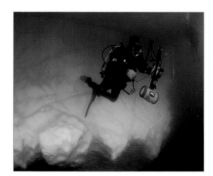

Exploring polar ecosystems
Divers equipped for conditions under Antarctic ice gather information about the diets of sea life, including leopard seals, and penguins.

Investigating marine ecosystems
Research into marine ecosystems includes studies of lemon shark (*Negaprion brevirostris*) populations in the Bahamas.

Monitoring endangered species
Scientists at Monterey Bay Aquarium Research Institute monitor the endangered California southern sea otter (*Enhydra lutris nereis*).

Studying marine mammals
At Long Beach Marine Laboratory, California, scientists research the physiological mechanisms that allow mammals to dive for long periods.

EXPLORING THE DEEP

Submarines must be built to withstand the crushing pressure of the water around them —a pressure that grows steadily with depth. Research submersibles are smaller than military submarines and can go much deeper. In 1960, with a crew of two, the heavily reinforced bathyscaphe *Trieste*, a Swiss designed "deep boat," reached the bottom of the Mariana Trench, the deepest part of the global sea. No existing submersible can go as deep.

Undersea craft such as the bathyscaphe *Trieste* and research submersibles *Alvin* and *Shinkai* have allowed historic studies of the sea depths.

Trieste   **Alvin**   **Shinkai**

Safe operating depth

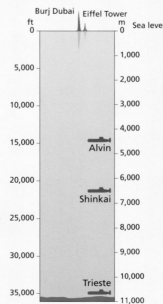

This one-person submarine, called *Deep Rover*, can descend to about 980 feet (300 m). Mechanical arms allow the operator to manipulate objects and collect samples.

From sunlit shallows to the greatest depths, the vast global sea is
always in motion. The physical and chemical properties of seawater
—salinity, the density or weight of water, its temperature, and the
availability of light below the surface—all help determine where
different marine species can survive. Seawater also continually
interacts with the land it washes and the atmosphere above it.

MARINE MECHANICS

THE SALTY SEA

Seawater is a relatively dense fluid that is 96.5 percent water and 3.5 percent salts including chloride, sodium, magnesium, and calcium. It also contains dissolved elements such as nitrogen and phosphorus. With increasing depth, water's density and pressure rise, its temperature and salinity drop, and less sunlight can penetrate it. These physical and chemical factors influence the movement of seawater and the bodily features of marine organisms. For example, until it is near freezing, deep, denser cold water remains at the bottom. Because light dims with depth, fish may have large eyes or rely on other senses to hunt or avoid predators. At great depths, fish typically have flabby bodies that require little food to sustain. Dissolved nitrogen and phosphorus in seawater are key nutrients for the floating phytoplankton that form the base of marine food webs. Corals, clams, and other marine invertebrates remove calcium from seawater to form protective calcium carbonate shells.

Chemical composition

The salinity of seawater varies around the globe. Salinity is greatest in semi-enclosed seas such as the Caribbean, Mediterranean, and the Red Sea, where more water is lost to evaporation of water from the sea surface than is replenished by rainfall and runoff. The lowest salinity occurs in areas where large rivers, such as the Yangtze, Ganges, Mississippi, and Amazon, discharge into the ocean.

Caribbean Sea
The shallowest areas of this warm, tropical sea off the western Atlantic are renowned for their "floatability"—the water's capacity to support swimmers due to its high salinity and, therefore, greatly increased density.

GLOBAL SALINITY

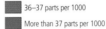

- Less than 33 parts per 1000
- 33–34 parts per 1000
- 34–35 parts per 1000
- 35–36 parts per 1000
- 36–37 parts per 1000
- More than 37 parts per 1000

SEAWATER COMPOSITION

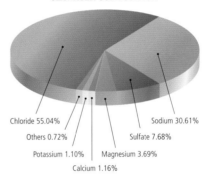

- Chloride 55.04%
- Others 0.72%
- Potassium 1.10%
- Calcium 1.16%
- Magnesium 3.69%
- Sulfate 7.68%
- Sodium 30.61%

Salts in seawater
Dissolved salts account for roughly 3.53 percent of the weight of seawater. Chloride and sodium represent more than 85 percent of this total. The chart shows percentages of these and other major salts by weight.

Dead Sea
This famous sea lies in the Jordan Rift Valley. Intense heat evaporates the water, making it approximately 10 times more saline than seawater and so dense that a human body cannot sink in it. As its name implies, there is little marine life there.

How the seas became salty

Approximately 4.3 billion years ago, Earth entered a 10-million-year period of intense rainstorms that helped form the first global sea. These storms eroded minerals from the hot rocks and picked up gases from the atmosphere. As a result, the first ocean was a complex solution of water and salts. Today there is a balance between salt inputs and losses, so salinity remains almost constant.

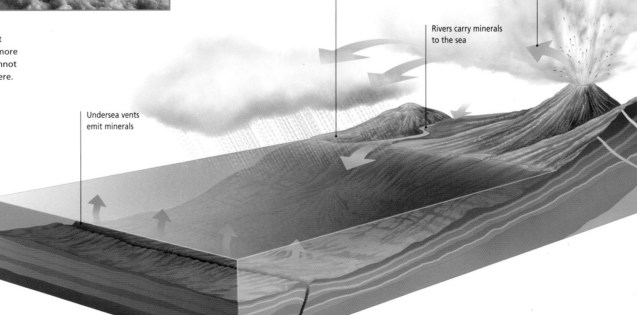

Rainwater dissolves salts from rocks

Rainwater dissolves volcanic gases

Rivers carry minerals to the sea

Undersea vents emit minerals

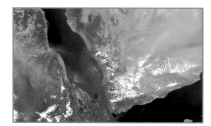

Red Sea
The extremely salty Red Sea formed when the Indian Ocean flooded an ancient rift valley. About 40 percent of the Red Sea is less than 330 feet (100 m) deep. It is known for its extensive coral reefs.

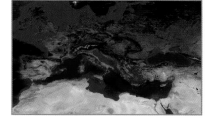

Mediterranean Sea
The Mediterranean connects to the Atlantic Ocean via the narrow Straits of Gibraltar, where its sapphire waters are about as saline as the Atlantic. The Mediterranean becomes saltier toward the sea's closed eastern end.

Antarctica
In the Weddell and Ross seas of the Southern Ocean, the seawater becomes unusually saline, and much denser, as sea ice forms. This dense water sinks and forms a deep water mass called Antarctic Bottom Water.

Calcium carbonate shells
Shallow seas have the richest supply of calcium, in the form of calcium carbonate. Shelled organisms such as clams and snails have evolved to take up dissolved calcium carbonate and use it to build their protective shells.

Conch
Conches are marine snails. Thousands of species are known, most in coral reef habitats where they are often harvested as seafood.

Spiral coiling
Like most gastropod snails, this species' shell consists of multiple calcium carbonate layers twisted into a spiral.

Prickly pen
This bivalve burrows into sand or gravel. It uses sticky byssus threads to anchor its shell to objects such as pebbles.

Abalone
An abalone's shell is lined with nacre or mother-of-pearl that is more than 95 percent calcium carbonate.

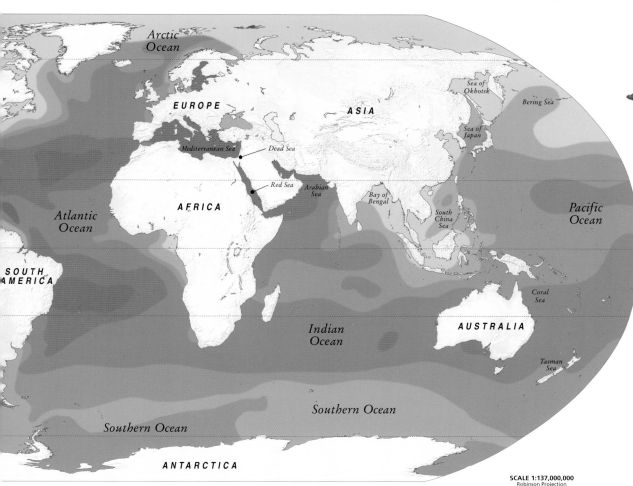

SCALE 1:137,000,000
Robinson Projection

DEPTH AND LIGHT
In seawater, light wavelengths corresponding to different colors of light are absorbed or scattered. Red light is absorbed quickly, so the sea surface usually appears blue. The longer green and blue wavelengths travel farther, but by about 4,265 feet (1,300 m) all the wavelengths have been absorbed even in clear waters. From that point onward the depths are completely dark except for the glow emitted from organisms having light-producing organs.

ESTUARY WATERS
COASTAL WATERS

MUDDY WATERS

OPEN OCEAN

Ocean water appears bluest where it holds less organic material. Increased material, including phytoplankton, containing the green pigment chlorophyll, makes water appear greenish, as in estuaries or along coasts. Turbid, muddy-looking water contains a heavy load of suspended soil particles.

In water, floating particles, density changes, and other factors change the trajectory of a light beam, a process called scattering that affects the water's color.

CURRENTS AND CIRCULATION

Currents are streams of moving water. Wind creates sea surface currents. Relatively warm water flows in some of these, including equatorial currents, while at higher latitudes water flows are much colder, such as the Labrador Current. The Gulf Stream and other boundary currents move along the edges of continents. Seawater also circulates in thermohaline currents, in which differences in temperature or salinity push water masses past one another, usually vertically. Thermohaline circulation distributes seawater into layers, with more salty, warmer water layered above colder, less saline water. Where surface currents drive water away from a coast, upwelling brings up deeper, nutrient-rich water to replace it. By contrast, downwelling occurs as surface water sinks when winds drive water toward a coast. In the largest oceans, surface currents include looping gyres in which water may be as much as 6.6 feet (2 m) higher in the center than at the edges. The combined effects of gravity and Coriolis forces drive the current in a horizontal spiral.

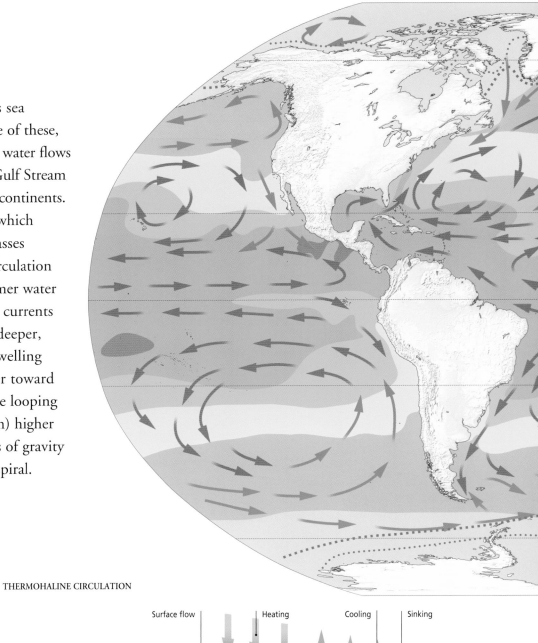

SURFACE AND DEEP OCEAN CIRCULATION

While dozens of small and large surface currents rapidly circulate upper ocean waters, deep-water masses simultaneously travel slowly around the global sea by thermohaline circulation. The North Atlantic Deep Water forms as water in the northern hemisphere sinks. Over an estimated 275 years it flows to the Antarctic, then onward to the deepest parts of the Indian and Pacific oceans before upwelling returns it to the surface.

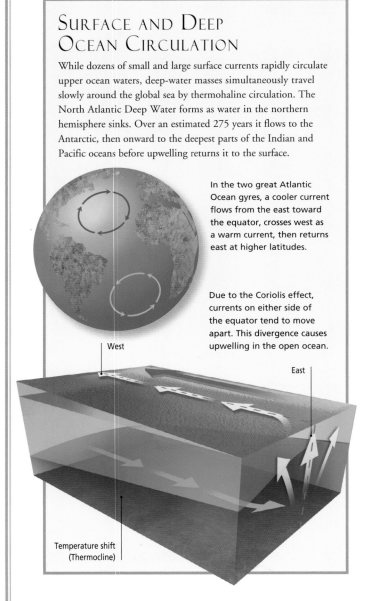

In the two great Atlantic Ocean gyres, a cooler current flows from the east toward the equator, crosses west as a warm current, then returns east at higher latitudes.

Due to the Coriolis effect, currents on either side of the equator tend to move apart. This divergence causes upwelling in the open ocean.

West

East

Temperature shift (Thermocline)

THERMOHALINE CIRCULATION

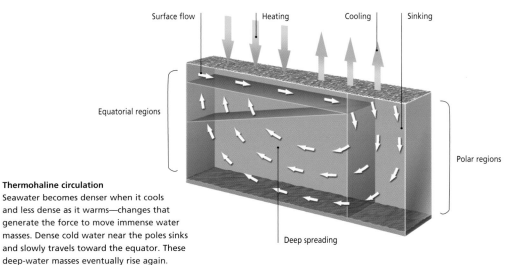

Surface flow   Heating   Cooling   Sinking

Equatorial regions

Polar regions

Deep spreading

Thermohaline circulation
Seawater becomes denser when it cools and less dense as it warms—changes that generate the force to move immense water masses. Dense cold water near the poles sinks and slowly travels toward the equator. These deep-water masses eventually rise again.

UPWELLING

Upwelling and downwelling
Vertical thermohaline water movements, also called upwelling and downwelling, are vital for marine ecosystems. Sinking surface water replenishes oxygen in the deepest parts of all ocean basins, while rising deep-water masses return valuable sunken nutrients to the surface. Most of these vertical water movements occur along continental coasts.

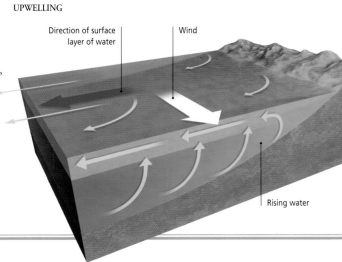

Direction of surface layer of water   Wind

Rising water

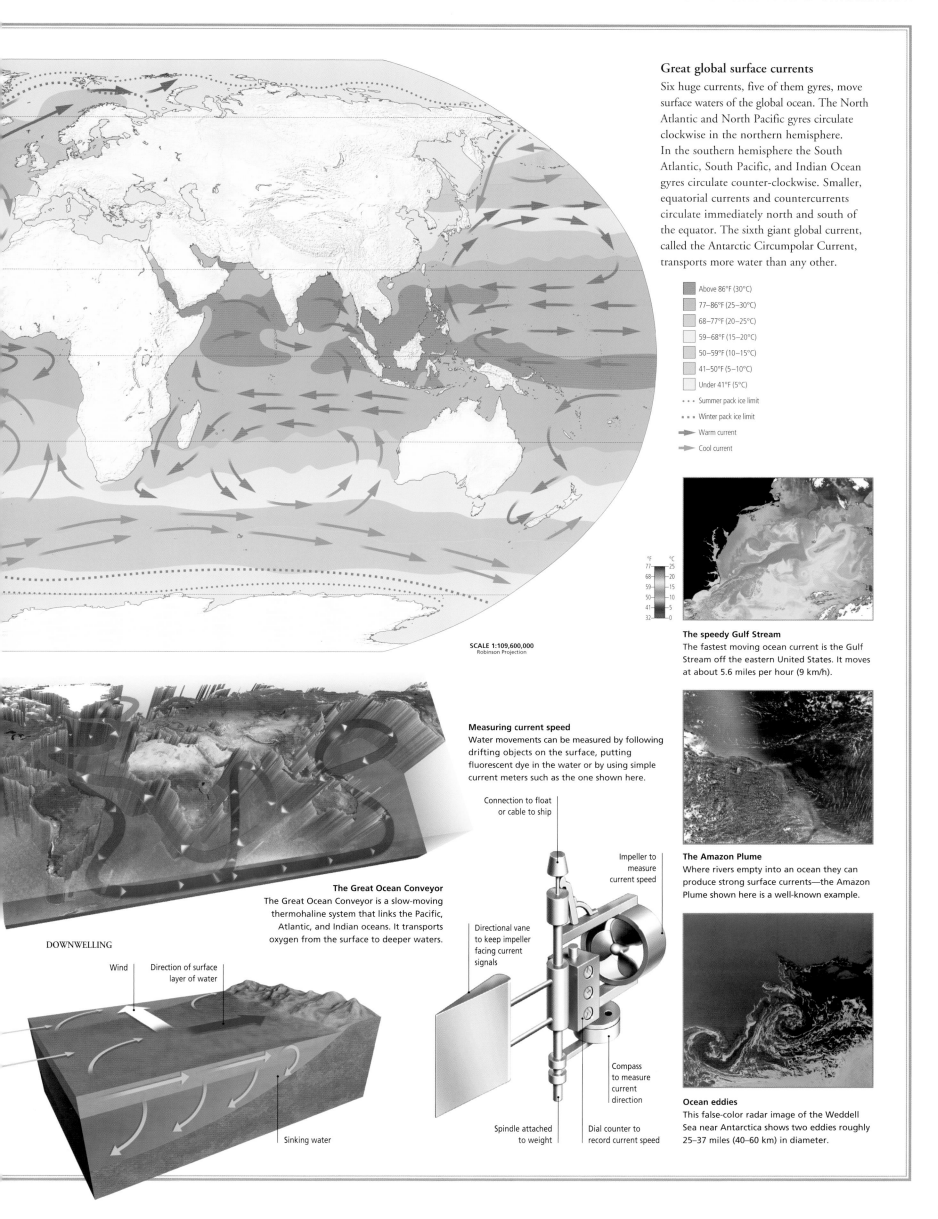

Great global surface currents

Six huge currents, five of them gyres, move surface waters of the global ocean. The North Atlantic and North Pacific gyres circulate clockwise in the northern hemisphere. In the southern hemisphere the South Atlantic, South Pacific, and Indian Ocean gyres circulate counter-clockwise. Smaller, equatorial currents and countercurrents circulate immediately north and south of the equator. The sixth giant global current, called the Antarctic Circumpolar Current, transports more water than any other.

Above 86°F (30°C)
77–86°F (25–30°C)
68–77°F (20–25°C)
59–68°F (15–20°C)
50–59°F (10–15°C)
41–50°F (5–10°C)
Under 41°F (5°C)

· · · Summer pack ice limit
· · · Winter pack ice limit
➜ Warm current
➜ Cool current

SCALE 1:109,600,000
Robinson Projection

The speedy Gulf Stream
The fastest moving ocean current is the Gulf Stream off the eastern United States. It moves at about 5.6 miles per hour (9 km/h).

Measuring current speed
Water movements can be measured by following drifting objects on the surface, putting fluorescent dye in the water or by using simple current meters such as the one shown here.

Connection to float or cable to ship

Impeller to measure current speed

Directional vane to keep impeller facing current signals

Compass to measure current direction

Spindle attached to weight

Dial counter to record current speed

The Amazon Plume
Where rivers empty into an ocean they can produce strong surface currents—the Amazon Plume shown here is a well-known example.

The Great Ocean Conveyor
The Great Ocean Conveyor is a slow-moving thermohaline system that links the Pacific, Atlantic, and Indian oceans. It transports oxygen from the surface to deeper waters.

DOWNWELLING

Wind

Direction of surface layer of water

Sinking water

Ocean eddies
This false-color radar image of the Weddell Sea near Antarctica shows two eddies roughly 25–37 miles (40–60 km) in diameter.

CLIMATE AND THE SEA

A region's climate is the long-term pattern of weather conditions there. The sea strongly influences climate all over Earth through its interactions with the atmosphere, where sunlight first reaches Earth. About 49 percent of incoming sunlight is reflected back to space; the remaining 51 percent is absorbed. In response to the combined effects of solar heating and Earth's rotation on its axis, air in the atmosphere warms, rises, cools, and descends in masses known as cells. This general scheme of atmospheric circulation produces the global water cycle, and influences climatic patterns of seasonal temperatures and precipitation. It also translates into the wind patterns that drive surface ocean currents, and it affects long-term movements of water masses between the surface and the depths of ocean basins. Changes to the composition of the atmosphere, especially an increase in so-called greenhouse gases, are warming the atmosphere in ways that have begun to rapidly alter global climate.

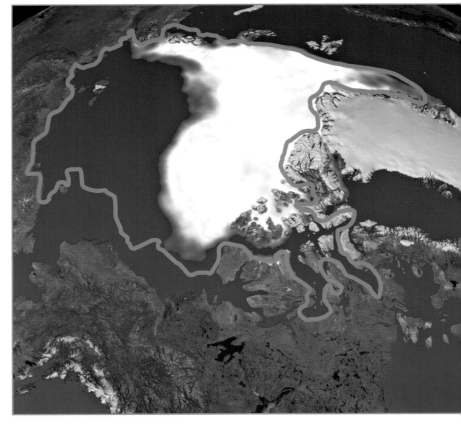

■ Sea ice extent in the mid-1970s

The global energy equation

About 30 percent of the Sun's energy beamed toward Earth is immediately reflected back to space. Clouds and the lower atmosphere absorb another 19 percent. The remaining 51 percent of solar energy is absorbed by the sea and land, including a small amount that is temporarily captured by photosynthesizing plants. Over time, however, all solar energy that reaches Earth's surface is radiated back to space.

Sea ice changes

Both permanent and annually renewed Arctic sea ice have been decreasing in recent decades due to global warming. Both types of Arctic ice have declined by 38 percent since the mid-1970s. Ice provides crucial habitat for both Arctic seals and polar bears. Although such species have survived previous climate shifts, the numbers of both are likely to decrease and in some areas populations may disappear altogether.

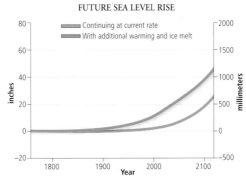

FUTURE SEA LEVEL RISE

— Continuing at current rate
— With additional warming and ice melt

Estimating sea level rise
At the current rate of sea level rise, sea level will gain 19 inches (480 mm) by 2100 (green line). Additional ice melting in Greenland or Antarctica could boost the increase to 39 inches (1,000 mm) or more (red line).

GLOBAL WARMING, CORAL THREAT

One of the major impacts of global warming is a rise in ocean temperature. In tropical regions a temperature increase of only 2.7–3.6°F (1.5–2°C) above normal can lead to the loss of the symbiotic algae called zooxanthellae that nourish coral polyps. As the polyps become malnourished, they turn white, a phenomenon called coral bleaching. Affected corals can sometimes recover, but only if the bleaching is quickly reversed.

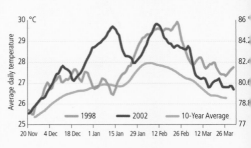

— 1998   — 2002   — 10-Year Average

During sustained periods of coral bleaching in 1998 and 2002 (yellow and orange lines), global sea temperatures were much higher than the 10-year average.

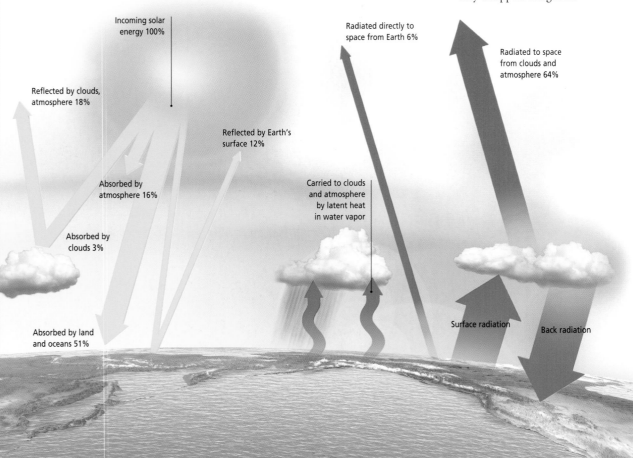

Incoming solar energy 100%

Radiated directly to space from Earth 6%

Radiated to space from clouds and atmosphere 64%

Reflected by clouds, atmosphere 18%

Reflected by Earth's surface 12%

Absorbed by atmosphere 16%

Carried to clouds and atmosphere by latent heat in water vapor

Absorbed by clouds 3%

Surface radiation

Back radiation

Absorbed by land and oceans 51%

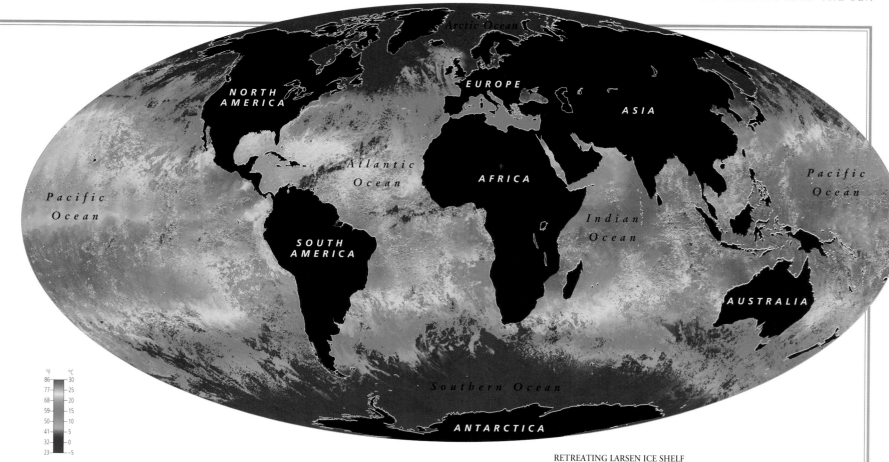

Monitoring sea surface temperature

Satellite-based instruments allow researchers to precisely measure the surface temperature of the world sea. The data used to generate this image was gathered over a period of 20 days in early spring. The coolest areas, around both the polar regions, show up as purple, while the warmest ocean regions show up as a red–orange band around the equator. A succession of such images allows scientists to monitor temperature shifts in different areas over time.

RETREATING LARSEN ICE SHELF

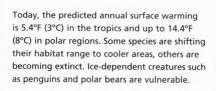

Atmospheric fireworks
As on land, a thunderstorm at sea can trigger the dramatic atmospheric discharge of electricity known as lightning. Bolts of lightning can travel an estimated 136,000 miles per hour (220,000 km/h).

1993
1947
1961
January 2002
March 2002

Retreating ice shelf
Over the years the extent of Antarctica's Larsen ice shelf has increased and decreased. In about 1960, however, the shelf began retreating due to prolonged global warming. Lines show ice shelf extent in 1947, 1961, 1993, and 2002.

Ice shelf collapse
In mid-March 2002, after shrinking steadily for 40 years, 1,255 square miles (3,250 km²) of the Larsen ice shelf collapsed, shattering into icebergs. The sudden event loosened 720 billion tons of ice into the sea.

Today, the predicted annual surface warming is 5.4°F (3°C) in the tropics and up to 14.4°F (8°C) in polar regions. Some species are shifting their habitat range to cooler areas, others are becoming extinct. Ice-dependent creatures such as penguins and polar bears are vulnerable.

Coral polyps secrete a calcium carbonate skeleton that is covered by a layer of living tissue containing zooxanthellae. Warming seawater upsets the symbiosis in which the coral shelters its algal partner in return for sugars and oxygen, which leads to coral bleaching.

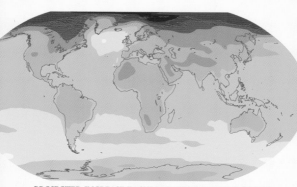

PROJECTED INCREASE IN SURFACE TEMPERATURE BY 2099

- 0–1.8°F (0–1°C)
- 1.8–3.6°F (1–2°C)
- 3.6–5.4°F (2–3°C)
- 5.4–7.2°F (3–4°C)
- 7.2–9°F (4–5°C)
- 9–10.8°F (5–6°C)
- 10.8–12.6°F (6–7°C)
- 12.6–14.4°F (7–8°C)

Corals stressed by warming seas may expel their resident zooxanthellae, or the algae may die. If conditions improve before the starving coral polyps die, they can take up new zooxanthellae and reestablish the life-sustaining symbiosis.

Healthy coral
1 Symbiotic zooxanthellae provide food and oxygen in exchange for protection.

Bleached coral
2 In bleached coral, polyp tissues no longer contain functioning zooxanthellae.

Dead coral
3 Surface algae blanket the bleached calcium carbonate skeletons.

EL NIÑO AND LA NIÑA

Interactions between the sea and Earth's atmosphere help shape both weather and climate. About 10 percent of seawater flows in wind-driven surface currents that have essential roles in climatic processes. In a roughly four-year cycle that unfolds along the coast of Peru, a tropical Pacific wind shift called the Southern Oscillation slows or reverses major currents. It also halts normal upwelling of cold, nutrient-rich water there. Spanish fishermen named this phenomenon El Niño (the Christ Child). It may last 18 months or longer. In the Americas and Southeast Asia, the abnormally warm, nutrient-poor El Niño current may mean disaster for fish and other wildlife that rely on seasonal upwelling for food. Increased evaporation of the warm surface water fuels an increase in severe storms that affect agriculture and other human activities. In an opposite phenomenon, La Niña, the sea surface remains uncharacteristically cool. It, too, produces abnormal weather patterns that extend around the globe.

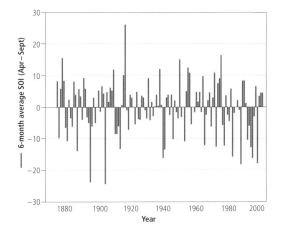

Southern Oscillation Index
The Southern Oscillation Index (SOI) tracks the air pressure difference between Tahiti and Darwin, Australia. When the SOI is strongly negative for several months, El Niño is underway. A strongly positive SOI marks La Niña.

Satellite monitoring of El Niño and La Niña
The TOPEX/Poseidon satellite monitors conditions in the oceans. Normal wind and current patterns were present in 2003. In 1997, however, satellite instruments tracked the development of El Niño. By October the mass of warm water (white area) had spread along the whole west coast of North and Central America. One year later, wind and current conditions had reversed and La Niña's cold water was upwelling.

Normal wind and current patterns
Normally in the tropical Pacific, surface winds blow westward, away from South America. Currents push warm water toward Indonesia, and upwelling replenishes nutrients and helps maintain normal weather patterns.

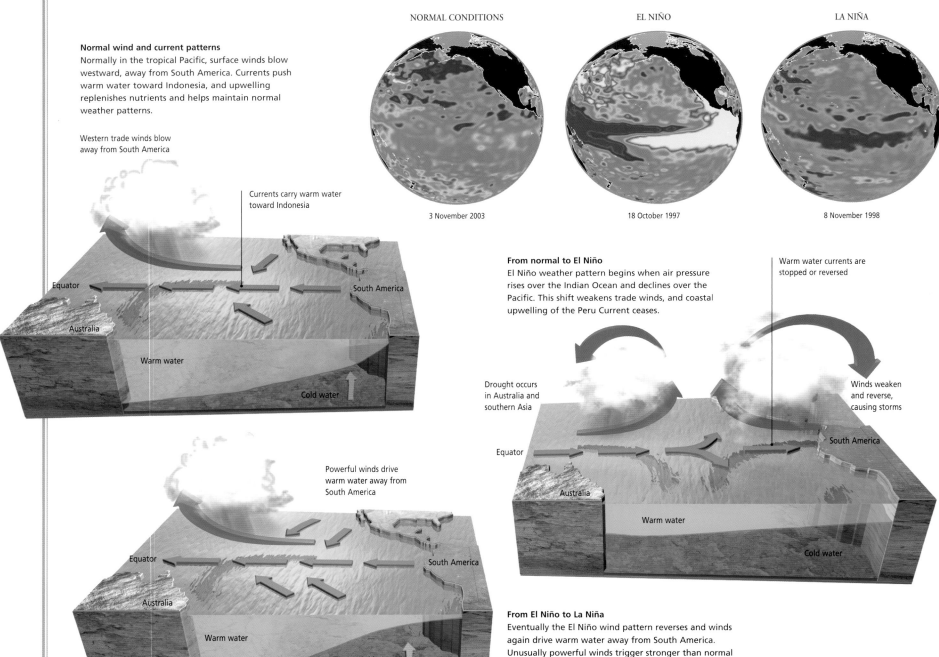

NORMAL CONDITIONS

3 November 2003

EL NIÑO

18 October 1997

LA NIÑA

8 November 1998

Western trade winds blow away from South America

Currents carry warm water toward Indonesia

Equator

South America

Australia

Warm water

Cold water

Powerful winds drive warm water away from South America

Equator

South America

Australia

Warm water

Cold water

From normal to El Niño
El Niño weather pattern begins when air pressure rises over the Indian Ocean and declines over the Pacific. This shift weakens trade winds, and coastal upwelling of the Peru Current ceases.

Warm water currents are stopped or reversed

Drought occurs in Australia and southern Asia

Winds weaken and reverse, causing storms

Equator

Australia

South America

Warm water

Cold water

From El Niño to La Niña
Eventually the El Niño wind pattern reverses and winds again drive warm water away from South America. Unusually powerful winds trigger stronger than normal upwelling of the Peru Current, setting La Niña in motion.

Shifting El Niño weather patterns

During El Niño, the arrival of an abnormal, large mass of warm water in the eastern Pacific may dramatically change precipitation patterns around the globe. Along the west coasts of North and South America, heavy downpours and tornadoes may wreak havoc in areas that are usually much drier, while extended drought develops in parts of Africa, Australia, and elsewhere.

- Dry and warm
- Warm
- Dry
- Wet and warm
- Wet
- Wet and cool

Starving seal
The 1997–98 El Niño had a serious impact on the marine food web along the west coast of the Americas. With its normal food supply of small fish greatly diminished, this sea lion pup (*Zalophus californianus*) is starving.

Coastal storm
Unusually frequent and severe storms and tornadoes are common during El Niño years. Coastal California has suffered huge losses in human life and property as storms triggered flooding, mud slides, and other damage.

Eye of the storm
Typhoon Fengshen slammed into coastal China, Macau, and the Philippines, causing over 1,400 deaths in 2008, La Niña year.

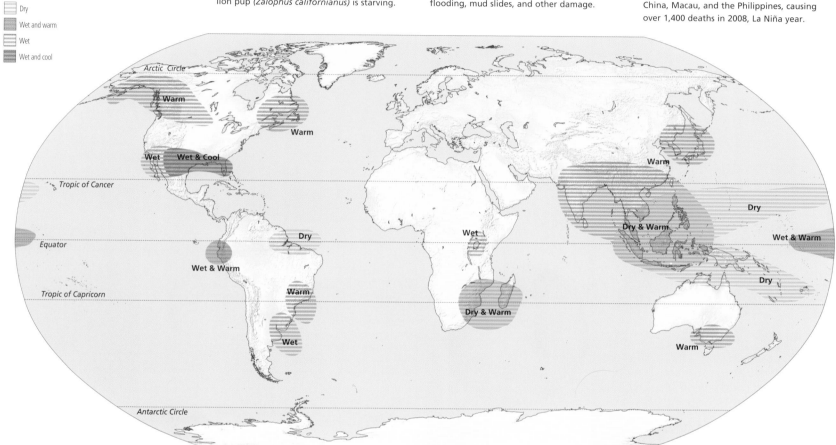

PERUVIAN ANCHOVY

The Peruvian anchovy (*Engraulis ringens*), or anchoveta, is a small fish that is used to manufacture high quality fish meal. It is the target of the world's largest fishery. The anchovies feed heavily on zooplankton. Their populations appear to grow, then contract in cycles of about 30 years. During El Niño, however, the population plummets when normal upwelling stops and zooplankton become scarce.

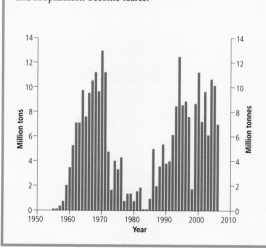

This diagram shows the relative habitats of several important fish species in the eastern Pacific. Peruvian anchovies are vulnerable in El Niño periods because they depend on coastal upwelling close to shore.

Peruvian anchovy populations have probably always cycled between highs and lows related to spawning success and food availability. Heavy commercial fishing contributed to steep crashes that began in El Niño periods of the early 1970s and late 1990s.

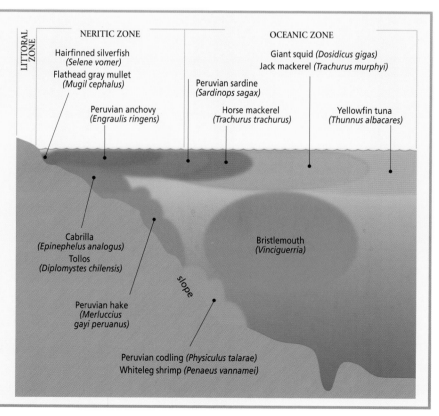

LITTORAL ZONE

NERITIC ZONE

OCEANIC ZONE

Hairfinned silverfish (*Selene vomer*)
Flathead gray mullet (*Mugil cephalus*)
Peruvian anchovy (*Engraulis ringens*)

Giant squid (*Dosidicus gigas*)
Jack mackerel (*Trachurus murphyi*)
Peruvian sardine (*Sardinops sagax*)
Horse mackerel (*Trachurus trachurus*)
Yellowfin tuna (*Thunnus albacares*)

Cabrilla (*Epinephelus analogus*)
Tollos (*Diplomystes chilensis*)
Peruvian hake (*Merluccius gayi peruanus*)

Bristlemouth (*Vinciguerria*)

slope

Peruvian codling (*Physiculus talarae*)
Whiteleg shrimp (*Penaeus vannamei*)

WIND

Wind is a force in driving ocean currents, including gyres that circulate around the fringes of the five largest ocean basins. Overall, air moves in patterns set by incoming solar energy. At lower latitudes, where sunlight is more intense, air warms, expands, and rises. At the poles air naturally cools, contracts, and falls. Earth's rotation shifts winds and currents to the right (clockwise) in the northern hemisphere and to the left (counter-clockwise) in the southern hemisphere. This shift is called the Coriolis effect. In addition, gravity pulls air from areas of high pressure, where the air mass is relatively cool, to areas of low pressure, where the air mass is warmer. Together these factors generate differing wind conditions over different ocean regions. In the ferocious rainstorms called cyclones or hurricanes, winds converge in an area of low pressure and spiral upward. An anticyclone develops over areas of high pressure and often correlates with fine weather.

WIND PATTERNS

Burga · Chinook · Santa Ana · Norte · Mistral · Foehn · Bora · Étesians · Seistan · Bise · Sirocco · Simoon · Sulawesi · Papagayo · Brisa · Shamai · Harmattan · Haboor dust storms · Berg · Brickfielder · Virazon · Brisa · Southerly Buster · Zonda · Pampero · Fremantle Doctor · Williwaw squalls · Canterbury Northwester

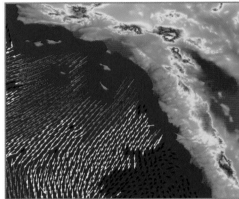

Wind speed and direction
Data from NASA's satellite-based Scatterometer precisely measure wind direction and speed. Shown here are the Santa Ana winds that buffet Southern California, USA. The colored arrows represent various ranges of wind speed.

The Coriolis effect
The Coriolis effect can be understood by imagining that someone sitting at the center of a moving roundabout (point A) throws a ball to someone sitting at a point on the rim (point B). By the time the ball reaches B, the person on the rim will have moved to point C. To this person, the ball will appear to have curved away from them.

North Pole
60°N
30°N
Equator
30°S
60°S
South Pole

Spinning planet
On our spinning planet, freely moving objects including weather systems appear to follow a curved path. They turn to the right in the northern hemisphere and to the left in the southern hemisphere.

Land and sea breezes
Coastal sea breezes develop early in the day when cooler air over the ocean rushes in to replace rising, warmer air over land. Overnight the process reverses, and land breezes develop.

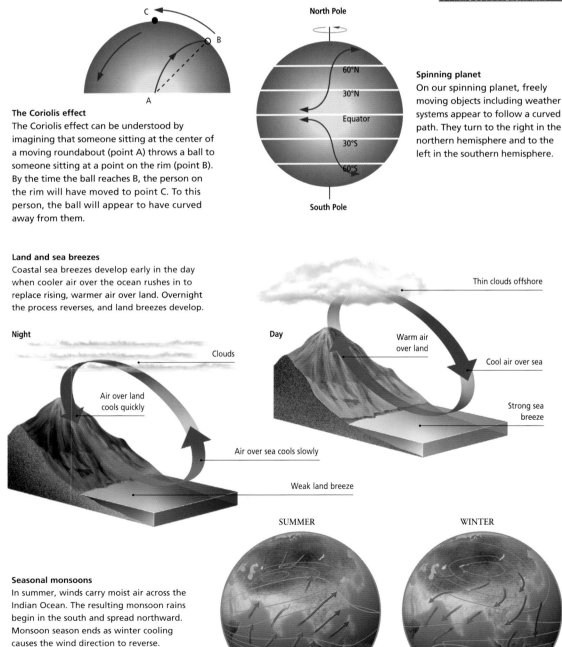

Night
Clouds
Air over land cools quickly
Air over sea cools slowly
Weak land breeze

Day
Thin clouds offshore
Warm air over land
Cool air over sea
Strong sea breeze

Seasonal monsoons
In summer, winds carry moist air across the Indian Ocean. The resulting monsoon rains begin in the south and spread northward. Monsoon season ends as winter cooling causes the wind direction to reverse.

SUMMER   WINTER

THE BERMUDA HIGH

A large, permanent region of high atmospheric pressure in the North Atlantic shifts with the seasons between the Azores and Bermuda. Air in this high picks up moisture from areas to the east. As the moist air circulates clockwise, it helps fuel the development of tropical storms and hurricanes that strike the Caribbean and the southeastern US during the summer and fall.

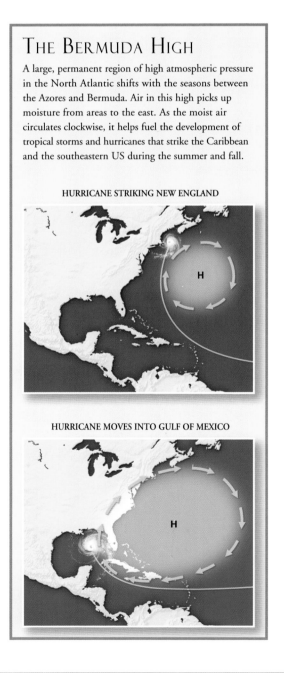

HURRICANE STRIKING NEW ENGLAND
H

HURRICANE MOVES INTO GULF OF MEXICO
H

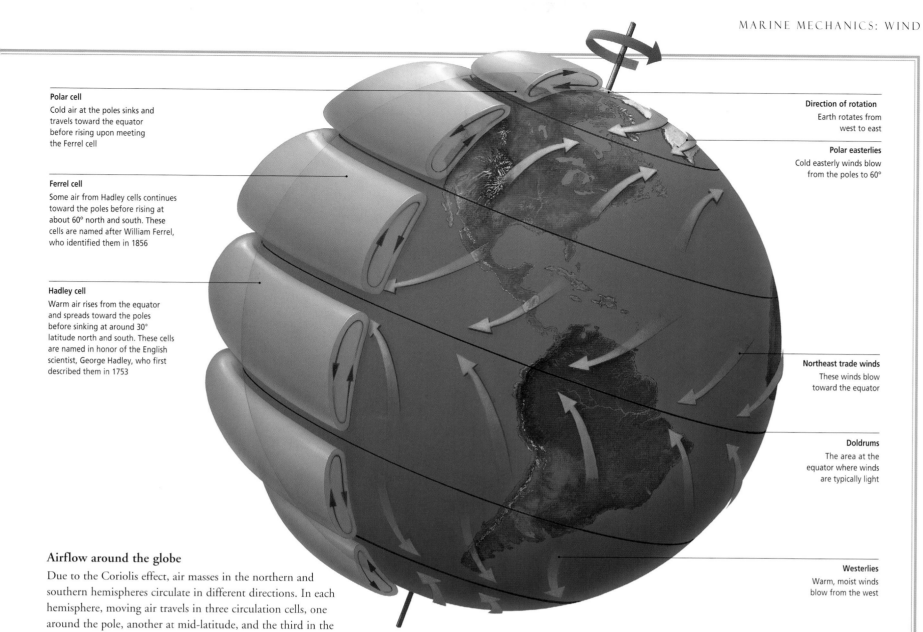

Polar cell
Cold air at the poles sinks and travels toward the equator before rising upon meeting the Ferrel cell

Ferrel cell
Some air from Hadley cells continues toward the poles before rising at about 60° north and south. These cells are named after William Ferrel, who identified them in 1856

Hadley cell
Warm air rises from the equator and spreads toward the poles before sinking at around 30° latitude north and south. These cells are named in honor of the English scientist, George Hadley, who first described them in 1753

Direction of rotation
Earth rotates from west to east

Polar easterlies
Cold easterly winds blow from the poles to 60°

Northeast trade winds
These winds blow toward the equator

Doldrums
The area at the equator where winds are typically light

Westerlies
Warm, moist winds blow from the west

Airflow around the globe

Due to the Coriolis effect, air masses in the northern and southern hemispheres circulate in different directions. In each hemisphere, moving air travels in three circulation cells, one around the pole, another at mid-latitude, and the third in the tropics bordering the equator. Among other effects, the circuits generate prevailing easterly winds in the tropics and high latitudes, and prevailing westerly winds in middle latitudes.

Stormy weather
Storms are atmospheric disturbances that develop when a region of high pressure envelops an area of low pressure. At sea, storm winds generate large, potentially dangerous waves.

Becoming becalmed
Mariners once dreaded becoming trapped in the doldrums, a belt of light winds in the tropics. A sail-powered ship might languish for days or weeks as supplies of food and drinkable water dwindle.

BEAUFORT WIND SCALE		
Force	Wind speed [mph (km/h)]	Description
0	below 1 (below 2)	calm
1	2–3 (3–5)	light air
2	4–7 (6–11)	light breeze
3	8–12 (12–19)	gentle breeze
4	13–18 (20–29)	moderate breeze
5	19–24 (30–38)	fresh breeze
6	25–31 (39–51)	strong breeze
7	32–38 (52–61)	near gale
8	39–46 (62–74)	gale
9	47–54 (75–86)	strong gale
10	55–63 (87–101)	whole gale
11	64–74 (102–120)	storm
12	above 74 (120)	hurricane

Beaufort Wind Scale

The Beaufort Wind scale ranks the force of wind at sea on a scale from zero (calm) to 12 (hurricane). The wind force determines how high wind-driven waves will be. It was devised to measure wind force on sailing ships.

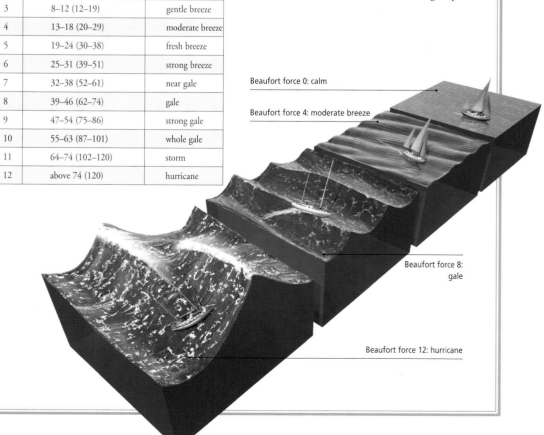

Beaufort force 0: calm

Beaufort force 4: moderate breeze

Beaufort force 8: gale

Beaufort force 12: hurricane

WAVES

From ripples to billowing swells and storm surges, waves are synonymous with the sea. All ocean waves are seawater set in motion by external energy. Most are wind waves that form as wind blows across the sea surface, its kinetic energy curling seawater up and forward. At a wave's crest, gravity pulls the water downward into a cuplike trough. Wind waves usually travel steadily across the surface, finally releasing energy when they reach the shore. Not surprisingly, the largest wind waves tend to occur in extremely windy ocean regions, such as the Southern Ocean encircling Antarctica. Along the southern coast of Australia, waves of nine–10 feet (2.7–3 m) are common. Storm winds often produce waves that reach 20 feet (6 m), although in areas such as the North Atlantic, wind and current conditions may produce so-called rogue waves that attain heights of 110 feet (33 m) or more.

PARTS OF A WAVE

wavelength

crest

steepness

height

trough

A shore thing
A shoreline's structure helps determine the characteristics of the waves that wash it. Towering, curling breakers develop where waves arrive at a steep shore, as here, in Waimea Bay off the Hawaiian island of Oahu.

Wave features
Wavelength is the distance between crests, while wave height is the vertical distance between a trough and a crest. Wave steepness is the angle from the bottom of a trough to the top of the neighboring crest.

Making waves

Wind moving over the ocean generates corresponding movement in surface water. Steady wind over great distances tends to generate long, smooth undulations called swells. In the surf zone close to shore, water particles move in circles that become larger closer to the surface. When the orbiting water particles strike bottom in the shallows, they flatten out. The forward thrust near shore forms crests and breakers.

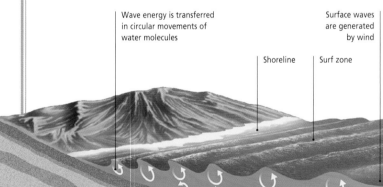

Wave energy is transferred in circular movements of water molecules

Surface waves are generated by wind

Shoreline

Surf zone

Movement of wind over the ocean generates corresponding movement in the water

Storm waves

As a storm builds, strengthening winds transfer a great deal of energy to the sea surface. Waves also interact with one another. This chaotic energy infusion may produce waves with a variety of wavelengths, heights, directions, and other physical characteristics, a phenomenon oceanographers term a wave sea. Rare rogue waves develop when many chaotic wind waves converge in a single spot.

1 Wind blowing across the sea surface produces small waves with rounded crests, narrow troughs, and a short wavelength.

2 As the waves continue to grow larger, the wave crests become more pointed and the troughs rounder.

3 Finally, the wave crests become less stable as gravity pulls them downward. Whitecaps form when the waves break.

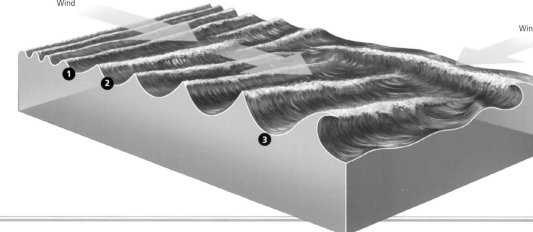

Wind

Wind

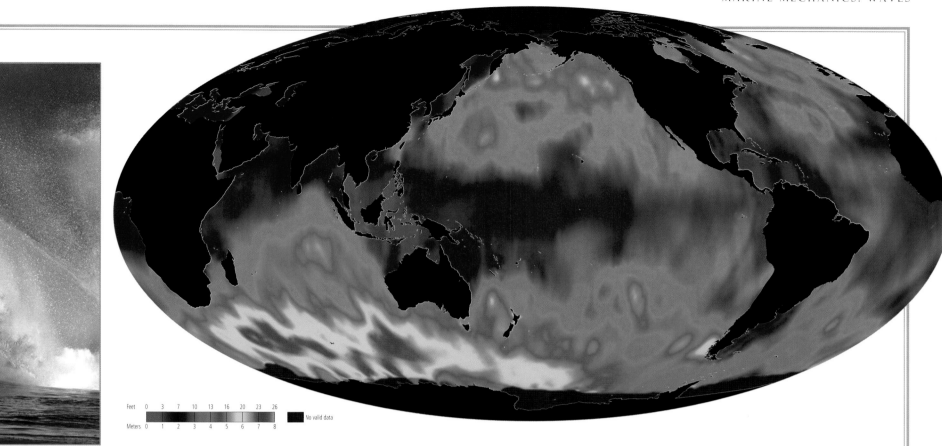

| Feet | 0 | 3 | 7 | 10 | 13 | 16 | 20 | 23 | 26 | No valid data |
| Meters | 0 | 1 | 2 | 3 | 4 | 5 | 6 | 7 | 8 | |

Wind waves on surface

Less dense water

Denser water

Internal wave
Waves can form below the sea surface, often at the bottom of a thermocline where a layer of warm water abuts a layer of colder, denser water. Generated by currents, tides, or winds, such internal waves can be more than 100 feet (30 m) high.

Waves around the world
This map shows the typical wave height in various regions of the global sea. Wave heights are color coded, from magenta for waves that are less than 3 feet (1 m) high, through blue, green, and yellow, to red for waves of 20–25 feet (7–8 m). The largest waves occur in the southern Indian Ocean and the Southern Ocean near Antarctica.

FIVE DIFFERENT WAVES

Capillary wave	A tiny ripple-like wave that carries only a little amount of wind energy.
Plunging wave	A breaking wave whose crest curls into a tube as the wave advances toward a steeply sloping shore.
Deepwater wave	A wave traveling through water deeper than half the wave length.
Spilling wave	A breaking wave whose crest crumbles onto the wave base as the wave advances up a gently sloping shore.
Forced wave	A wave that persists because the energy that generated it continues.

Sea swell
The gently rising and falling ocean surface motion called "swell" consists of longer period waves that do not break. The arrival of swell in calm waters can indicate a storm is coming.

Storm-battered shores
Storm waves crashing on a Nova Scotia coast transfer their considerable energy to the shore. Many shorelines are regularly reshaped by the pounding force of storm waves.

Underwater
The slope of the bottom effects the way waves break over it. In this shallow Micronesian reef, the reef structure disperses the wave energy, so that the waves break gently on the shore.

WAVE POWER
Several coastal nations are exploiting ocean waves and winds as a renewable source of electrical energy that does not contribute to global warming. Technologies already in place include wave-powered generators, underwater turbines, and coastal wind farms that take advantage of steady sea breezes. The ceaseless motion of tides can also be used to produce electricity.

In a tidal power-generating system, a pump in a buoy drives seawater through a turbine, which in turn drives a generator connected to the shore.

Hydraulic pump encased in a buoy

Anchor and turbine

Generator in a canister

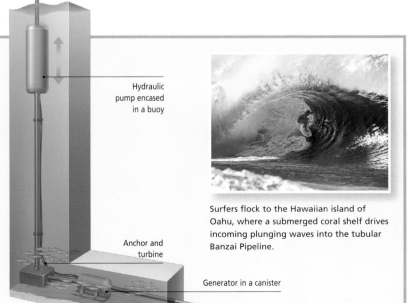

Surfers flock to the Hawaiian island of Oahu, where a submerged coral shelf drives incoming plunging waves into the tubular Banzai Pipeline.

TSUNAMIS

One of the most potentially dangerous ocean waves is a tsunami, a massive flood of water caused by a seismic shift such as a seafloor earthquake or an erupting undersea volcano. The term tsunami describes a speeding wall of water that can reach heights of 100 feet (30 m) or more and travel at a speed of 500 miles per hour (800 km/h). Typically, the triggering event launches a succession of huge waves as much as 45 minutes apart. Such waves may be imperceptible in the deep open ocean, but as a tsunami nears shore its height increases dramatically. In 1960, a tsunami generated by an earthquake off the coast of Chile raced 9,000 miles (14,500 km) to Japan where it caused massive damage and took 180 lives. Even more destructive was a 2004 tsunami that destroyed the Indonesian city of Banda Aceh and killed a total of more than 225,000 people.

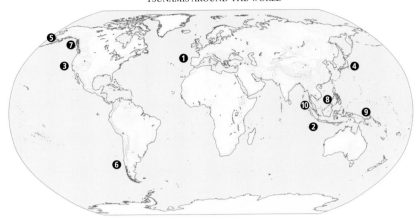

TSUNAMIS AROUND THE WORLD

Ten Worst Tsunamis		
1	1775	An earthquake in Lisbon generates a tsunami. More than 60,000 people die.
2	1883	Krakatau erupts and a tsunami sweeps over Indonesia; 36,000 people die.
3	1896	A tsunami hits Los Angeles on the Californian coast.
4	1896	The Sanriku tsunami strikes Japan and kills more than 26,000 people.
5	1946	Alaskan quake generates a tsunami. Hours later it kills 159 people in Hawaii.
6	1960	A tsunami kills 1,000 people in Chile, 61 people in Hawaii, and 180 people in Japan.
7	1964	Waves from an Alaskan quake sweep down the west coast, killing 122 people.
8	1976	A tsunami kills more than 5,000 people in the Philippines.
9	1998	A tsunami strikes the north coast of Papua New Guinea, killing 2,000 people.
10	2004	A powerful earthquake triggers waves that travel thousands of miles to crash onto the coastlines of at least 14 Asian and African countries. More than 225,000 people die.

Great wave in art
In the 1820s, Japanese artist Katsushika Hokusai captured the awesome power of huge ocean waves in his famous woodblock print *The Great Wave off Kanagawa*. The Japanese word tsunami roughly translates as "harbor wave."

Progress of a tsunami

After a shock launches a tsunami, it can travel across an ocean in less than a day. At sea the gathering tsunami may be less than 40 inches (1 m) high and vessels may hardly notice it. Nearing shore, the speed of tsunami waves slows and their height increases. The tsunami arrives as a series of wave crests and troughs 10 to 45 minutes apart.

Alaska 1964
In 1964, a tsunami struck southeastern Alaska with deadly force. Generated by a magnitude 9.2 earthquake beneath Prince William Sound, the gigantic wall of water wiped out several coastal villages and took 122 lives.

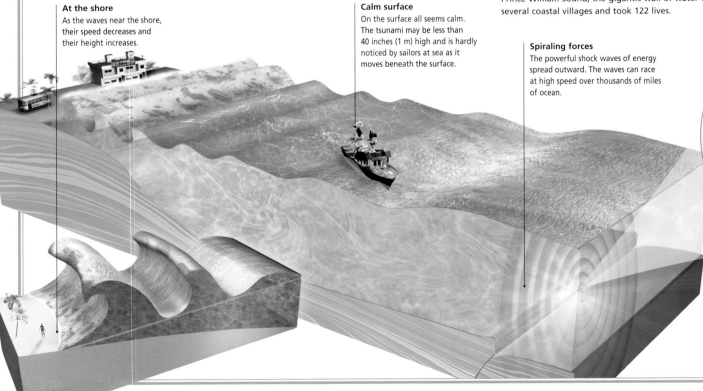

At the shore
As the waves near the shore, their speed decreases and their height increases.

Calm surface
On the surface all seems calm. The tsunami may be less than 40 inches (1 m) high and is hardly noticed by sailors at sea as it moves beneath the surface.

Spiraling forces
The powerful shock waves of energy spread outward. The waves can race at high speed over thousands of miles of ocean.

Submarine shock
Most tsunamis develop when an earthquake occurs deep in the ocean. Seafloor tectonic plates shift against one another, producing powerful shock waves. The energy of these waves then is transferred to the sea above.

Pre-tsunami
The Indonesian province of Aceh took the brunt of the December 2004 Indian Ocean tsunami. This aerial view shows the town of Lhokna in 2003.

Washed away
The tsunami washed away most buildings and vegetation in Lhokna, drowned nearby agricultural areas, and removed sand from the nearby beaches.

Monster tsunami

Throughout coastal Indonesia, the morning of December 26, 2004 held no sign of impending danger from the tsunami. Shortly before the first wave struck, however, the ocean off Aceh receded as water was pulled out toward the growing wave offshore. Then a series of waves up to 50 feet (15 m) high rushed toward the shore, crashed upon the beach, and pushed inland with massive force.

BEFORE THE TSUNAMI

WATER RETREATS

DISASTER STRIKES

AN ASIAN EARTHQUAKE AND TSUNAMI

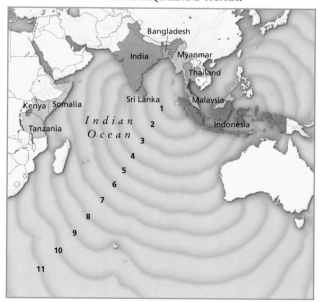

Bangladesh

India   Myanmar

Thailand

Kenya   Somalia   Sri Lanka   Malaysia
                                        1
Tanzania   *Indian*   2   Indonesia
            Ocean   3
                    4
                    5
                6
                7
            8
        9
    10
11

DEATH TOLL

▮ >100 000	▮ 10 000–100 000	▮ 1 000–10 000
▮ <1 000	▢ no data	**2** hours after event

Path to destruction
The Richter magnitude 9.2 or 9.3 earthquake that occurred on December 26, 2004 caused movement along a fault to the west of Sumatra. The sudden displacement in the sea floor sent a shock wave across the ocean. This map shows the hour-by-hour progress of the wave over 11 hours. When the wave reached shallow water it piled up into a devastating tsunami.

DETECTION AND WARNING

Tsunamis can hit coastlines both near to and far from the site of origin. In coastal nations around the world, early-warning systems help civil defense personnel predict when and where a tsunami will strike, and to inform the populace. The systems include sensors that monitor undersea earthquakes and other seismic shifts, and devices mounted on specialized buoys that track unusual shifts in the height of the sea surface.

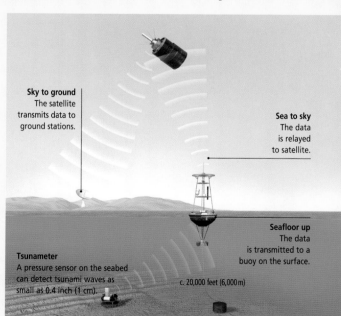

Sky to ground
The satellite transmits data to ground stations.

Sea to sky
The data is relayed to satellite.

Seafloor up
The data is transmitted to a buoy on the surface.

Tsunameter
A pressure sensor on the seabed can detect tsunami waves as small as 0.4 inch (1 cm).

c. 20,000 feet (6,000 m)

This sign provides tsunami evacuation instructions at the beach on Koh Lipe, Thailand. Similar signs now appear in many beach areas vulnerable to tsunamis.

Hurricanes

Tropical cyclones are among the most powerful of all natural events. Called hurricanes in the Atlantic and eastern Pacific and typhoons in the western Pacific, these huge swirling storms generally develop over tropical seas where warm air soaks up evaporating surface water. Over several days, the air mass starts spinning counterclockwise in the northern hemisphere, attaining hurricane status when the wind speed reaches 74 miles per hour (118 km/h). Air in the calm center or "eye" of a hurricane is warmer and under lower pressure than in the spiraling rain bands farther out. The greater the pressure difference between the inner and outer regions, the greater a hurricane's intensity and the potential threat to life and property. The largest and most intense tropical cyclone on record is Super Typhoon Tip, which struck southern Japan in 1979 and caused major flooding and loss of life. Measuring 1,380 miles (2,220 km) in diameter, Tip generated maximum winds of 190 miles per hour (305 km/h).

Eye of a hurricane
In 2005, Hurricane Hernan developed into a huge storm off California and northwestern Mexico. Maximum winds measured 165 miles per hour (266 km/h). This satellite image clearly shows its eye, the calm area at a hurricane's center.

Pressure systems
In a low-pressure system, surface air converges counterclockwise toward the center, then rises and diverges in the opposite direction. The reverse happens in a high-pressure system. Air flows from high to low pressure, creating wind.

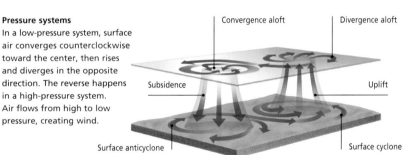
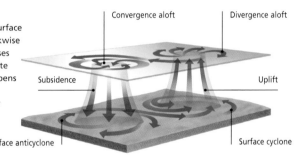

Convergence aloft   Divergence aloft

Subsidence   Uplift

Surface anticyclone   Surface cyclone

Southern hemisphere hurricane
A satellite tracks Hurricane Monica, building strength off northeastern Australia in April 2006, the southern hemisphere autumn. Its winds eventually peaked at 215 miles per hour (370 km/h). Colored areas correlate with rainfall, with red being the heaviest.

How a hurricane works

A hurricane forms when rising humid air begins rotating counterclockwise. As the air rises, it creates intense low pressure that essentially sucks in additional air over the sea surface. The circulating warm air typically holds a great deal of water vapor—a large hurricane can dump 20 billion tons (18 billion t) of rainwater in a day. Paired with high winds, the deluge can cause severe damage on land.

❶ Eyewall
The calm eye of a hurricane is surrounded by an eyewall—massive, dark storm clouds that produce the heaviest rain and strongest winds.

❷ Spiraling air
An upward spiral of warm, moist air is drawn into the central area of low pressure. Moisture sustains the formation of the storm clouds.

❸ Rain bands
As the storm builds, spiraling bands of rain clouds form. The outer bands may be more than 200 miles (320 km) from the eye.

❹ Approaching land
The eye forms and the hurricane is at its most dangerous approaching land.

❺ Over land
Without moisture from the sea, the hurricane starts to lose some of its energy.

❻ Hurricane dies
Farther inland the hurricane dissipates.

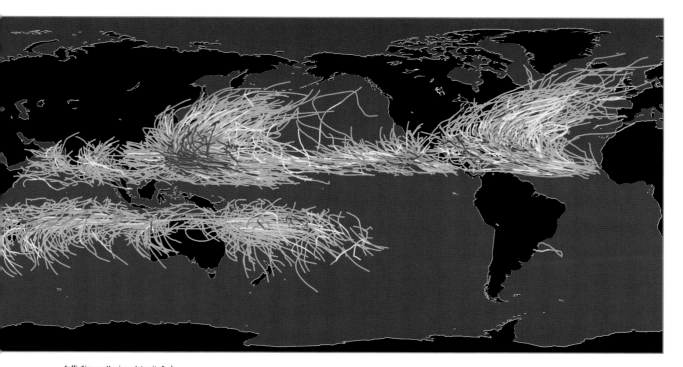

Hurricane Andrew's destruction, Florida, 1992

Saffir-Simpson Hurricane Intensity Scale

| TD | TS | 1 | 2 | 3 | 4 | 5 |

Measuring hurricane intensity

Climatologists use the Saffir-Simpson Scale shown at right to categorize a hurricane's intensity. The most powerful hurricanes typically develop in the western Pacific, which historically has tallied more category 4 and 5 storms than anywhere else. By contrast, hurricanes are virtually unknown in the South Pacific and southern Atlantic oceans, where cold currents translate into cool air that gives off less water vapor to the atmosphere.

THE SAFFIR-SIMPSON SCALE

Category number	Wind speed [mph (km/h)]	Storm surge [ft (m)]	Damage
1	74–95 (118–152)	4–5 (1.2–1.6)	Minimal
2	96–110 (153–176)	6–8 (1.7–2.5)	Moderate
3	111–130 (177–208)	9–12 (2.6–3.7)	Extensive
4	131–155 (209–248)	13–18 (3.8–5.4)	Extensive
5	More than 155 (248)	More than 18 (5.4)	Catastrophic

Shrimp boats blown ashore by Hurricane Katrina, 2005

TEN WORST HURRICANES   H = Hurricane, T.S. = Tropical Storm, T = Typhoon

	Year	Name and place	Deaths
1	1998	H. Mitch, Central America	11,000
2	1900	No name, Texas	6,000–12,000
3	1974	H. Fifi, Honduras	5,000
4	2004	T.S. Jeanne, Haiti	3,000
5	2005	H. Katrina, Louisiana & Mississippi	1,193
6	1979	H. David, Caribbean, Florida, Georgia, New York	1,000
7	1994	T. Fred, China	1,000
8	2004	T. Winnie, Philippines	(dead/missing) 1,000
9	1944	T. Cobra, Philippine Sea	790
10	2005	H. Stan , Central America	725

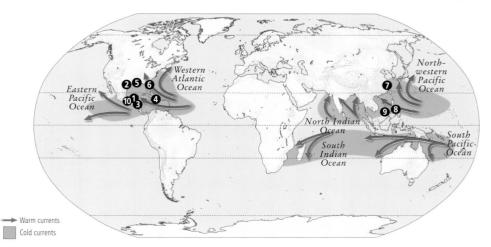

Warm currents
Cold currents

WATERSPOUTS

A tornado is a funnel of air rapidly spiraling upward into a cloud. It is the most violent of all climatic phenomena. Waterspouts are tornadoes that develop or pass over warm, shallow water, sucking up a whirling column of water that may rise as high as 300 feet (100 m). Waterspouts usually develop during tropical storms when masses of cold and warm air interact with the sea surface.

Not all waterspouts develop at sea. Some begin to form over land and then move to warm coastal waters offshore.

Mariners of old recounted frightening encounters with waterspouts. This 19th century painting clearly depicts multiple waterspouts threatening the sailing ship *Trombes*.

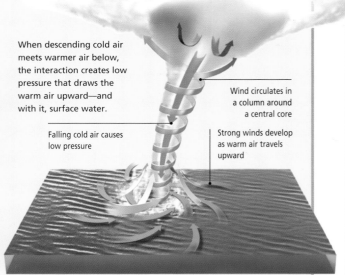

When descending cold air meets warmer air below, the interaction creates low pressure that draws the warm air upward—and with it, surface water.

Wind circulates in a column around a central core

Falling cold air causes low pressure

Strong winds develop as warm air travels upward

Tides

Tides may be the sea's most predictable changes. In each tide cycle, the sea surface rises, then falls in conjunction with the shifting pull of gravity from the Moon and the Sun as Earth rotates on its axis. Lunar gravity exerts the strongest pull, so the sea bulges below the Moon's position above Earth. A corresponding bulge occurs on the planet's opposite side. As Earth rotates through the bulges, the result is a pattern of shallow, planet-sized waves that are visible as rising and falling water levels along the shore. The highest and lowest tides, called spring tides, occur year-round at two-week intervals corresponding to the full and new moon. "Neap tides"—the lowest high and highest low tides—occur during the Moon's first- and third-quarter phases. Regardless, because the Moon rises 51 minutes later each day, a tide cycle lasts 24 hours and 51 minutes and high tide occurs 51 minutes later each day.

Spring and neap tides

Spring tides result when Earth, the Moon, and the Sun all align. The combination of their gravitational effects increases both high tide height and low tide levels. Neap tides occur when Earth, the Moon, and the Sun form the points of a triangle. In this configuration, the Moon's gravitational pull is at right angles to that of the Sun and the Sun's gravity partly cancels it out.

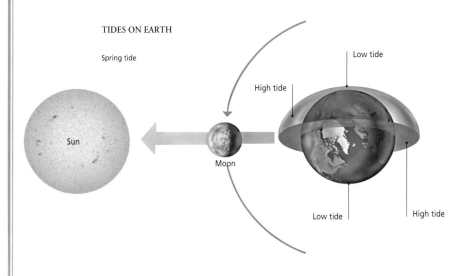

TIDES ON EARTH

Spring tide

Low tide

High tide

Sun

Moon

Low tide

High tide

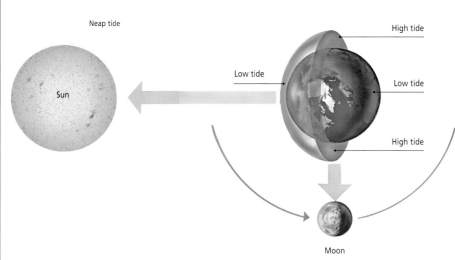

Neap tide

High tide

Low tide

Sun

Low tide

High tide

Moon

Tides around the globe

Three general tide patterns occur along Earth's coastlines. Most coastal areas experience semidiurnal, or twice daily, tides in which the levels of high or low tides are about equal. Also common are mixed tides—semidiurnal tides in which the levels of highs or lows are unequal. Along some coastlines tides follow a simpler diurnal pattern of one high and one low a day.

Highest high tide
The shape and depth of the Bay of Fundy, on Canada's east coast, give it perhaps the greatest tidal range in the world—56 feet (17 m). This photograph shows Hopewell Rocks at high tide, when the rock bases are submerged.

Lowest low tide
At low tide, Hopewell Rocks are completely above the water line and the shore is a broad mudflat. Tidal action has scoured out the rocks' pedestal-like bases and eventually will erode them away completely.

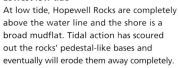

Bea
S

NOR
AMER

Gulf
Mexi

Pacific Ocean

▨	Semidiurnal tides
▫	Diurnal tides
▨	Mixed tides

SCALE 1:146,000,000
Robinson Projection

Reef revealed
At Montgomery Reef in northwest Australia, the exposed reef visible at maximum low tide, when all the seawater drains into the ocean, extends over nearly 116 square miles (300 km²).

TIDE INFORMATION	
1 Nature of tide waves	Shallow water wave
2 Tide wave wavelength	About 12,400 miles (20,000 km)
3 Diurnal tide interval	24 hours, 50 minutes
4 Semidiurnal tide interval	6 hours, 12.5 minutes (high/low roughly equal)
5 Mixed tide interval	6 hours, 12.5 minutes (high/low unequal)
6 Speed of tide wave energy through ocean	About 435 miles per hour (700 km/h)

Hidden reef
At high tide at Montgomery Reef, the spectacular reef is submerged. The tidal range is about 33 feet (10 m), ranking second in the world after the Bay of Fundy in Nova Scotia.

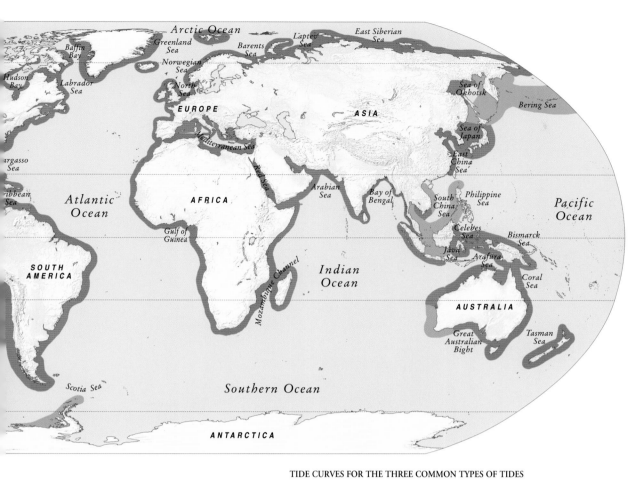

Bright red tide
A so-called "red tide" is a "bloom" of millions of rusty-hued phytoplankton called dinoflagellates. Toxic to fish or shellfish and other marine life, red-tide organisms can also cause poisoning and allergic reactions in humans.

TIDE CURVES FOR THE THREE COMMON TYPES OF TIDES

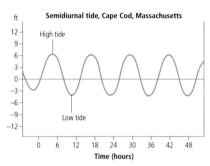
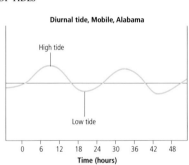
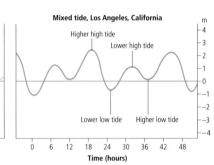

Tide curves
These graphs plot how water levels fluctuate during different types of tides over a 48-hour period. Although the water levels are unequal in mixed tides (pink), the shifting pattern repeats about every 12 hours 25 minutes.

THAMES BARRIER

In some harbor areas where extreme high tides or storm surge may threaten cities and towns, engineers have created barriers that can be moved into place to block the tidal flow. One of the largest protects areas of London, England from tidal flooding of the river Thames. Its water-filled, crescent-shaped steel gates can be rotated upward to block floodwater, then rotated back underwater when danger is past.

The Thames Barrier is just over 1,700 feet (520 m) long. Each of its 10 submerged gates spans 200 feet (61 m) and can rise 35 feet (10.7 m) above the Thames River's normal water level.

Barrier raised
The Thames Barrier is raised to protect against an impending flood and a remotely controlled gate arm pivots each gate upward. The gates can also be rotated 180 degrees for maintenance and are put through a test run every month.

Barrier lowered
The Thames Barrier is lowered when not in use and its curved gates nest in concave concrete foundations sunk into the riverbed. The depth of the channels above allows normal vessel traffic on the river.

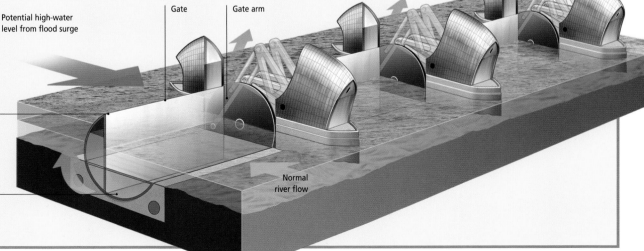

This photograph shows colonies of coral animals, each a polyp that resembles a slender, white-tipped stalk. The polyps grow, they are nourished, and they reproduce as they undulate with the current in tropical shallows. The catalog of marine life encompasses a striking array of animals, plants, and microorganisms, each with structures and functions suited to survival in a particular undersea environment.

SEA ENVIRONMENT

SEA DEPTHS

All forms of life on Earth are profoundly affected by their physical surroundings. In the sea, two of the most crucial physical factors are light and temperature conditions at different depths. Oceanographers divide the three-dimensional marine environment into the pelagic zone of open water and the bottom or benthic zone—each home to a striking diversity of marine life. The layers of the pelagic zone are defined by the amount of sunlight reaching them. The upper sunlight zone, where the most light penetrates, ranges from the surface to about 660 feet (200 m). Here marine life is most abundant, with the seas teeming with organisms ranging from bacteria to a wealth of fish and other species. Below, a dimmer, cooler, and less populated "twilight" zone extends down from 660–3,300 feet (200–1,000 m). The deep sea is a frigid, dark world where relatively few types of organisms survive.

Life at different depths

Similarly to land animals, sea creatures need a particular set of environmental conditions to survive. For example, like plants, phytoplankton and algae can only survive where there is enough sunlight for photosynthesis. Far more conspicuous are the thousands of species of marine fishes, some adapted for life near the surface of the sea, others that survive in mid-waters, and still others with features that suit them for great depths.

Surface for air
Sperm whales (*Physeter macrocephalus*) must surface to breathe, but they may dive as deep as 3,300 feet (1,000 m) in search of their giant squid prey.

Environments for life

Away from shore, the sea becomes a deepening universe of interacting physical and chemical factors. Although overall water depth varies greatly within different ocean basins, each of Earth's five oceans is subdivided into parts having different features. Horizontally an ocean includes nearshore and open waters. Vertically it has layered zones where depth-related shifts in temperature, salinity and other conditions set the ground rules for survival of marine species.

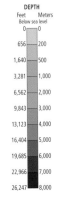

DEPTH	
Feet	Meters
Below sea level	
0	0
656	200
1,640	500
3,281	1,000
6,562	2,000
9,843	3,000
13,123	4,000
16,404	5,000
19,685	6,000
22,966	7,000
26,247	8,000

Ocean zones
Ocean waters are subdivided broadly into a nearshore neritic realm and the oceanic realm. The pelagic realm encompasses the sunlit epipelagic and dimmer mesopelagic zones, the dark bathypelagic and abyssopelagic zones, and the hadal zone of seafloor trenches.

SCALE 1:143,100,000
Mercator Projection

THE FOOD-RICH SURFACE

The upper two percent of the global sea contains more living organisms than the rest of the ocean combined. Here sunlight fuels the growth of vast pastures of plant-like phytoplankton that sustain themselves by photosynthesis. They are the vital foundation for a global food web that includes zooplankton, tiny drifting animals preyed upon by species ranging from shrimps to whales. Food-rich surface waters also sustain a tremendous variety of fish species.

This species of krill (*Euphausia superba*) and the sea butterfly (*Clione limacina*) are types of zooplankton that drift or swim weakly with surface sea currents.

Krill

Sea butterfly

Diatoms are mostly single-celled phytoplankton with a hard, shell-like casing of silica that often forms an intricate pattern characteristic of each species.

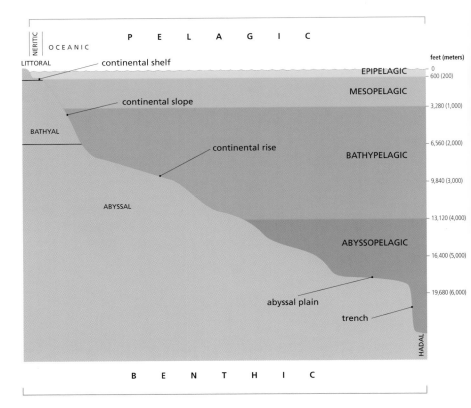

			feet (meters)
NERITIC	OCEANIC	P E L A G I C	
LITTORAL	continental shelf	EPIPELAGIC	0 / 600 (200)
	continental slope	MESOPELAGIC	3,280 (1,000)
BATHYAL	continental rise	BATHYPELAGIC	6,560 (2,000)
			9,840 (3,000)
ABYSSAL		ABYSSOPELAGIC	13,120 (4,000)
			16,400 (5,000)
	abyssal plain		19,680 (6,000)
		trench	
		HADAL	
B E N T H I C			

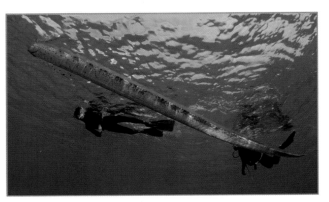

Marine snow
Researchers deploy fine-mesh nets to collect "marine snow"—wastes and other decaying particles that drift toward the bottom. A crucial food source for many marine organisms, this material is the energy base for most deep-sea ecosystems.

Ribbon-like body
The longest bony fish in the ocean—the oarfish (*Regalecus glesne*)—grows to about 50 feet (15 m) and lives as deep as 3,000 feet (914 m). This specimen photographed in Kasari Bay, Japan, dwarfs the two divers swimming alongside.

Fast swimmer
The blue and silver mahi mahi *(Coryphaena hippurus)* closely match the hues of the upper ocean waters where these speedsters live and pursue darting flying fish.

Upward migrator
Lanternfish *(Diaphus* sp.) spend the day away from surface predators between 1,000 and 3,300 feet (303–1,000 m), but migrate upward at night to feed in the dark.

Deep-sea dweller
Humpback anglerfish *(Melanacetus johnsoni)* have a luminous fin spine on the head that attracts prey and potential mates. Several species live as deep as 6,600 feet (2,000 m).

Into the abyss
The abyssal cuskeel *(Abyssobrotula galatheae)* lives at extreme depths below 13,000 feet (4,000 m) in the abyssopelagic zone, where daylight never penetrates.

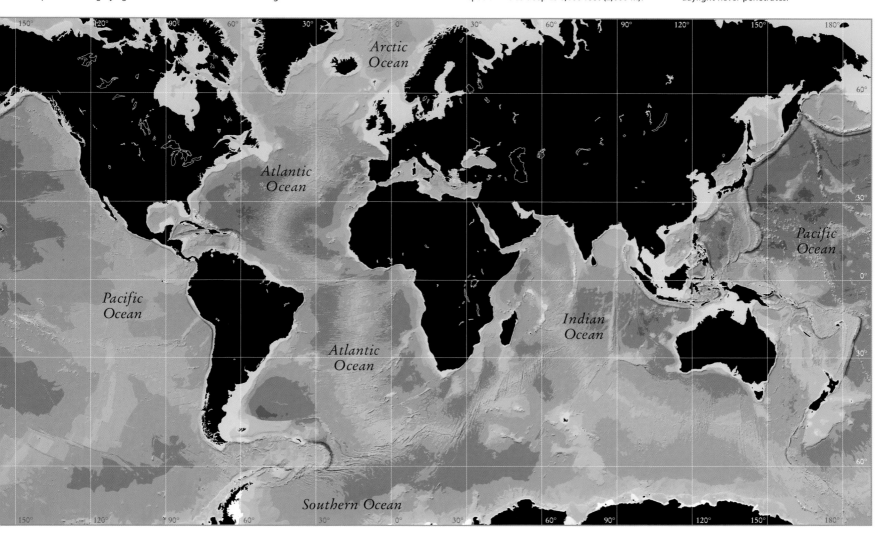

Deep-Sea Vents

Hydrothermal vents may develop along crustal cracks where seafloor spreading is occurring. Dozens are known, all spewing a scalding blend of water and chemicals that may exceed 600°F (350°C). Some vents build into "smokers" that spout water chemically tinted gray or black. These towering structures have been known to rise 15 stories before collapsing. Vent communities include some of the strangest of all marine animals.

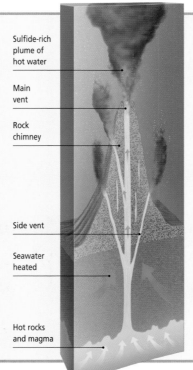

Sulfide-rich plume of hot water

Main vent

Rock chimney

Side vent

Seawater heated

Hot rocks and magma

Black smokers are the hottest vents. This one is releasing its chemical-laced plume at a hydrothermal spring in the mid-ocean ridge of the Atlantic.

Pale, oversized mussels *(Bathymodiolus* sp.) blanket an area near a hydrothermal spring in the Pacific. They share their real estate with crabs, shrimp, and limpets.

This aptly named, 2-inch (5-cm) spiny crab (species unknown) scuttles through a vent community hunting for live food, sometimes including other crabs.

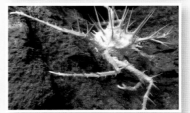

Minerals in vent plumes harden into whitish rock chimneys that can be more than 63 feet (19 m) high. This relatively small example is about 3.3 feet (1 m) across.

UNDERWATER TOPOGRAPHY

It took centuries for marine scientists to begin to grasp the remarkable diversity of Earth's undersea landscapes. With the advent of increasingly sophisticated sonar, manned and remote-operated submersibles, advanced underwater cameras, and other methods, researchers today have a much fuller understanding of the sea's major topographic features. This physical portrait includes: the submerged, sloping margins of the continents; scores of submarine canyons; the vast plains of the deep abyss; plunging ocean trenches; approximately 20,000 inactive volcanoes that form structures known as seamounts and guyots; and about 40,400 miles (65,000 km) of sinuous undersea mountain ranges marking the submerged seams of crustal plates. Similar diversity marks the seafloor surface, which may be rocky, sandy, or a blend of sand and mud. Where tectonic events are actively producing new seafloor, surface sediments are usually thin. In contrast, at the "rise" where a continental shelf tapers to the deep ocean floor, deep blankets of soft sediments can develop.

The undersea landscape

Tools including satellite-based sensors and sonar are the stock-in-trade of bathymetry—literally measuring "the deep." Today, their computer-processed data provides a revealing and detailed portrait of the undersea landscape, with its varied array of continental shelves, huge undersea canyons, mid-ocean ridges, soaring peaks, vast trenches, and abyssal plains. These features include the deepest point on Earth and its tallest mountain—a peak that breaks the surface as the island of Hawaii.

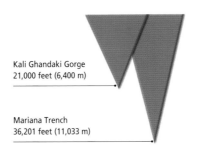

Kali Ghandaki Gorge
21,000 feet (6,400 m)

Mariana Trench
36,201 feet (11,033 m)

Mauna Kea
33,000 feet (10,000m)

Mount Everest
29,029 feet (8,848 m)

Deepest trenches
The Mariana Trench, the deepest part of the world seas, is more than 15,000 feet (4,572 m) deeper than the deepest land trench, Nepal's Kali Ghandaki Gorge.

Highest mountains
The marine volcano visible above the sea surface as Hawaii's Mauna Kea rises about 4,000 feet (1,219 m) higher than the tallest mountain on land, Mount Everest.

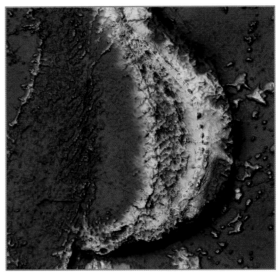

The Mariana Trench
The deepest point on Earth, the sickle-shaped Mariana Trench in the western Pacific, slices more than 36,100 feet (11,022 m) into Earth's crust. Due in part to the lack of food at that depth, life there is scarce.

Volcanic legacy
Researchers have ample evidence of past undersea volcanoes. These images compare the crater of an extinct land volcano, Crater Lake in the US state of Oregon, and the crater of an extinct marine volcano in the western Pacific.

SEDIMENTARY BASINS

Sediment blankets about 75 percent of the ocean basins and much of the continental shelves. Some of these sediments enter the marine environment as weathering rock and eroding soil washed or blown into the sea or carried there by rivers. Some form muddy deposits while others are converted to sticky clays. Still other sediments are soft "oozes" consisting of the decomposing remains of marine organisms.

SEDIMENTARY DEPOSITS

Onshore sedimentary deposits

Offshore sedimentary deposits

CRATER LAKE, OREGON, USA

feet	meters
8200	2500
6560	2000
4920	1500
3280	1000

sea level

-1640	-500
-3280	-1000
-4920	-1500
-6560	-2000
-8200	-2500
-9840	-3000
-11480	-3500

122°10'W   122°00'W

WEST ROTA, SOUTHERN MARIANA ARC

14°30'N
14°20'N
14°10'N

144°40'E   144°40'E   144°40'E

0   10 miles
0   10 km

Under the sea
Deep ocean basins make up more than half of Earth's surface. Some of their most notable geologic features are canyons cleaving the continental slopes, mid-ocean mountain ridges, steep trenches, and broad, flat abyssal plains.

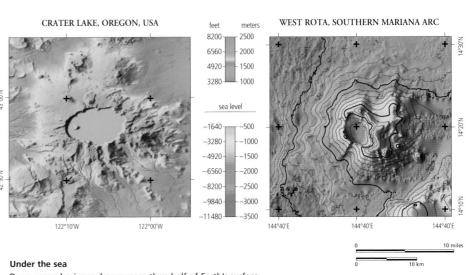

Continental shelf   Continental slope   Mid-ocean ridge   Trench
Continental rise
Abyssal plain

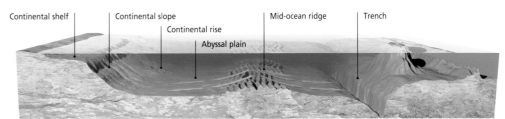

Sedimentary rock on land reveals the gradual layering of sediments over spans of time. This formation is in Death Valley National Park, California, USA.

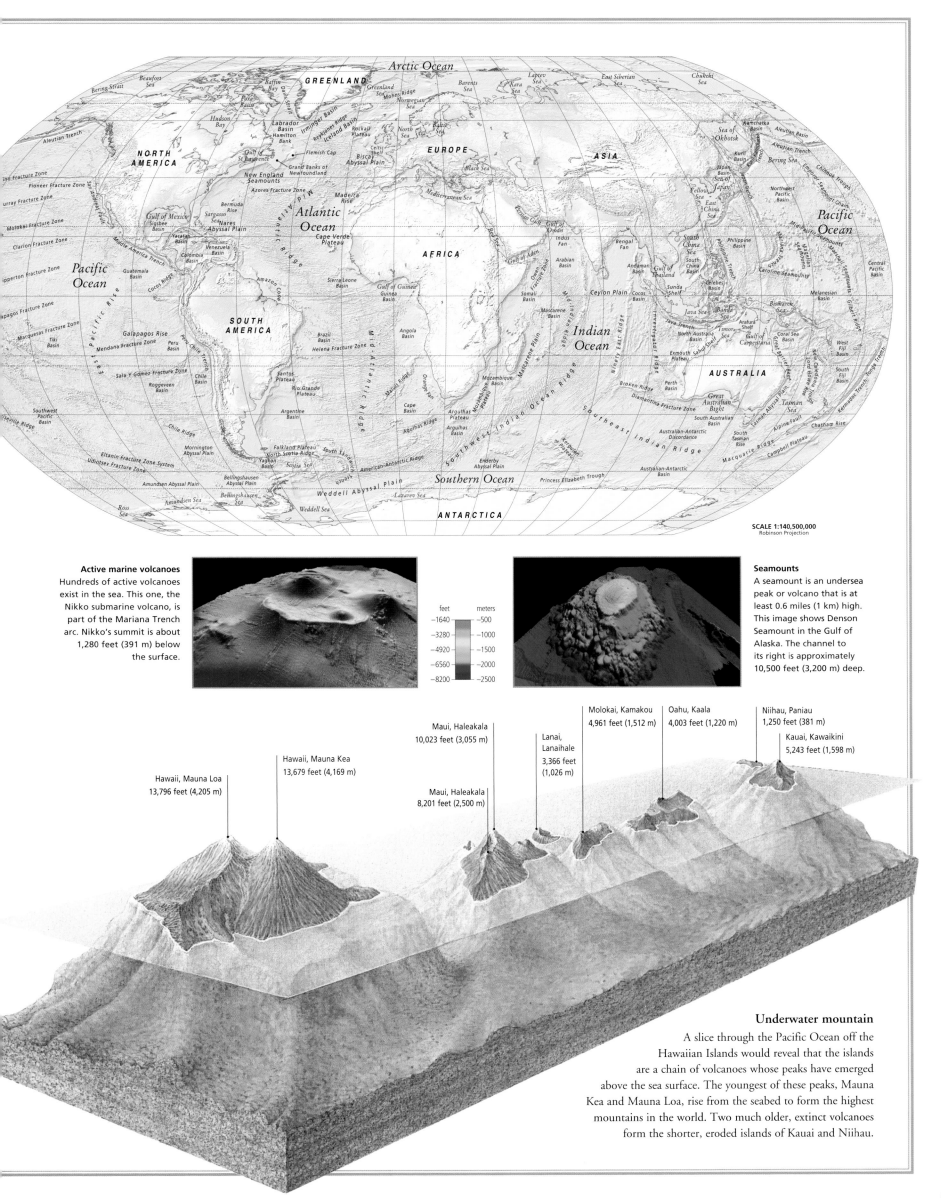

SCALE 1:140,500,000
Robinson Projection

Active marine volcanoes
Hundreds of active volcanoes exist in the sea. This one, the Nikko submarine volcano, is part of the Mariana Trench arc. Nikko's summit is about 1,280 feet (391 m) below the surface.

feet	meters
–1640	–500
–3280	–1000
–4920	–1500
–6560	–2000
–8200	–2500

Seamounts
A seamount is an undersea peak or volcano that is at least 0.6 miles (1 km) high. This image shows Denson Seamount in the Gulf of Alaska. The channel to its right is approximately 10,500 feet (3,200 m) deep.

Hawaii, Mauna Loa
13,796 feet (4,205 m)

Hawaii, Mauna Kea
13,679 feet (4,169 m)

Maui, Haleakala
10,023 feet (3,055 m)

Maui, Haleakala
8,201 feet (2,500 m)

Lanai, Lanaihale
3,366 feet (1,026 m)

Molokai, Kamakou
4,961 feet (1,512 m)

Oahu, Kaala
4,003 feet (1,220 m)

Niihau, Paniau
1,250 feet (381 m)

Kauai, Kawaikini
5,243 feet (1,598 m)

Underwater mountain
A slice through the Pacific Ocean off the Hawaiian Islands would reveal that the islands are a chain of volcanoes whose peaks have emerged above the sea surface. The youngest of these peaks, Mauna Kea and Mauna Loa, rise from the seabed to form the highest mountains in the world. Two much older, extinct volcanoes form the shorter, eroded islands of Kauai and Niihau.

HOT SPOTS

Volcanoes constantly reshape Earth's crust both on land and under the sea. The vast majority of volcanoes, including more than 450 in the famous Pacific Ring of Fire, result from collisions between crustal plates. Geologists estimate that there may be as many 10,000 hidden from view under the sea, most situated along mid-ocean ridges. Many are associated with some of the seafloor's most striking oddities, including hydrothermal vents, hot and cold seeps, and towering smokers, all home to an array of unusual species such as giant, rose-hued tube worms. Volcanoes also develop at so-called hot spots where heat from a site in the mantle erupts at the surface of the crust above it. The resulting volcano remains active until plate movements shift it away from the hot spot. Because the hot spot does not move, a new volcano then arises in crust that has moved into place above it. Iceland, the Galapagos Islands, and the Hawaiian Islands are examples of hot-spot activity.

HOT SPOTS AROUND THE WORLD

10 Most Active Hot Spots	
1	Hawaii
2	Iceland
3	Galapagos Islands
4	Réunion Island (Indian Ocean)
5	Yellowstone National Park (continental)
6	Azores
7	Bowie (Queen Charlotte Islands, Canada)
8	Samoa
9	Marquesas
10	Tristan (Tristan da Cunha island, southern Atlantic)

Yellowstone geysers
Every 60 to 90 minutes, Old Faithful Geyser, a geothermal vent in Yellowstone National Park in the US state of Wyoming, spews a fountain of boiling water heated by hot-spot activity far below in Earth's mantle.

Iceland hot spot
Iceland's Strokkur Geyser erupts every five to 10 minutes, venting superheated water and steam as high as 70 feet (20 m). Iceland currently lies over one of the world's most active hot spots.

Réunion Island
Réunion Island in the Indian Ocean is one of the best known hot spots in the world. Its active volcano, Piton de la Fournaise, spews molten lava almost daily. The most recent major eruption occurred in 2007.

Galapagos Islands
Hot-spot volcanic activity that gave rise to the Galapagos Islands of Ecuador produced both the islet of Bartolomé and its landmark Pinnacle Rock. Eroding lava of various colors makes up much of Bartolomé's landscape.

The Ring of Fire

The Pacific Ocean basin contains numerous hot spots marked by features such as the Hawaiian and Samoan island chains. In addition, more than 50 percent of Earth's active continental volcanoes form the "Ring of Fire" that nearly encircles the basin. Unlike hot-spot volcanoes, these plate-boundary volcanoes rise where crustal plates are colliding. Volcanoes in Japan, Indonesia, and along the west coast of North and South America are prime examples.

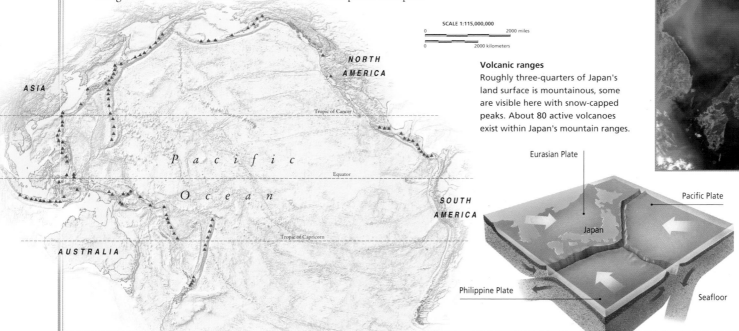

SCALE 1:115,000,000

Volcanic ranges
Roughly three-quarters of Japan's land surface is mountainous, some are visible here with snow-capped peaks. About 80 active volcanoes exist within Japan's mountain ranges.

The Japan split
There are three tectonic plates beneath Japan, but the Pacific Plate is moving about twice as fast as the Philippine Plate. This difference underlies the geologic activity that has formed many of Japan's volcanoes and that causes its frequent earthquakes.

UNIQUE HAWAIIAN SPECIES

Hawaii's isolated location in the Pacific Ocean has triggered the evolution of a striking mix of endemic plants and animals—native species that occur nowhere else. Uniquely Hawaiian marine species include marine mammals, seabirds, fishes, and crustaceans. Endemic species may be unusually vulnerable to extinction if they face introduced predators or diseases against which they have few or no natural defenses.

The endemic Hawaiian monk seal (*Monachus schauinslandi*), Hawaii's state mammal, has become critically endangered due to hunting and other pressures. It is estimated only 1,200 individuals remain.

The Laysan albatross (*Phoebastria immutabilis*) is one of the most common of Hawaiian seabirds. Although they range widely over the North Pacific, the birds return to Hawaii to breed.

This banded spiny lobster (*Panulirus marginatus*) is a relatively common denizen of nearshore waters. Its distant cousins include spiny lobsters of the Caribbean and other tropical seas.

Divers may observe schools of these brightly colored Hawaiian squirrelfish (*Sargocentron xantherythom*) browsing among the coral heads of Hawaii's reefs.

Formation of an island chain

Hawaii is a prime example of how hot spots may create marine island chains. The site of a hot spot's magma plume remains fixed while an oceanic plate slowly travels over it. Discharged magma gradually builds a volcano that breaks the surface as an island. As the plate moves over millions of years, a series of volcanic islands form, move away from the hot spot, become extinct, and erode.

Kilauea in action
Molten lava cascades regularly down the flanks of Hawaii's Mount Kilauea to the sea. Kilauea's current position atop the Hawaii hot spot makes it the most active volcano on Earth, erupting almost daily since January 1983.

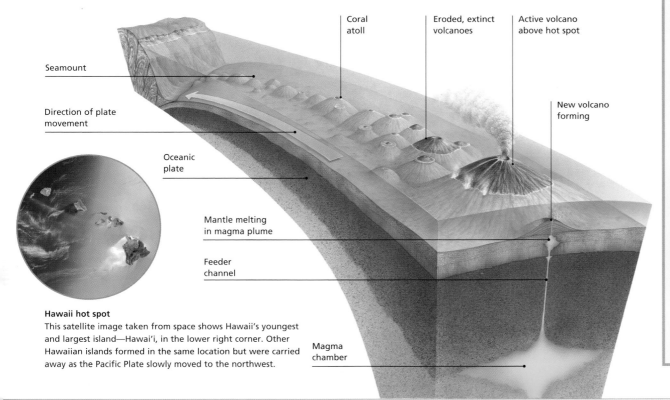

Seamount

Direction of plate movement

Oceanic plate

Mantle melting in magma plume

Feeder channel

Coral atoll

Eroded, extinct volcanoes

Active volcano above hot spot

New volcano forming

Magma chamber

Hawaii hot spot
This satellite image taken from space shows Hawaii's youngest and largest island—Hawai'i, in the lower right corner. Other Hawaiian islands formed in the same location but were carried away as the Pacific Plate slowly moved to the northwest.

Coastlines

Coastlines, the boundaries where the sea meets land, are among the most dynamic places on Earth. Over geologic time, tectonic forces that move continents determine the location and overall shape of coastlines. A geologically young, emergent coast occurs where tectonic movements are pushing up the edge of a continent. Conversely, older coasts may gradually subside partly because of the weight of accumulating sediments. Sea level changes also submerge or expose coastal land as ice caps and glaciers form or melt, crustal plates shift, and the seafloor expands at mid-ocean ridges. Erosion by wave action, tides, and river flows mold the contours of the shore, forming beaches where the substrate is soft material such as sandstone. Along high-energy coastlines, where wave action is intense, erosion may sculpt dramatic features such as cliffs, caves, and arches. Seawalls and other human-made structures designed to forestall these natural processes attest to the sea's power to shape the land.

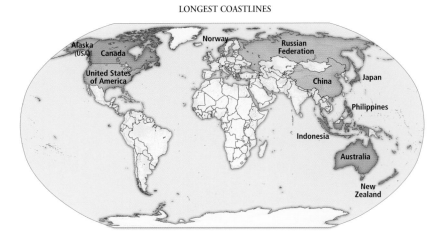

LONGEST COASTLINES

10 Countries with the Longest Coastlines	
1	Canada	151,485 miles (243,791 km)
2	Indonesia	33,999 miles (54,716 km)
3	Russia	23,396 miles (37,652 km)
4	Philippines	22,559 miles (36,305 km)
5	Japan	18,486 miles (29,750 km)
6	Australia	16,007 miles (25,761 km)
7	Norway	13,624 miles (21,926 km)
8	United States of America	12,380 miles (19,924 km)
9	New Zealand	9,404 miles (15,134 km)
10	China	9,010 miles (14,500 km)

Tectonically uplifted cliffs
The pale color of the famous cliffs along England's Dover coast comes from their main constituent calcium carbonate, remains of ancient marine zooplankton. The highest cliff rises 350 feet (106 m) above the sea.

Glacial coast
An ice-age glacier sculpted the rolling headlands typical of Orkney, an archipelago of more than 70 islands in northern Scotland. Erosion of underlying sandstone and volcanic granite produced the dark rock-strewn beach.

Lava flow coast
In geologic time, the Hawaiian island of Maui formed relatively recently as a hot-spot volcano and much of its coastline consists of lava rock. Over time, grinding wave action may produce beaches of coarse black lava bits.

Barrier island
Barrier islands form from sand deposited between two tidal inlets.

Coastal landforms

Vigorous waves and tides cut into rocky coasts, producing cliffs, terraces, blowholes and other landforms. The sea deposits the eroded material elsewhere, building sandbars and spits, and extending beaches. When sand accumulates and links an offshore rock or island with the mainland, the formation is called a tombolo, from an Italian word for mound.

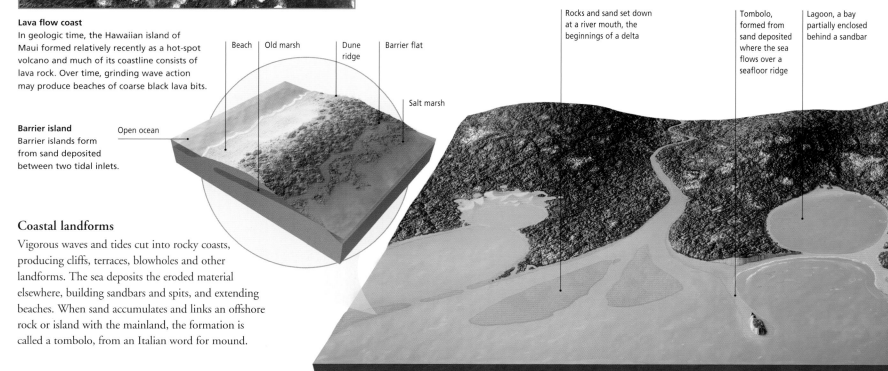

Beach | Old marsh | Dune ridge | Barrier flat

Salt marsh

Open ocean

Rocks and sand set down at a river mouth, the beginnings of a delta

Tombolo, formed from sand deposited where the sea flows over a seafloor ridge

Lagoon, a bay partially enclosed behind a sandbar

The Twelve Apostles
A set of 12 distinct sea stacks off the southern coast of Australia was named the Twelve Apostles in the 1950s. Since then, ongoing erosion has toppled four of the original stacks—a fate that will eventually claim them all.

Coast of barrier islands
Bald Head Island is one of a string of barrier islands along the coast of North Carolina, USA. Barrier islands typically are huge sandbars that develop where ocean currents and wave action promote the deposition of sand.

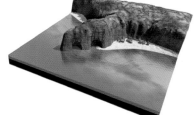 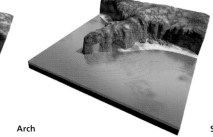 

Cave
When coastal currents erode softer rocks from the face of a headland, a sea cave is hollowed out.

Arch
Wave action continues to widen the cave and eventually wears through the headland, producing an arch.

Stack
The top of the arch thins and collapses, leaving a sea stack separated from the shore.

Coastal formations
Coastal cliffs form when waves erode hills along the shore. As this process continues, the cliffs gradually retreat inland. Erosion due to wave action and weathering continues to play a major role in shaping subsequent coastal features, such as sea stacks, arches, and caves.

PROTECTING THE COAST

Coastal areas have always been vulnerable to damage from storm surges as well as day-to-day impacts of wave action and tidal fluxes. Seawalls and structures called groins are common solutions to these ongoing problems. A seawall protects developed coastal areas by deflecting wave energy back toward the ocean. Grouped groins help establish and maintain beaches by preventing the loss of sand or other sediments.

Sets of groins, typically constructed of rocks, wood or concrete, are a common sight in coastal areas where beach erosion is a recurring problem.

Modern seawalls are often reinforced concrete. This one in Zeeland, Holland was erected following major storm surge damage in 1953.

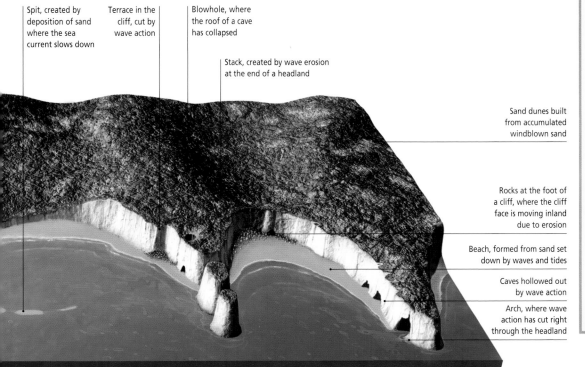

Spit, created by deposition of sand where the sea current slows down

Terrace in the cliff, cut by wave action

Blowhole, where the roof of a cave has collapsed

Stack, created by wave erosion at the end of a headland

Sand dunes built from accumulated windblown sand

Rocks at the foot of a cliff, where the cliff face is moving inland due to erosion

Beach, formed from sand set down by waves and tides

Caves hollowed out by wave action

Arch, where wave action has cut right through the headland

BEACHES AND DUNES

Along every coast a shoreline threads between the water's edge and the uppermost splash zone. Punctuating this seam between land and sea are beaches, some consisting mainly of sand or rocks, others of pebbles or mud. Beaches develop where coastal topography encourages the build-up of sediments. Depending on the location and other characteristics of a coast, beach material may be deposited by river or lava flows, nearshore currents and waves, by the wind or glacial action, or another source. Worldwide, sand beaches are the most common, often backed by dunes in places where strong onshore winds push beach sand landward. The largest coastal dunes may grow to more than 330 feet (100 m). Bangladesh claims the world's longest unbroken sand beach, which stretches some 80 miles (129 km) along the Bay of Bengal. Yet all beaches and dunes are in constant flux, shifting in size and shape in tune with shifts in the forces that mold them.

Beach makeup

Geologically a beach is a blanket of loose sediment particles deposited along the shore. Grinding wave action and erosion by wind and water produce these deposits from bedrock, coral, or lava, creating beaches of cobbles, pebbles, or sand. Many dazzling white tropical beaches consist of coral sand, while the dramatic black beaches of Iceland and some Hawaiian islands are the remains of lava flows.

Copacabana
The 2.5-mile (4 km) Copacabana Beach in Rio de Janeiro, Brazil, is one of the most famous beaches in the world.

SAND FILTER

Some of the water in waves advancing up a sand or shingle shore immediately returns to the sea, but some percolates down into the beach. This water is filtered of particulate matter as it trickles down through the beach sediments. Most of the filtered water eventually seeps back to sea, but some remains trapped in tiny spongelike spaces between the beach sediments.

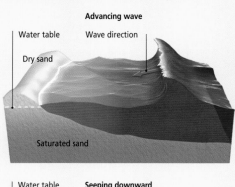

Advancing wave

Water table — Wave direction

Dry sand

Saturated sand

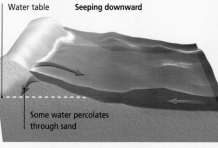

Water table — **Seeping downward**

Some water percolates through sand

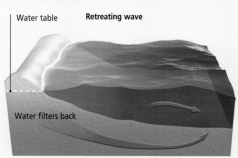

Water table — **Retreating wave**

Water filters back

Dune systems

Coastal sand dune systems form where onshore winds pick up and redeposit sand from drier parts of a beach. A combination of factors determines dune size. The available supply of sand, grain size, and the strength of prevailing winds all contribute. Strong winds and abundant sand may sculpt dunes hundreds of feet high. Similarly, powerful storms may shift their location.

Towering dunes
The world's tallest dunes occur in the Namib Desert of western Africa. A narrow beach separates them from the Atlantic Ocean.

WIND-SHAPED DUNES

Transverse
Where sand is abundant, dune ridges develop at right angles, or transverse, to the wind.

Barchan dunes
Crescent-shaped dunes, with tips pointing downwind, form where the wind direction is constant but the sand supply is limited.

Star
Where winds come from three or more opposing directions, star dunes form as tall as 1,000 feet (300 m).

Longitudinal
Linear dunes form parallel to the average wind direction where sand is plentiful and wind direction is slightly variable.

Parabolic
Tips of these U-shaped dunes point upwind. They form when wind direction is more or less constant.

Lava sand beach
This black beach at Vík í Mýrdal is one of numerous Icelandic beaches formed when basalt lava flowed into the sea.

Beach in transition
The sand beach at Cape Cod National Seashore, USA, is in transition. Rising sea level consumes as much as 3 feet (0.9 m) annually.

Coral sand beach
Bora Bora, part of the South Pacific nation of French Polynesia, is renowned for its sparkling white, often secluded coral sand beaches.

Brighton's shingle beach
Large pebbles mark a shingle beach at Brighton, England. Shingle beaches are composites of pebbles and sand.

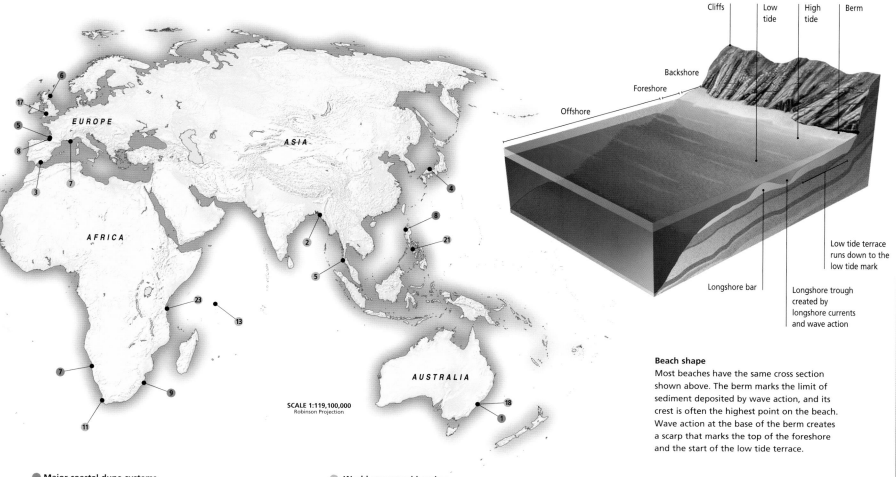

SCALE 1:119,100,000
Robinson Projection

Low tide terrace runs down to the low tide mark

Longshore bar

Longshore trough created by longshore currents and wave action

Beach shape
Most beaches have the same cross section shown above. The berm marks the limit of sediment deposited by wave action, and its crest is often the highest point on the beach. Wave action at the base of the berm creates a scarp that marks the top of the foreshore and the start of the low tide terrace.

● Major coastal dune systems

1 Cronulla Sand Dunes/Kurnell Peninsula, Sydney, NSW, Australia
2 Nags Head, North Carolina, USA
3 Oregon Dunes National Recreation Area, Florence, Oregon, USA
4 Tottori Sand Dunes, Honshu, Japan
5 Great Dune of Pilat, Arcachon Bay, France
6 Sands of Forvie, Ythan Estuary, Scotland
7 Soussusvlai Dunes, Walvis Bay, Namibia
8 Paoay Dunes, Ilocos, Philippines
9 St. Lucia, South Africa

● World-renowned beaches

1 Poipu Beach, Hawaii, USA
2 Cox's Bazar, Bangladesh
3 Costa del Sol, Spain
4 Ipanema Beach, Brazil
5 Khao Lak, Thailand
6 Matira Beach, Bora Bora
7 Saint Tropez, France
8 Biarritz, France
9 South Beach/Miami Beach, Florida, USA
10 Bandon Beach, Oregon, USA
11 Clifton Beach, South Africa
12 Pink Sand Beach, Bahamas (UK)
13 Anse Sourse Beach, Seychelles
14 Maroma Beach, Mexico
15 Cabo San Lucas, Mexico
16 Sarasota, Florida, USA
17 Swansea Bay, Wales, UK
18 Bondi Beach, Sydney, NSW, Australia
19 Big Sur, California, USA
20 Paracas Beach, Peru
21 Boracay Beach, Philippines
22 Palm Beach, Aruba
23 Spice Island, Zanzibar
24 Gold Coast, Barbados
25 Cape Cod National Seashore, Massachusetts, USA

RIP CURRENTS

A rip current, or a rip tide or undertow, is a small, strong current that flows out to sea. The current develops when a series of approaching waves causes water to accumulate in the surf zone faster than normal circulation patterns can disperse it. Some of this water then rushes back out to sea, possibly carrying a swimmer along with it.

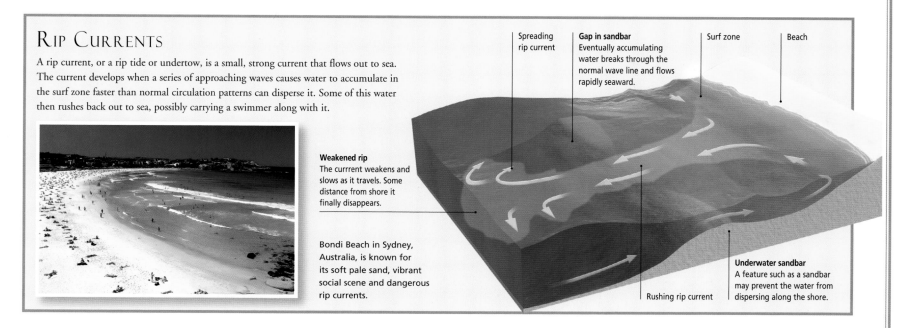

Weakened rip
The currrent weakens and slows as it travels. Some distance from shore it finally disappears.

Bondi Beach in Sydney, Australia, is known for its soft pale sand, vibrant social scene and dangerous rip currents.

Spreading rip current

Gap in sandbar
Eventually accumulating water breaks through the normal wave line and flows rapidly seaward.

Surf zone

Beach

Underwater sandbar
A feature such as a sandbar may prevent the water from dispersing along the shore.

Rushing rip current

CONTINENTAL MARGINS

A continent's dry land stops at the shore but the continent itself extends below the waves, its edge forming a gently sloping, submerged continental shelf that has "land" features such as hills and canyons blanketed with a thin layer of sediments. At plate boundaries, as off western South America, continental shelves are narrow but elsewhere they may be vast. In parts of the Arctic Ocean the shelf is more than 750 miles (1,200 km) wide. Shallow shelf waters are the most accessible areas of the sea where marine resources are most abundant. Continental shelves thus are the prime focus for fisheries and undersea mining. The outer edge of a shelf forms a feature called a continental slope. Beyond this steeply tilting area is the continental rise, where the continent ends. Where there is little or no tectonic activity, deep-sea sediments accumulate at continental rises. The sediment layer can be as thick as 6 miles (10 km) in some oceans.

From shore to sea

The continental shelf and slope make up the continental margin—the area of seafloor nearest the shore. The sloping transition from the edge of the sea to the ocean depths follows the same pattern around all continents. The continental slope and continental rise beyond give way to oceanic crust where the abyssal plain begins. Although these transitional areas vary greatly in their width and depth, by international agreement coastal nations claim jurisdiction over the first 200 nautical miles off their shores.

Continental shelf

Continental margin

200 nm (nautical miles)

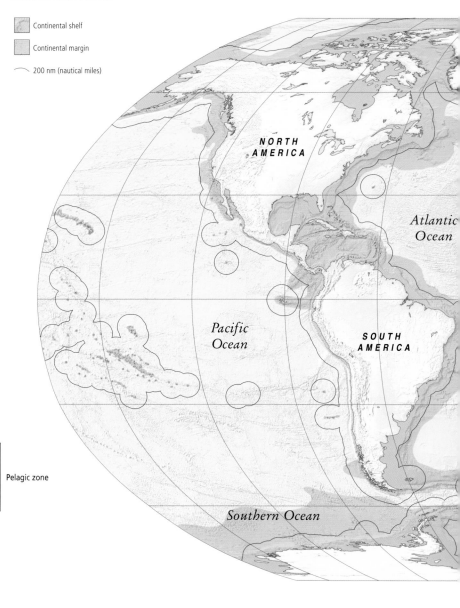

NORTH AMERICA

Atlantic Ocean

Pacific Ocean

SOUTH AMERICA

Southern Ocean

Shallow shelf waters
Despite regional variations in the slope and the contours of continental shelves, the seas covering them are shallow. Shelf waters encompass only the epipelagic zone, the upper 660 feet (200 m) of the sea where light and life are abundant.

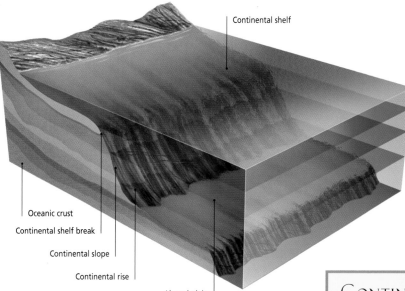

Continental shelf

Pelagic zone

Oceanic crust

Continental shelf break

Continental slope

Continental rise

Abyssal plain

Meeting the shelf
The Ganges Delta, the world's largest river delta, is 220 miles (354 km) wide where it meets the coast of the Indian Ocean. Although very fertile, the delta is vulnerable to tidal flooding.

CONTINENTAL SHELF OFF EASTERN NORTH AMERICA

Off eastern North America the continental shelf overall is broad with a shallow incline. The northern portion of the shelf illustrated at the right also clearly shows the effects of the last ice age, when the sea level was much lower and the shelf was exposed to erosion. The shelf's submerged canyons, deep channels, and fanlike deltas were all carved by ancient river flows and similar events.

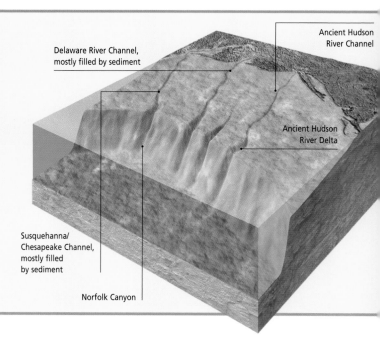

Delaware River Channel, mostly filled by sediment

Ancient Hudson River Channel

Ancient Hudson River Delta

Susquehanna/ Chesapeake Channel, mostly filled by sediment

Norfolk Canyon

Trailing a school of tropical fish, this large Pacific jellyfish (*Thysanostoma* sp.) navigates open shelf waters propelled by undulations of its bell.

This photograph shows eggs that have been deposited by a waved whelk (*Buccinum undatum*), a North Atlantic snail. The species is a bottom dweller of the continental shelf.

A banded butterflyfish (*Chaetodon striatus*) forages among yellow tube sponges (*Aplysina fistularis*). Both are denizens of a coral reef in the Caribbean Sea.

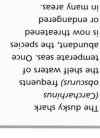

The dusky shark (*Carcharhinus obscurus*) frequents the shelf waters of temperate seas. Once abundant, the species is now threatened or endangered in many areas.

Canyons and gorges
Erosion by moving water and sediment, often river flows or ancient flowing glaciers, creates steep-walled V-shaped submarine canyons and gorges cut deeply into the shelf and slope.

Geologic faulting
Where a continental plate and the adjoining oceanic plate are actively shifting, cracks or faults between plates may also alter the contours of the continental shelf.

Ice age erosion
During the last ice age, so much seawater was locked in ice caps that previously submerged continental shelves were exposed. Ice streams and rivers carried exposed sediments seaward.

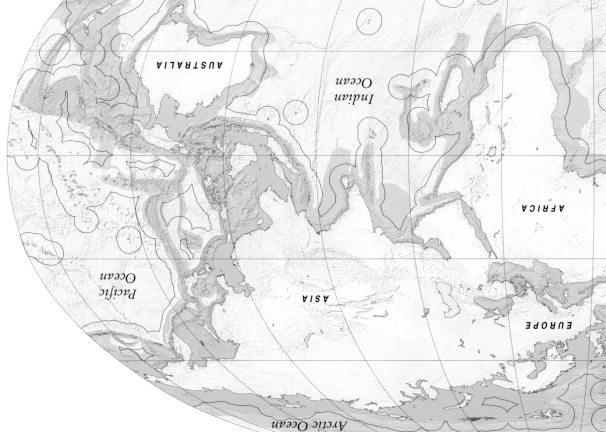

SCALE 1:115,400,000
Robinson Projection

ANTARCTICA
Southern Ocean
AUSTRALIA
Indian Ocean
Pacific Ocean
ASIA
AFRICA
EUROPE
Arctic Ocean

Cliff edge
Strong coastal currents, sometimes in combination with other factors, may scour out sediments and other material from the seaward edge of a continental shelf.

Barrier reefs
In shallow, tropical shelf areas the long-term activity of coral communities may produce a barrier reef landscape both below and above the sea surface.

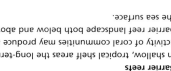

Broad and gentle
A broad gentle shelf with offshore ridges and sandbars often occurs at the boundary of the continent and an abutting oceanic plate with limited recent tectonic activity.

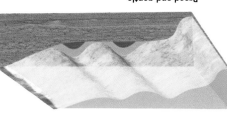

Shelf variations
On mountainous coastlines, shelf zones are narrow, rough and steep. By contrast, they are smooth and gently sloping where plains meet the sea. Everywhere the shelf ends at a steep drop-off called the shelf break.

CORAL REEFS AND ATOLLS

Coral reefs occur mostly in warm, shallow seas. Home to diverse communities of corals, fishes, sponges, and other species, coral reefs are the work of match head-sized coral polyps. Algae living within a polyp's tissues manufacture most of its food by the process of photosynthesis. Reef-building corals secrete a hard, protective limestone casing over their soft bodies, and over centuries, polyps of different species may produce vast reef systems such as Australia's Great Barrier Reef. At 1,250 miles (2,000 km) long and up to 95 miles (150 km) wide, it is the largest structure ever made by living organisms. A barrier reef is higher than the adjacent land, while fringing reefs form in the shallows around volcanic islands. A coral atoll develops when a volcanic island erodes gradually or sinks back into the sea, leaving sections of the reef behind. Recent coral bleaching—the untimely starvation of corals when their resident algae die—now threatens many coral reefs around the globe.

LARGEST KNOWN CORAL REEF AREAS

Location	Area [square miles (km²)]	% of world total
1 Indonesia	31,700 (51,020)	17.95
2 Australia	30,400 (48,960)	17.22
3 Philippines	15,570 (25,060)	8.81
4 France (French Overseas Departments)	8,870 (14,280)	5.02
5 Papua New Guinea	8,600 (13,840)	4.87
6 Fiji	6,220 (10,020)	3.52
7 Maldives	5,540 (8,920)	3.14
8 Saudi Arabia	4,140 (6,660)	2.34
9 Marshall Islands	3,800 (6,110)	2.15
10 India	3,600 (5,790)	2.04

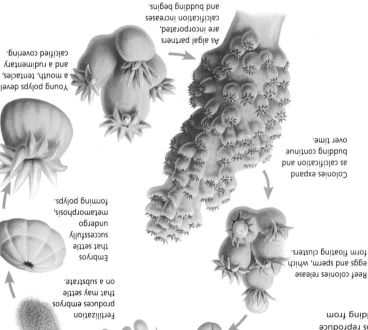

Coral life cycle
Most coral species have a multi-step life cycle. Eggs and sperm are released into the sea and unite. Fertilized eggs develop into young coral polyps. Colonies also expand as growing coral polyps reproduce asexually, by budding from the parent.

Reef colonies release eggs and sperm, which form floating clusters.

Clusters rise to the sea surface, where they break up.

Sperm from different colonies fertilize eggs at random, preventing inbreeding.

Fertilization produces embryos that may settle on a substrate.

Embryos that settle successfully undergo metamorphosis, forming polyps.

Colonies expand as calcification and budding continue over time.

Young polyps develop a mouth, tentacles, and a rudimentary calcified covering.

As algal partners are incorporated, calcification increases and budding begins.

ATOLLS

An atoll consists of a shallow lagoon surrounded by a coral reef. Hundreds exist in the global sea, although most occur in the central and southern Pacific. Atolls can be round, oval, or some other shape and usually occur in groups. Pacific atolls have generally developed as fringing reefs around a subsiding volcano. Elsewhere they may be atop subsided blocks of continental or oceanic crust.

FORMATION OF AN ATOLL

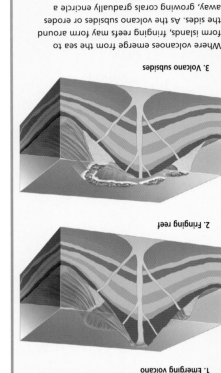

1. Emerging volcano

2. Fringing reef

3. Volcano subsides

Where volcanoes emerge from the sea to form islands, fringing reefs may form around the sides. As the volcano subsides or erodes away, growing corals gradually encircle a central lagoon, forming an atoll.

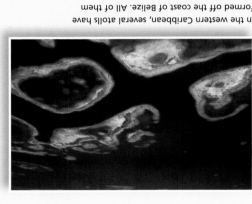

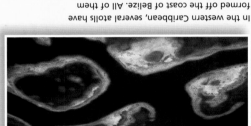

This atoll in the Maldives is still developing. As the coral heads grow together they will eventually encircle a shallow lagoon.

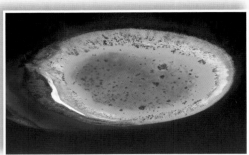

In the western Caribbean, several atolls have formed off the coast of Belize. All of them developed atop a now-subsided fault block.

Harlequin Shrimp

Reef animals often specialize in their diet, a natural mechanism for allotting resources in a highly competitive environment. The crimson spotted harlequin shrimp *(Hymenocera picta)*, found in the Indo-Pacific, preys mainly on sea stars, often grazing on the echinoderm's tube feet. With a maximum size of only about 2 inches (5 cm), harlequin shrimps may devour their much larger but less mobile prey over a period of days.

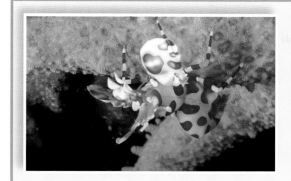

Sea fan
The colonies of some coral species form branching fan-shaped structures that superficially seem plant-like. This bright crimson sea fan was photographed in its tropical habitat on a reef off the Fiji Islands.

Brain coral
French grunts *(Haemulon flavolineatum)* forage around a giant brain coral *(Colpophyllia natans)* in the Florida Keys National Marine Sanctuary. Under ideal conditions, brain corals can live for an estimated 200 years, growing slowly to a maximum height of 7 feet (2 m).

Cold-water coral communities
Anemones, warty sponges, and species of soft corals take hold on the rocky bottom in the cold waters of the Gulf of St Lawrence in eastern Canada.

Corals around the globe

Coral reefs occur in every ocean region except the Arctic and South Atlantic. Tropical reefs range in age from 6,000 to 9,000 years and have the most diverse array of species. Researchers are just beginning to identify aggregations of cold-water soft corals, some of which occur at great depths. To date they have been discovered in the territorial waters of more than 40 countries.

Warm ocean
Cold ocean
Warm-water coral reefs
Deep cold-water coral reefs

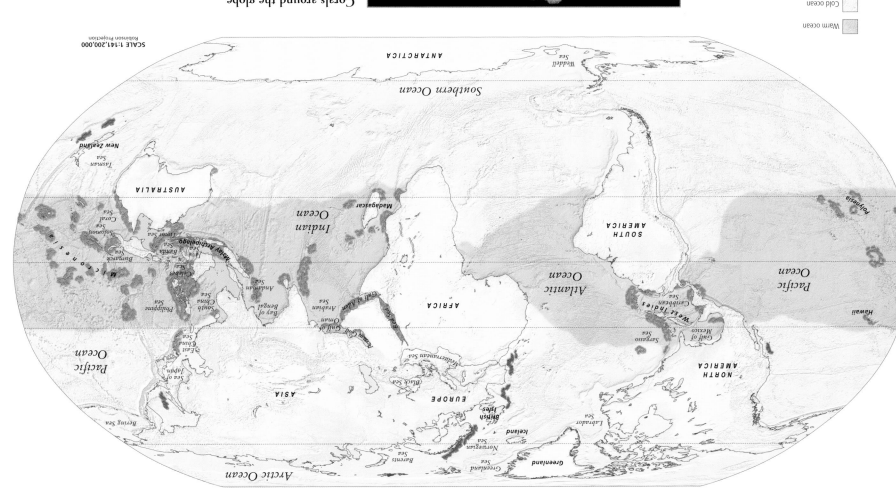

SCALE 1:141,200,000
Robinson Projection

Arctic Ocean · Greenland Sea · Barents Sea · Norwegian Sea · Iceland · Greenland · British Isles · Labrador Sea · Bering Sea · Sea of Japan · East China Sea · Black Sea · Mediterranean Sea · Sargasso Sea · Gulf of Mexico · Caribbean Sea · West Indies · Hawaii · Pacific Ocean · Atlantic Ocean · NORTH AMERICA · SOUTH AMERICA · EUROPE · ASIA · AFRICA · Red Sea · Gulf of Aden · Arabian Sea · Gulf of Oman · Bay of Bengal · South China Sea · Philippine Sea · Celebes Sea · Sulu Sea · Java Sea · Banda Sea · Timor Sea · Andaman Sea · Flores Sea · Bismarck Sea · Solomon Sea · Coral Sea · Indian Ocean · Madagascar · AUSTRALIA · Tasman Sea · New Zealand · Micronesia · Melanesia · Polynesia · Southern Ocean · Weddell Sea · ANTARCTICA

SEA AND ICE

In polar seas, ice is a fact of life. Surface waters freeze into sea ice for much of the year in the Arctic. In the Antarctic, most sea ice melts during the southern hemisphere summer. Off Antarctica, Canada, and Greenland, ice shelves as thick as 3,300 feet (1,000 m) extend from the land and float on the sea surface. Antarctica's huge Ross Ice Shelf covers about 188,000 square miles (487,000 km²), nearly twice the area of New Zealand. Species in and around icy seas include fish with blood containing natural antifreeze, giant squids, whales, seals, Antarctic penguins, and Arctic polar bears. Antarctic ice shelves also produce the largest recorded icebergs. Propelled by ocean currents and winds, these bergs pose serious hazards to ocean-going vessels. As warming related to global climate change speeds the collapse of ice shelves, the risk of icebergs will rise, as will the threats to wildlife that depend on polar ice for their survival.

Arctic life

The Arctic Ocean boasts a wealth of species. Summer phytoplankton blooms support grazing copepods and amphipods, both in the water and in pores in the ice. These in turn are food for jellyfish, whales, and fish such as Arctic cod. Seabirds pluck prey from both water and ice. Skates and walruses feed on abundant clams and other invertebrates on the seafloor. Apex predators include huge sleeper sharks.

Forms of sea ice

Sea ice comes in various types. So-called frazil ice is a thin, loose coating of ice crystals. In calm waters they may freeze into a thin layer called nilas ice. Other physical processes produce pancake ice and pack ice.

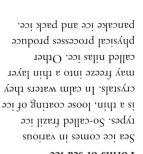

Frazil ice
Here a patchy glaze of frazil ice surrounds icebergs along the coast of Greenland. This type of sea ice is also called grease ice.

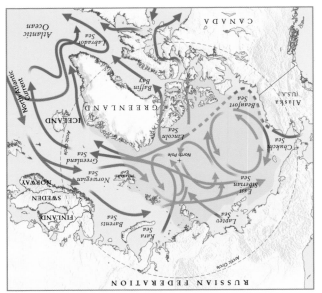

Shrinking Arctic sea ice
More or less permanent ice once covered up to 5.6 million square miles (14.6 million km²) of the Arctic Ocean. Historically, only the outer portions of this frozen salt water melted in warmer months. Since the early 1950s, however, the maximum extent of Arctic sea ice has been steadily shrinking due to global warming.

Arctic seawater circulation
Currents flow in complex patterns in the Arctic. Warm surface water from the North Atlantic cools, sinks, and flows back southward, and influences Earth's climate.

- Ice extent
- Cool currents
- Warm currents

SEAFLOOR

Sponges (Halichondria panicea)
Feather star (Phylum echinodermata)
Brittle stars (Echinodermata ophiuroidea)
Sea anemones (Bolocera tuediae)
Arctic skate (Amblyraja hyperborea)
Walrus (Odobenus rosmarus)
Bowhead whale (Balaena mysticetus)
Herring (Clupea harengus)
Beluga (Delphinapterus leucas)
Jellyfish (Cyanea capillata)
Capelin (Mallotus villosus)
Greenland shark (Somniosus microcephalus)
Arctic cod (Arctogadus glacialis)
Water column
UNDER ICE ZONE
MARGINAL ICE ZONE
PERMANENT ICE COVER
Glaucous gulls (Larus hyperboreus)
Eiders (Somateria fischeri)
Harp seal (Phoca groenlandica)
Razorbills (Alca torda)
Polar bear (Ursus maritimus)
Bearded seal (Erignathus barbatus)
Ivory gulls (Pagophila eburnea)
Arctic tern (Sterna paradisaea)
Arctic skua (Stercorarius parasiticus)
Northern fulmar (Fulmarus glacialis)

Nilas ice
Recently formed nilas ice is thin enough to be transparent. As it thickens from the bottom up it eventually turns white.

Pancake ice
Flat plates of pancake ice form as swells and waves consolidate freezing slush that has formed on the sea surface.

Pack ice
Over time sea ice may be compressed into large, thick sheets called pack ice. Arctic pack ice is thickest, up to 9 feet (3 m).

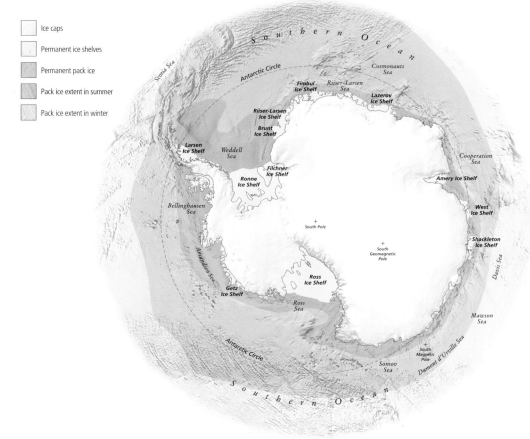

- Ice caps
- Permanent ice shelves
- Permanent pack ice
- Pack ice extent in summer
- Pack ice extent in winter

Sea ice in the Antarctic
In the Antarctic, sea ice covers about 7.7 million square miles (20 million km²) in the depths of winter. It typically shrinks drastically, to about 1.5 million square miles (4 million km²), by summer's end. In contrast to the Arctic, the maximum extent of Antarctic sea ice has remained relatively stable. Even so, the Antarctic ice cap is melting more rapidly than scientific models predicted.

Icebergs
Icebergs are large, sometimes massive, chunks of ice that have broken off an ice sheet or glacier. This process, called calving, occurs when wave action, currents, or other forces produce enough physical stress to cut the berg away.

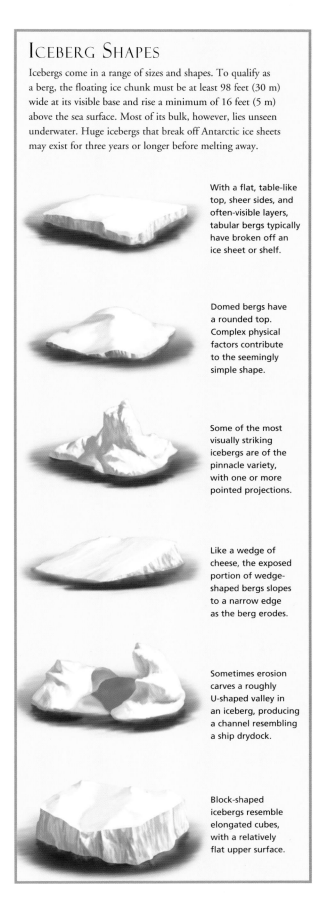

ICEBERG SHAPES

Icebergs come in a range of sizes and shapes. To qualify as a berg, the floating ice chunk must be at least 98 feet (30 m) wide at its visible base and rise a minimum of 16 feet (5 m) above the sea surface. Most of its bulk, however, lies unseen underwater. Huge icebergs that break off Antarctic ice sheets may exist for three years or longer before melting away.

With a flat, table-like top, sheer sides, and often-visible layers, tabular bergs typically have broken off an ice sheet or shelf.

Domed bergs have a rounded top. Complex physical factors contribute to the seemingly simple shape.

Some of the most visually striking icebergs are of the pinnacle variety, with one or more pointed projections.

Like a wedge of cheese, the exposed portion of wedge-shaped bergs slopes to a narrow edge as the berg erodes.

Sometimes erosion carves a roughly U-shaped valley in an iceberg, producing a channel resembling a ship drydock.

Block-shaped icebergs resemble elongated cubes, with a relatively flat upper surface.

BETWEEN LAND AND SEA

An estuary is a partially enclosed body of water in which seawater mingles with fresh water from rivers and streams. Some estuaries are glacier-carved fjords, including Norway's Sognefjorden, the world's deepest estuary at just over 4,290 feet (1,300 m). Others are coastal lagoons protected by islands or sandbars and coastal plain estuaries such as Chesapeake Bay on the east coast of the United States. California's San Francisco Bay is a famed example of a tectonic estuary formed when seawater floods an area that is sinking due to movements of crustal plates. In tropical and some subtropical locales mangrove swamps line the fringes of estuaries, while elsewhere, brackish salt marsh skirts the water's edge. Conditions in estuaries constantly change. Salinity shifts with tidal fluxes and variations in rainfall and runoff from rivers and streams. Seasonal water temperature variations may also be extreme. Even so, estuaries are renowned for supporting abundant wildlife.

Estuary habitats

Estuaries are common features along the coastlines of every continent except Antarctica. Regardless of where an estuary occurs, however, it contains specialized communities of plants and animals adapted to cope with the ever-changing conditions. In temperate regions, grassy salt marshes fringe estuaries. In the tropics and subtropics, the shrubby tree species called mangroves are the dominant plant life. Each plant community supports a diverse assemblage of wildlife.

Pacific Ocean

NORTH AMERICA

Salt marshes

Mangrove forests

Roaming otter
In addition to living in totally freshwater habitats, southern river otters *(Lontra provocax)* may also thrive in estuaries and along rocky seacoasts.

Salt marsh zones
A salt marsh has two zones that place differing demands on plant and animal life. Organisms in the low marsh must cope with daily flooding at high tide. Flooding is intermittent or rare in the drier upper marsh.

Upland area

Upper marsh

Pool

Low marsh

Marsh edge

Tidal mudflat

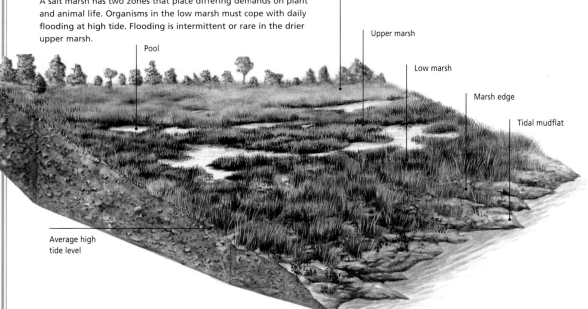

Average high tide level

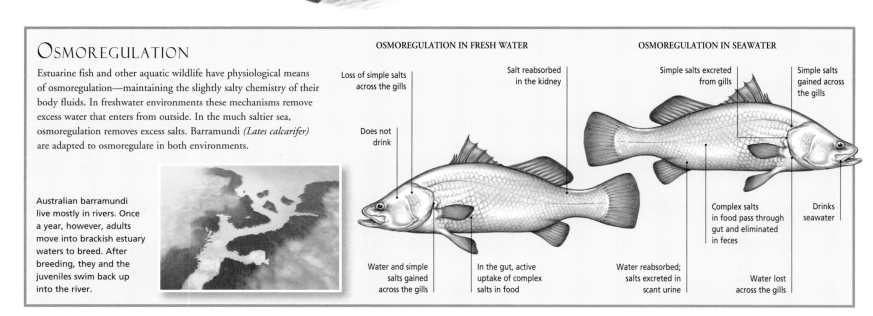

Salt marshes
Salt marshes occur worldwide except in polar areas. This example is at the head of the Bay of Fundy, Nova Scotia, Canada, where North Atlantic high tides flood its lower zone with brackish water twice daily.

OSMOREGULATION

Estuarine fish and other aquatic wildlife have physiological means of osmoregulation—maintaining the slightly salty chemistry of their body fluids. In freshwater environments these mechanisms remove excess water that enters from outside. In the much saltier sea, osmoregulation removes excess salts. Barramundi *(Lates calcarifer)* are adapted to osmoregulate in both environments.

Australian barramundi live mostly in rivers. Once a year, however, adults move into brackish estuary waters to breed. After breeding, they and the juveniles swim back up into the river.

OSMOREGULATION IN FRESH WATER

Loss of simple salts across the gills

Salt reabsorbed in the kidney

Does not drink

Water and simple salts gained across the gills

In the gut, active uptake of complex salts in food

Water reabsorbed; salts excreted in scant urine

OSMOREGULATION IN SEAWATER

Simple salts excreted from gills

Simple salts gained across the gills

Complex salts in food pass through gut and eliminated in feces

Drinks seawater

Water lost across the gills

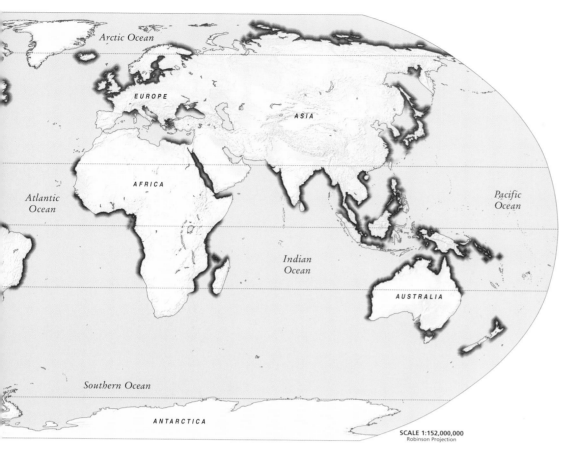

SCALE 1:152,000,000
Robinson Projection

Submerged aquatic grasses

Submerged grasses and other aquatic vegetation flourish in the shallows of San Quintin Bay in Baja California, Mexico. Like mangrove habitats, such brackish coastal waters are vitally important nurseries for the young of many fish species. They also attract diverse wetlands birds, such as rails and herons. Clams and other small invertebrates live on or in the muddy bottom.

Floating through
The upside down jellyfish (*Cassiopeia xamachana*) inhabits a variety of tropical waters, such as mangroves. This specimen was photographed in a red mangrove swamp in the Bahamas.

Scarlet ibis
The scarlet ibis (*Eudocimus ruber*), native to northern South America, roams between coastal marshes and interior wetlands —a behavior common to many bird species that visit estuaries.

Estuaries
Various geological processes of formation, such as erosion and sedimentation, are used as part of a scheme to classify estuaries. The four main types are drowned river valleys, fjords, bar-built estuaries, and tectonic estuaries.

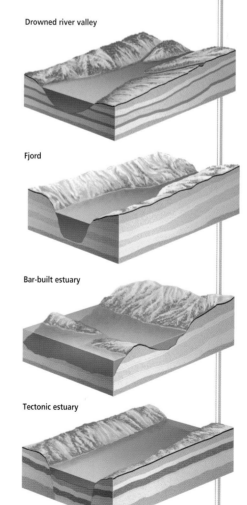

Drowned river valley

Fjord

Bar-built estuary

Tectonic estuary

Mangrove forests

Red mangroves, photographed here in Florida, USA, are the dominant vegetation in saltier tropical estuaries. Black mangroves and white mangroves inhabit less saline estuarine environments.

Calm waters
Mangrove habitats occur in tropical coastal areas having shallow, calm waters. This intertidal zone is a perfect nursery and feeding ground for many small aquatic creatures.

Targeting its prey
Unerring aim with a forceful jet of water shot from its mouth allows the archerfish to knock insects from overhanging foliage.

Mangrove menagerie
Stilt-like mangrove roots support a diverse community of animal life. Gobies and other small fishes find food and shelter there, while fiddler crabs inhabit mud burrows below.

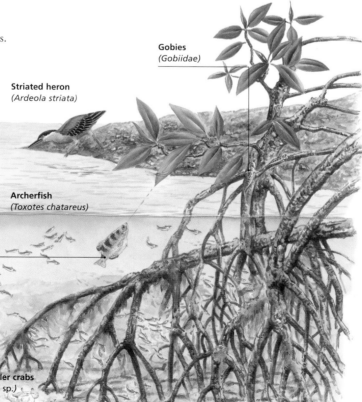

Gobies
(Gobiidae)

Striated heron
(*Ardeola striata*)

Archerfish
(*Toxotes chatareus*)

Fiddler crabs
(*Uca* sp.)

Stilt roots

INLAND SEAS

Inland seas are branches of ancient oceans that are now enclosed by land. The Caspian Sea between southern Russia and northern Iran is the largest of these lakelike bodies of water, covering some 143,000 square miles (370,000 km²). Famous for its caviar-producing sturgeon, the Caspian is also home to abundant birdlife and other animals. The Caspian and the neighboring Black and Aral seas were cut off from the prehistoric Tethys Sea as plate movements raised the Himalaya and surrounding lands. The Aral Sea, in present-day Kazakstan and Uzbekistan, is rapidly disappearing because of diversions of feeder river water for human use such as irrigated farming. The world's saltiest inland sea is the Dead Sea, once a branch of the Mediterranean Sea. Like many other inland seas, the Dead Sea has no outlets. Evaporation and mineral build-up in the region's arid climate make the Dead Sea roughly nine times saltier than the ocean—far too saline for most life to survive.

Disappearing Dead Sea
The Dead Sea is actually a hypersaline lake in a basin created by the separation of crustal plates underlying the continents of Asia and Africa. Fed by rivers such as the Jordan, the Dead Sea has steadily been shrinking—and becoming saltier—as nearby countries divert river flows for agriculture and other uses.

Salty support
It is relatively easy to float in salt water because salt water is denser than the human body. The Dead Sea is roughly nine times saltier than any ocean. Floating in it is as simple as wading in and reclining.

Ancient inland sea
Some 300 million years ago an inland sea spread across the site of Arches National Park in Utah, USA. Slowly over time the sea evaporated and a thick layer of sandstone developed atop the salt bed left behind. Geologic upheavals and erosion produced the park's famous arches and other striking rock formations.

A nautical heritage
Tour boats and fishing vessels have long been a part of life along the shore of the Sea of Galilee. Today, the lake is mainly a tourist site, although small fishing operations still thrive.

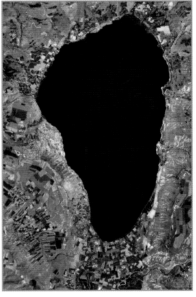

Misnamed "Sea" of Galilee
Warm water and abundant life make the freshwater lake known as the Sea of Galilee a major aquatic resource in Israel. This "sea" is also the lowest freshwater lake on Earth, filling a shallow basin that is 686 feet (209 m) below sea level.

EVAPORITE DEPOSITS

Evaporite deposits are sediments laid down by the evaporation of salty water. During geologic time, multiple cycles of evaporation and replenishment of Dead Sea waters have created thick layers of evaporite salts, including halite—the rock salt from which table salt (sodium chloride) is refined. Chemical conditions near the bottom cause crystals of these salts to precipitate out on the lake floor. They also wash up along the shore.

Dead Sea salt deposits are the raw material of valuable commercial operations. Some consumers believe that salt-laden mud in the lake bottom also has health benefits.

As a salt lake dries out, minerals are deposited in predictable ring-like layers around what were once the margins of the original lake.

Rock salt

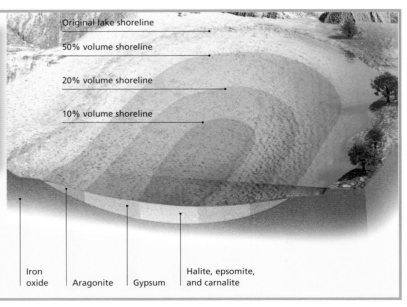

Original lake shoreline

50% volume shoreline

20% volume shoreline

10% volume shoreline

Iron oxide | Aragonite | Gypsum | Halite, epsomite, and carnalite

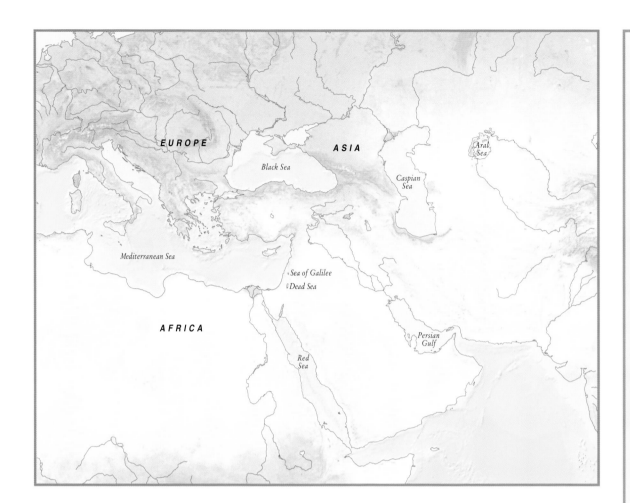

Cluster of inland seas

This map reveals the clustering of some major inland seas, including the Caspian and the Aral seas and the lakes known as the Dead Sea and the Sea of Galilee. These large bodies of water occur in rifts or basins created by tectonic shifts that slowly realigned crustal plates underlying the Arabian Peninsula and Eurasia. The plate movements correlate with the opening of the Indian Ocean about 300 million years ago.

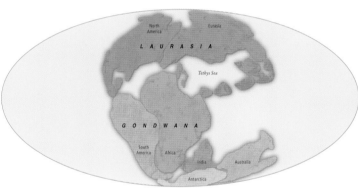

The prehistoric Tethys
A large, ancient Tethys Sea formed as Earth's supercontinent Pangea broke up into smaller landmasses. Drifting continents slowly produced the Indian Ocean and isolated remnants of the Tethys, including the Caspian and Aral seas.

Caspian Sea

The Caspian Sea is Earth's largest inland sea. Although some 130 rivers deliver fresh water to it, none flows out. Intensive fisheries, river-borne industrial pollution, and development along the shore have all taken a toll on the Caspian's ecological health. The discovery of significant oil and gas deposits under the Caspian is increasing pressure on the Caspian's natural systems and wildlife, including the sevruga sturgeon, seals, and birdlife.

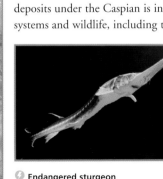

 Endangered sturgeon
The sevruga sturgeon (*Acipenser stellatus*) has become endangered because of overharvesting of its eggs for sevruga caviar, pollution, and disruption of its natural spawning areas.

Caspian tern
The outsized Caspian tern (*Hydroprogne caspia*) has a maximum wingspan of about 4 feet (1.2 m). Caspian terns use freshwater and saltwater habitats around the globe.

A DYING ARAL SEA

The Aral Sea was a vast lake that has been shrinking due to the loss of the river flows that once replenished it. Since the early 1960s, upstream damming and diversions for agriculture have dramatically reduced the lake's size, which can be seen in the photographs below. Today, only a few hypersaline ponds remain and the Aral Sea is rapidly becoming only a memory.

May 29, 1973
A NASA satellite photograph taken in the late spring of 1973 provided a baseline for monitoring changes in the Aral Sea coastline.

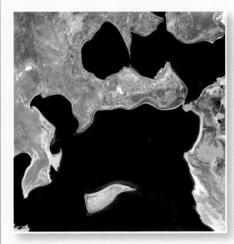

August 19, 1987
Fourteen years later, far more of the lake floor was exposed. Air-quality monitoring showed an increase in airborne dust and other pollutants in the region.

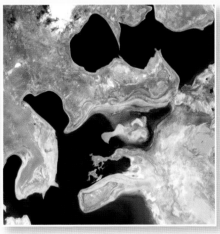

July 29, 2000
By 2000, the Aral Sea was seriously depleted and its wildlife all but wiped out. By 2008 less than 10 percent of the original lake remained.

Once considered a limitless trove of food fish and other commodities, the sea is a complex and fragile natural system. The modern challenge is finding ways to balance rising demand for marine resources with the need to sustain ecologically vulnerable marine habitats and species. Included in this category are green sea turtles (*Chelonia mydas*), an endangered species shown here amid colorful tropical fish.

SEA LIFE
& RESOURCES

SEA HABITATS

At least several hundred thousand species of animals, plants, and other organisms inhabit the sea's varied environments. Roughly 98 percent of these marine organisms live in, on, or just over the seafloor that extends from the shore downward to the deepest abyss. The rest, from floating phytoplankton to sleek swimmers such as tunas, inhabit open waters—the pelagic realm. Water temperature establishes four overall marine regions: polar waters, the coldest; cold temperate seas; warm temperate seas; and the warmest, tropical seas. In all four regions, sunlight profoundly affects the abundance of marine life, with most species living within the sunlight zone that extends down to about 660 feet (200 m). Most marine animals, including familiar sharks, whales, and finfish, inhabit this top layer in temperate and tropical seas. Regardless of exactly where a species occurs, however, its biological design allows it to meet the constant challenges of living, finding food, reproducing, and evading predators in the undersea world.

Climate zones

Based on temperature, scientists divide Earth into four major climate zones. These zones correlate with the paths of warm and cold ocean currents, but they do not coincide exactly with geographic regions. For example, as the map at the right shows, cold currents extend the cold temperate zones up the west coasts of Africa and South America.

■ **Warm temperate zone**
Greek islands in the Aegean Sea are in the warm temperate climatic zone extending over the Mediterranean region and parts of western Asia. In this late-summer satellite view, much of the region's vegetation is brown.

- ☐ Tropical (over 69°F / 20°C)
- ☐ Warm temperate (50–69°F / 10–20°C)
- ☐ Cold temperate (40–50°F / 5–10°C)
- ☐ Polar (less than 40°F / 5°C)

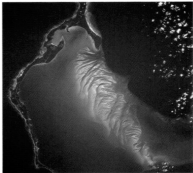

■ **Tropical zone**
The western Atlantic island of Eleuthera is a popular tropical destination. Warmed by equatorial currents and the Gulf Stream, the surrounding sea ranges in temperature from 70°F (21°C) in winter to 80°F (27°C) in summer.

Oceanic zones

Living space in the sea is divided into two major realms: pelagic, up in the water column; and benthic, on the seafloor. The majority of marine creatures are benthic. Sunlight, temperature, pressure, and animal life change dramatically with depth, and the ocean can be divided into three main vertical layers: the narrow upper band of the sunlight zone, the dim middle layer of the twilight zone, and the inky depths of the midnight zone below.

OCEANIC ZONES

ZONE	DESCRIPTION
1 Sunlight zone Surface to 660 feet (200 m)	With enough light for plants to perform photosynthesis, this zone contains most of the ocean's life.
2 Twilight zone 660–3,300 feet (200–1,000 m)	Some sunlight filters down into the twilight zone, but not enough to sustain plants.
3 Midnight zone 3,300 feet (1,000 m) to bottom	Apart from bioluminescence produced by deep-sea species, this deep zone is pitch-black.

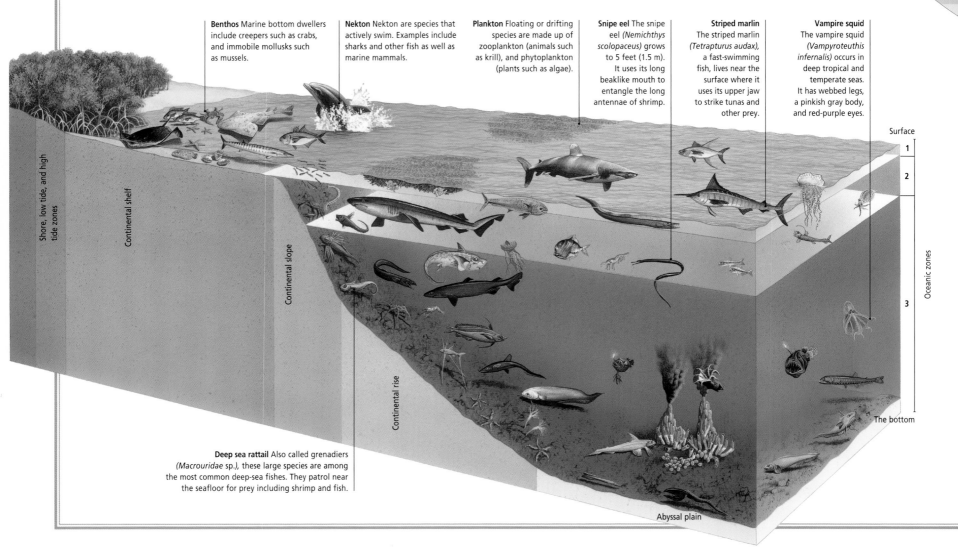

Benthos Marine bottom dwellers include creepers such as crabs, and immobile mollusks such as mussels.

Nekton Nekton are species that actively swim. Examples include sharks and other fish as well as marine mammals.

Plankton Floating or drifting species are made up of zooplankton (animals such as krill), and phytoplankton (plants such as algae).

Snipe eel The snipe eel (*Nemichthys scolopaceus*) grows to 5 feet (1.5 m). It uses its long beaklike mouth to entangle the long antennae of shrimp.

Striped marlin The striped marlin (*Tetrapturus audax*), a fast-swimming fish, lives near the surface where it uses its upper jaw to strike tunas and other prey.

Vampire squid The vampire squid (*Vampyroteuthis infernalis*) occurs in deep tropical and temperate seas. It has webbed legs, a pinkish gray body, and red-purple eyes.

Deep sea rattail Also called grenadiers (*Macrouridae* sp.), these large species are among the most common deep-sea fishes. They patrol near the seafloor for prey including shrimp and fish.

Shore, low tide, and high tide zones

Continental shelf

Continental slope

Continental rise

Abyssal plain

Surface

Oceanic zones

The bottom

Warm temperate

Tropic

Pa

Oc

Cold temperate zone
Influenced by the warm North Atlantic Current, a cold temperate climate prevails across the Scandinavian Peninsula, which includes Norway and Sweden. Glacier-carved fjords are common along the edges of the peninsula. Finland lies to the northeast.

Polar zone
Polar regions are colder than elsewhere because less solar heat reaches the poles. Around Antarctica the mixing of cold and warm ocean currents helps moderate climate. There is much less mixing in the nearly landlocked Arctic Sea.

SURVIVAL STRATEGIES

All ocean species have body features and behaviors that help them survive in their habitats and produce young. These adaptations range from gills that enable fishes to acquire oxygen from seawater to the hydrodynamic body shape of fast swimmers such as mako sharks. Many adaptations are for defense. Camouflage, poisonous venom, and the ability to burrow into seafloor sediments all help protect the species from predation.

This common dab (*Limanda limanda*), a flounder relative, burrows into bottom sediments as a means of avoiding the notice of both predators and prey.

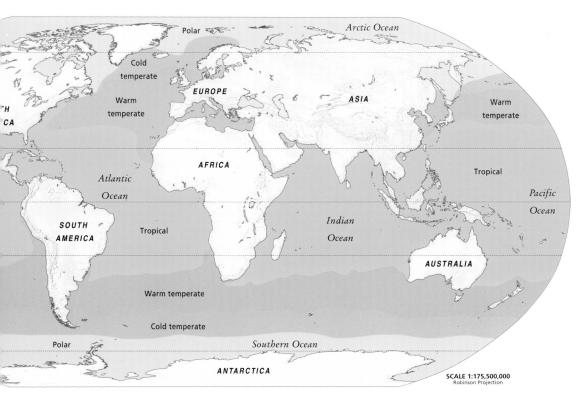

SCALE 1:175,500,000
Robinson Projection

Mats of sargassum, a brown alga, provide floating camouflage for small fish such as this sargassum frogfish (*Histrio histrio*) and other marine life.

Phytoplankton soup
A gallery of phytoplankton from the tropical waters of the Great Barrier Reef, Australia, includes slender copepods, spiky radiolarians, larvae of marine mollusks, and photosynthesizing microorganisms known as cyanobacteria.

The coloration pattern of a pygmy seahorse (*Hippocampus bargibanti*) enables it to almost disappear against a gorgonian coral.

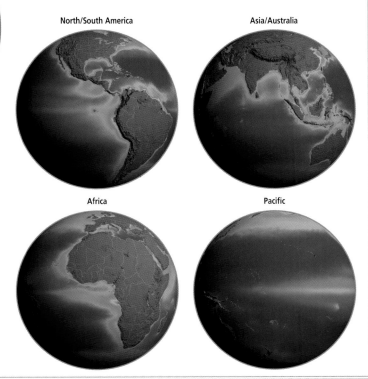

North/South America   Asia/Australia

Africa   Pacific

Monitoring the food base

The marine food web starts with phytoplankton, which survive by using photosynthesis to make their own food. Satellite instruments monitor light reflected from the sea surface to reveal how well or poorly this process occurs. The instruments measure chlorophyll, a pigment used in photosynthesis. Less photosynthesis occurs and food-web nutrients are scarcest in dark blue areas, but more plentiful in red and green areas.

Equipped with unusually long pectoral fins, an Atlantic flying fish (*Cypselurus melanurus*) glides through the air to escape predators.

Life Along the Shore

The sea begins where tides ebb and flow—the intertidal or littoral zone. Whether this narrow ribbon consists of rocks, sand, or mud, it is populated by communities of organisms equipped to survive its challenges. Buffeted by waves, high-energy rocky shores are home to organisms that attach to the hard substrate, such as barnacles, limpets, sea stars, and kelps and other seaweeds. Sandy shores are suited to burrowers such as clams, worms, and shrimplike amphipods. Mudflats may also have large populations of clams and worms. Shorebirds are a feature of every littoral community, and meadows of sea grass abound in areas of soft sediments, providing food and shelter for animals ranging from tiny shrimps to massive sea turtles. Intertidal habitats are increasingly threatened by coastal development, sewage, and accumulating trash. Globally, tens of millions of tons of garbage —an estimated 80 percent of it plastic—pile up along the shore, entangling or poisoning wildlife and degrading the seaside's natural beauty.

Mud communities

Muddy sediments conceal a thriving community of grazers, burrowers, and other life. In this illustrated community, mud snails graze along the surface, and moon snails and dog whelks hunt prey. Below the surface are buried worms, shrimps, and clams. These species extract food deposited on the surface or suspended in the water above it. Many more microscopic creatures inhabit the spaces between sediment particles.

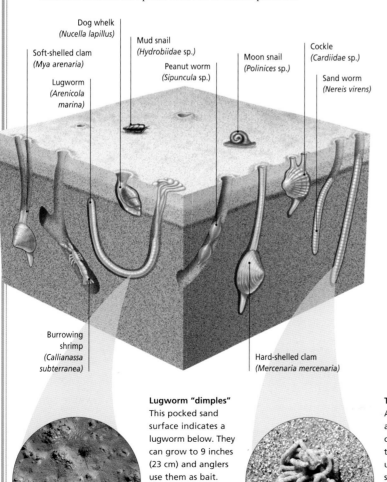

Dog whelk
(*Nucella lapillus*)

Soft-shelled clam
(*Mya arenaria*)

Mud snail
(*Hydrobiidae* sp.)

Lugworm
(*Arenicola marina*)

Peanut worm
(*Sipuncula* sp.)

Moon snail
(*Polinices* sp.)

Cockle
(*Cardiidae* sp.)

Sand worm
(*Nereis virens*)

Burrowing shrimp
(*Callianassa subterranea*)

Hard-shelled clam
(*Mercenaria mercenaria*)

Lugworm "dimples"
This pocked sand surface indicates a lugworm below. They can grow to 9 inches (23 cm) and anglers use them as bait.

Telltale cast
A lugworm takes in sand and digests microscopic organisms living between the grains. It expels the unwanted sand to the surface, leaving a cast.

Rocky and sandy coasts

Rock beaches, cliffs, and caves are prime features of erosional coasts, where wave action slowly wears away hard material forming the shore. Sandy beaches are a hallmark of depositional coasts, where rivers or wave action deposit sediment particles. Over a long time, erosional coasts retreat as the base material is worn away. Sandy coastlines tend to be more stable, but rising sea levels erode them.

Sea cucumber
Sea cucumbers occur in rocky or sandy shallows as well as on the deep seafloor. This specimen of sea cucumber (*Bohadschia argus*) is native to the Indian and southwestern Pacific oceans.

Venus clam
Venus clams (*Pitar* sp.) and other bivalves form colonies on sandy seafloors. Like other clams, they burrow into the soft substrate and filter bits of food from seawater.

Sediment life

Sand or mud beaches are extremely challenging environments. The Sun's heat, salt water, salt-laden winds, and constant wave action all are potential threats to survival. As a result, many species in the intertidal zone spend much or all of their time burrowed beneath the surface or in the shelter of driftwood and washed-up seaweeds and shells. Microscopic animals thrive in the spaces between sand grains.

Coastal cruiser
Purple sea urchins (*Strongylocentrotus purpuratus*) are common inhabitants of rocky coastal areas of western North America. They feed on kelps and other algae.

● Significant rocky coastlines
● Significant sandy coastlines

NORTH AMERICA

SO
AM

Isopod
Isopods (*Cyathura* sp.) are crustaceans with pairs of leg-like appendages and a flattened tail called a telson.

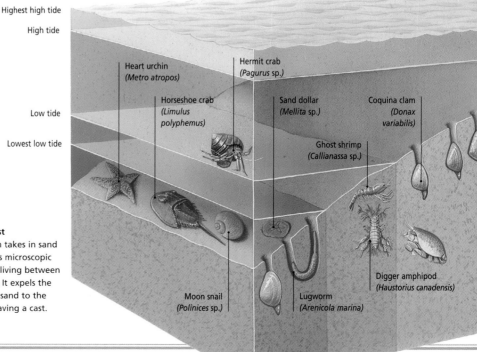

Highest high tide

High tide

Low tide

Lowest low tide

Heart urchin
(*Metro atropos*)

Hermit crab
(*Pagurus* sp.)

Horseshoe crab
(*Limulus polyphemus*)

Sand dollar
(*Mellita* sp.)

Coquina clam
(*Donax variabilis*)

Ghost shrimp
(*Callianassa* sp.)

Moon snail
(*Polinices* sp.)

Lugworm
(*Arenicola marina*)

Digger amphipod
(*Haustorius canadensis*)

Southern sea otter
Southern sea otters *(Enhydra lutris nereis)* are marine mammals native to rocky coasts of the northeastern Pacific. They feed on urchins, shellfish, and small fish.

Blue-banded goby
The Galapagos blue-banded goby *(Lythrypnus gilberti)* darts through rocky nearshore reefs. It is 1.5 inches (4.5 cm) long and an aggressive predator.

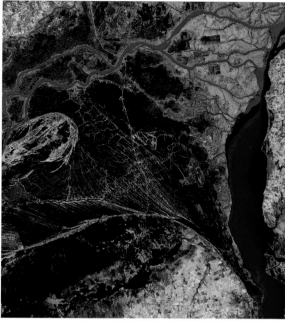

River-borne sediments
Rivers transport sediments to coastal areas, sometimes creating sprawling, fertile deltas. The forested and densely vegetated Parana River Delta shown here is northeast of Buenos Aires, Argentina.

Rocky shore life

Complex communities of marine organisms survive along rocky shores. Most of those living in the intertidal zone have shells or other adaptations that help protect them from wave action and the drying effects of air. Mussels, oysters, limpets, sea stars, chitons, and snails attach to the hard substrate. Small fish and creatures such as sea urchins are found only underwater, in the subtidal zone.

Beach flea
Beach fleas *(Orchestia* sp.) belong to the crustacean group called amphipods. Like fleas, they move by hopping.

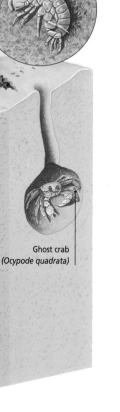

Clam worm
(Nereis sp.)

Ghost crab
(Ocypode quadrata)

Mole crab
(Emerita sp.)

Bloodworm
(Glycera dibranchiata)

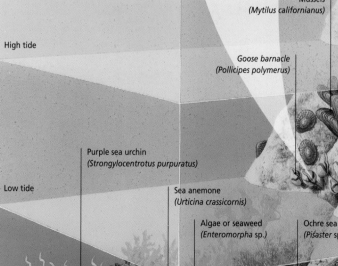

Gooseneck barnacle
Chunky gooseneck barnacles *(Pollicipes polymerus)* may attach to intertidal rocks or to floating debris such as driftwood.

Rock louse
(Ligia occidentalis)

Periwinkle
(Littorina littorea)

Limpet
(Patellacea)

White acorn barnacles
(Balanus glandula)

Chiton
(Chitonidae)

Highest high tide

High tide

Mussels
(Mytilus californianus)

Goose barnacle
(Pollicipes polymerus)

Blue mussels
(Mytilus edulis)

Purple sea urchin
(Strongylocentrotus purpuratus)

Low tide

Sea anemone
(Urticina crassicornis)

Algae or seaweed
(Enteromorpha sp.)

Ochre sea star
(Pisaster sp.)

Hermit crab
(Ceonobita sp.)

LIFE IN SHALLOW SEAS

Shallow, sunlit seas extend from the shore to the outer margins of continental shelves. This realm harbors the great bulk of sea life and also the greatest overall numbers of marine animals, plants, and other kinds of organisms. There are approximately 230,000 documented marine species, including thousands of bony fishes, sharks and their relatives, marine mammals and sea turtles, and invertebrates such as squids, shrimps, and the tiny floating animals collectively called zooplankton. Many more, yet undiscovered species of marine life are thought to exist, and some researchers estimate that the true tally may approach 1 million. Most fish and other pelagic marine animals spend their entire lives in shelf waters, while others pass through during seasonal migratory journeys. Sea grasses and an estimated 9,000 species of seaweeds live in coastal areas. In many parts of the world the cornucopia of life in shallow seas is under siege from overfishing, pollution, and the effects of global climate change.

SEA GRASS SPECIFICS

Type of sea grass	Ocean climatic zone	Interesting fact
Eelgrass	Temperate	Like other seagrasses, has tiny flowers at base of leaves
Widgeon grass	Temperate	Favorite food of wild ducks
Turtle grass	Subtropical Florida and Caribbean	Favored food of sea turtles and parrotfish
Shoal grass	Tropical, subtropical	Short, narrow blades only 0.08–0.1 inch wide (2–3 mm)
Posidonia	Temperate	May form colonies tens of thousands of years old
Johnson's seagrass	Subtropical Florida	Occurs only in Indian River Lagoon, Florida

Food from sunlight
Photosynthesis is the process by which green plants capture solar energy and use it to form sugars. These compounds fuel the plant's own growth and are also stored in plant tissues animals use as food. Specialized plant pigment molecules, mainly chlorophylls, initially trap sunlight. Its energy then drives chemical reactions that convert water and carbon dioxide into sugar. The reactions simultaneously release oxygen.

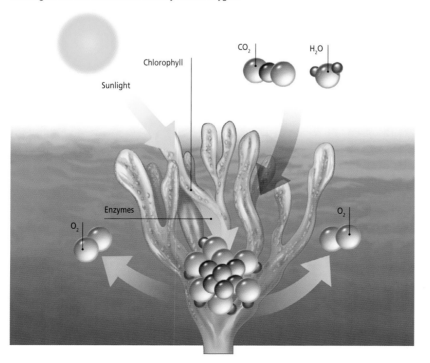

Sunlight
Chlorophyll
CO_2
H_2O
Enzymes
O_2
O_2

Kelp forest
A California bat ray (*Myliobatis californica*) navigates a kelp forest in the Channel Island National Marine Sanctuary off southern California, USA. Kelps rise rapidly toward the sunlit surface. Some species grow as much as 20 inches (50 cm) a day.

Sea grass meadows
Sea grasses undulate with the waves. Rooted in the soft bottom, sea grasses and algae growing on them provide food for grazing snails and small crustaceans. These densely vegetated beds also serve as cover for crabs and juvenile fish.

HUNTING ON THE WING

Keen-eyed seabirds have evolved a variety of methods for finding food. Some simply scavenge dead material floating at the sea surface. Others actively dive to snare fish or other prey near the surface. Still other seabirds excel at underwater hunting and are able to stay submerged for extended periods. Scientists have observed some penguins diving for eight minutes or longer without surfacing to breathe.

Shallow-water corals
Coral reefs in shallow, warm waters, like this strikingly colorful one in the Red Sea, are extraordinarily diverse marine habitats. Many species may coexist in a small area.

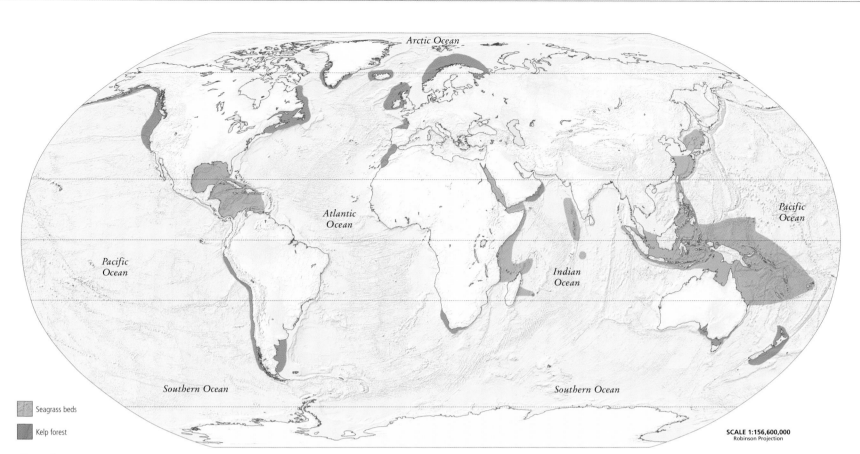

Seagrass beds

Kelp forest

SCALE 1:156,600,000
Robinson Projection

Coastal pastures

In tropical and temperate waters, sea grasses and the large seaweeds called kelp are crucial parts of many coastal marine communities. Growing in the nearshore shallows, this submerged vegetation provides small fish and other marine creatures with both food and shelter from predators. Sea grasses are common along sandy shores. Kelps form lush forests along some rocky coasts.

Giant clam
The tropical Pacific is home to giant clams (*Tridacna gigas*). This vulnerable species can grow, over many years, up to 4 feet (1.2 m) wide and can weigh 440 pounds (220 kg).

Versatile snake eel
The goldspotted snake eel (*Myrichthys ocellatus*) hunts after dark for crabs in sandy sea grass beds of tropical seas. It also burrows into the bottom with its hard, pointy tail.

Bottlenose dolphin
Bottlenose dolphins (*Tursiops truncatus*) occur in shallow waters of tropical and temperate regions of the global ocean. These sociable animals often travel in groups in search of fish.

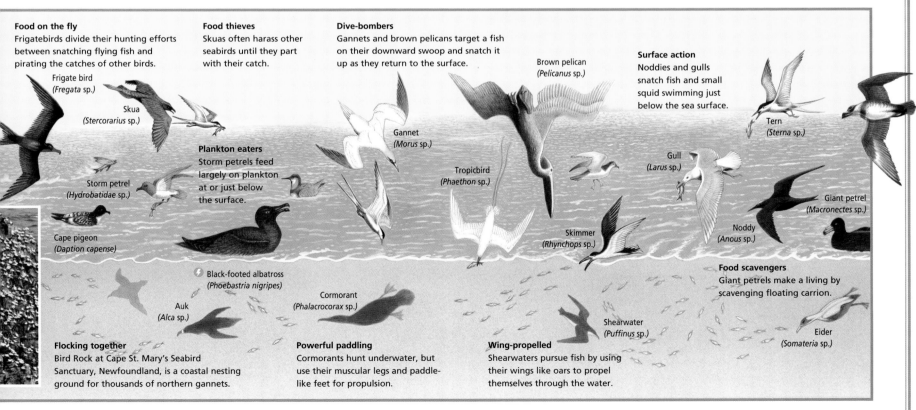

Food on the fly
Frigatebirds divide their hunting efforts between snatching flying fish and pirating the catches of other birds.

Food thieves
Skuas often harass other seabirds until they part with their catch.

Dive-bombers
Gannets and brown pelicans target a fish on their downward swoop and snatch it up as they return to the surface.

Surface action
Noddies and gulls snatch fish and small squid swimming just below the sea surface.

Brown pelican
(*Pelicanus* sp.)

Frigate bird
(*Fregata* sp.)

Skua
(*Stercorarius* sp.)

Tern
(*Sterna* sp.)

Plankton eaters
Storm petrels feed largely on plankton at or just below the surface.

Gannet
(*Morus* sp.)

Gull
(*Larus* sp.)

Storm petrel
(*Hydrobatidae* sp.)

Tropicbird
(*Phaethon* sp.)

Giant petrel
(*Macronectes* sp.)

Cape pigeon
(*Daption capense*)

Skimmer
(*Rhynchops* sp.)

Noddy
(*Anous* sp.)

Black-footed albatross
(*Phoebastria nigripes*)

Food scavengers
Giant petrels make a living by scavenging floating carrion.

Auk
(*Alca* sp.)

Cormorant
(*Phalacrocorax* sp.)

Shearwater
(*Puffinus* sp.)

Eider
(*Somateria* sp.)

Flocking together
Bird Rock at Cape St. Mary's Seabird Sanctuary, Newfoundland, is a coastal nesting ground for thousands of northern gannets.

Powerful paddling
Cormorants hunt underwater, but use their muscular legs and paddle-like feet for propulsion.

Wing-propelled
Shearwaters pursue fish by using their wings like oars to propel themselves through the water.

BEYOND THE SHELF

The open ocean begins where continental shelves end and ocean basins slope downward to the deepest seafloor. Sunlit and relatively warm near the surface, these waters become dimmer as the depth increases, and their temperature drops sharply as well. At about 3,300 feet (1,000 m), sunlight no longer penetrates and the temperature averages roughly 39°F (4°C). It stabilizes at a frigid 30°F (-1°C) in the deep abyss. Warmer surface waters teem with uncountable billions of floating phytoplankton, tiny plantlike organisms that are the foundation of the marine food web. Species with light-producing organs are common in the dimmer, cooler twilight zone below. Casting an eerie glow are many species of squids, red shrimps, and fishes whose eyes are 100 times more sensitive to light than those of humans. The sea becomes increasingly inhospitable to life with depth. Although the deep ocean contains more than 75 percent of the sea's total volume, relatively few species survive there.

Humpback whales
Humpback whales (Megaptera novaeangliae) are known for their acrobatic breaching—here, a rare double breach in the Pacific Ocean off Hawaii. Humpbacks occur around the globe, migrating seasonally between polar and temperate seas. They feed on fish and krill.

Built for speed
From its bullet-like body to its crescent-shaped tail, a bluefin tuna's (Thunnus thynnus) adaptations make it a powerful high seas predator. Its cruising speed is about 2 miles per hour (1.3 km/h), fast for a fish. When chasing prey, however, a tuna can accelerate in a burst of speed, reaching 12–18 miles per hour (20–30 km/h) in less than 10 seconds.

Crescent-shaped tail
The bluefin tuna has a narrow, stiff tail fin shaped like a crescent moon. This shape, and the "keels" on the sides of the tail, reduce turbulence or "drag" that can slow the tuna.

Dorsal fin | A predator's large eyes

Gills

Warm muscles
A network of blood vessels called a rete mirabile, or "wonderful net," keeps warm blood flowing to a tuna's muscles. This allows tunas to swim fast in cold waters.

Powerful swimming muscles
A tuna needs strong muscles for its lifetime of swimming. The bluefin tuna is globally endangered largely because its muscles are the "meat" that so many people prize as food.

Countershading
The back of a bluefin tuna is dark blue, while its underside and flanks are silvery. This countershading makes it harder for both predators and prey to see a bluefin in the water.

High seas shark
The oceanic white tip (Carcharinus longimanus) is one of the open ocean's large predators, growing up to 13 feet (4 m) long. Its sizable fins make this shark a target for fishers who slice off the fins and throw the doomed fish overboard.

Ocean sunfish
An adult sunfish (Mola mola) can weigh 2,200 pounds (1,000 kg) and feeds mainly on jellyfish. Sharks and killer whales prey on sunfish.

Chambered nautilus
The chambered nautilus (Nautilus pompilius), related to the octopus and squid, retracts its tentacled body into a multichambered shell.

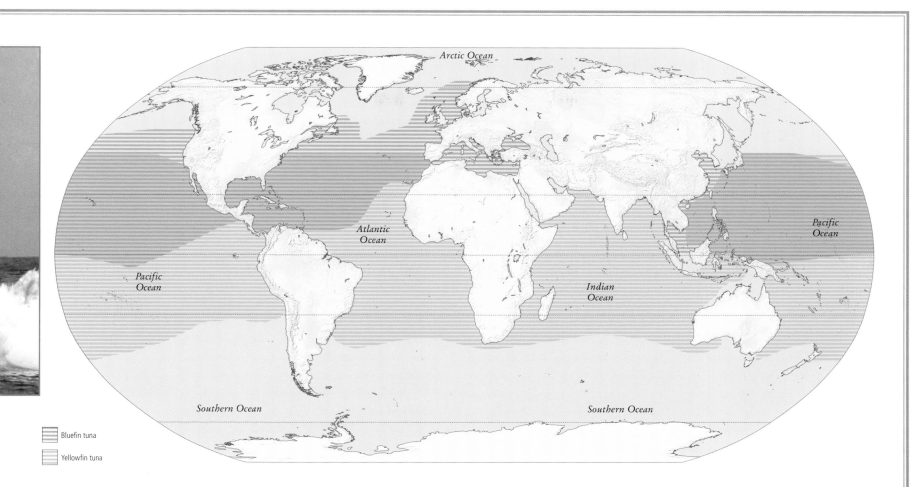

- Bluefin tuna
- Yellowfin tuna

Tuna geographic range

Two of the best-known tunas are the bluefin *(Thunnus thynnus)* and yellowfin *(Thunnus albacares).* Both are somewhat "warm-blooded," with dense arrays of blood vessels that are warmed by the swimming muscles. This mechanism is most efficient in bluefin tunas, which spawn in tropical and subtropical regions but range in summer well up into cold temperate seas. Yellowfin tunas are restricted to tropical and subtropical waters year-round.

TUNA VITAL STATISTICS		
Common name	Bluefin tuna	Yellowfin tuna
Scientific name	*Thunnus thynnus*	*Thunnus albacares*
Average length	6.6 feet (2 m)	4.6 feet (1.4 m)
Maximum length	10 feet (3 m)	9 feet (2.8 m)
Maximum weight	1,500 pounds (680 kg)	880 pounds (400 kg)
Top speed	62 miles per hour (100 km/h)	50 miles per hour (80 km/h)
Maximum depth	3,000 feet (914 m)	820 feet (250 m)
Average life span	15 years	9 years

DEEP DWELLERS

In the eerie realm of the deep sea, many species including fishes, brittle stars, and squids are bioluminescent. Below about 3,300 feet (1,000 m) fishes and other creatures have soft bodies, and the fish species are small with large mouths. Some have large eyes; others are blind. Food is relatively scarce in this environment. Some predators have light organs that lure prey while others hunt using keen senses of smell and touch.

Normal fish eye
Eyes of upper and mid-water fish are rounded, with a moderate-sized lens and retina. This design works reasonably well for gathering ambient light.

Iris
Choroid layer
Suspensory ligament
Tough outer layer
Retina
Lens
Optic nerve

Tubular eye
Some deep-sea fishes have tubular eyes. The large lens and specialized, multi-layered retina help maximize the detection of available light in the depths.

Optic nerve
Choroid layer
Retina
Lens
Tough outer layer
Auxiliary lens
Reflective layer

Blackbelly dragonfish
This blackbelly dragonfish *(Stomias* sp.) is native to the central eastern Pacific, where it may be found as deep as 4,900 feet (1,500 m). Females sport long chin barbells equipped with light organs that may attract both prey and potential mates.

Atlantic longarm octopus
The delicate-looking Atlantic longarm octopus *(Octopus defilippi)* is named for elongated arms that stretch about five times the length of its body. It lives on or near the seafloor.

MIGRATIONS

Migration is a basic survival strategy for many marine creatures. Species ranging from fish and jellyfish to squids and plankton move vertically between the surface and deeper, darker waters in a daily rhythm that affords a balance between finding food and being less visible to predators. Sea turtles, whales, salmon, some sharks, and many seabirds migrate long distances to find mates, food, or to avoid harmful environmental shifts as seasons change. Cues from the sun, odors, sounds, or Earth's magnetic field are thought to guide these remarkable journeys. Female sea turtles are renowned for their long, magnetism-guided migrations to the nesting beach where they themselves were hatched. Humpback whales hold the record for a migrating marine mammal; they travel as much as 5,600 miles (9,000 km) between summer feeding grounds and winter breeding grounds. An Arctic tern traverses as much as 22,000 miles (35,400 km) in its annual migratory journey between the poles—the longest animal migration known.

Migration paths

Most migrating marine animals remain in their home hemisphere, even though they may travel long distances. Birds have no such limits, however, and may migrate from pole to pole. Whales migrate from polar regions where they feed in summer to the tropics where they mate and have their young. Seals migrate to bear their young on islands or other coasts in subpolar latitudes.

WINTER MIGRATIONS

➡ Humpback whale
➡ Arctic tern
➡ Short-tailed shearwater
➡ Southern right whale

Phytoplankton

Phytoplankton species are known for their striking body architecture, which ranges from spiky or boxy to feathery, ball-like, and helical.

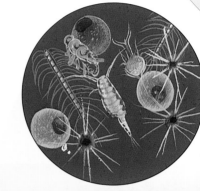

Pacific Ocean

Daily vertical migration

Shifting light levels trigger the most massive marine migration, a vertical journey by numerous species moving up and down in the water column. For example, as day gives way to night copepods and jellyfish move upward, followed by their predators. The pattern reverses with the rising dawn. Some seabirds hunt at or near the surface regardless of the time of day.

GULF STREAM TRAVELERS

🔵 Loggerhead sea turtles *(Caretta caretta)* are among a variety of marine migrators that take advantage of the powerful Gulf Stream traveling clockwise around the North Atlantic. Using different types of tracking devices, scientists have been able to monitor both the turtles' routes and the length of time they remain in the Gulf Stream. Loggerheads can detect and use Earth's magnetic field to navigate.

Satellite tags have revealed crucial information about loggerhead migration. The simpler "living tag" shown here is a pale plug from the turtle's plastron transplanted to its dark carapace. Living tags are used to mark wild turtles under study.

Loggerhead turtles hatched on Florida beaches navigate into the Gulf Stream, which carries them northeast, then south around the North Atlantic. Six to 12 years later the turtles are carried to the US as large juveniles.

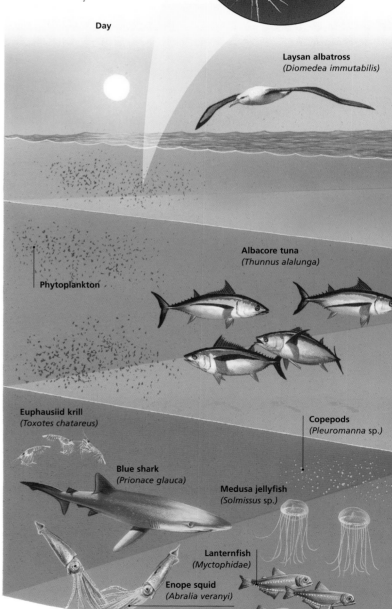

Day

Surface

100 feet (30 m)

660 feet (200 m)

3,300 feet (1,000 m)

Laysan albatross *(Diomedea immutabilis)*

Phytoplankton

Albacore tuna *(Thunnus alalunga)*

Euphausiid krill *(Toxotes chatareus)*

Copepods *(Pleuromanna sp.)*

Blue shark *(Prionace glauca)*

Medusa jellyfish *(Solmissus sp.)*

Lanternfish *(Myctophidae)*

Enope squid *(Abralia veranyi)*

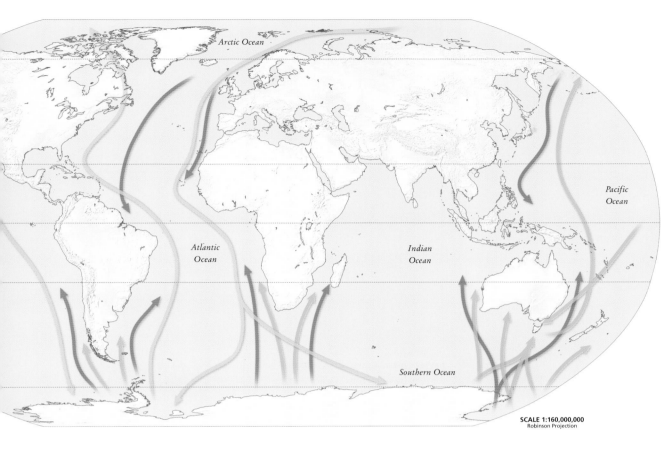

Arctic Ocean

Pacific Ocean

Atlantic Ocean

Indian Ocean

Southern Ocean

SCALE 1:160,000,000
Robinson Projection

Short-tailed shearwater
Short-tailed shearwaters (*Puffinus tenuirostris*) migrate about 20,000 miles (32,000 km) around the Pacific. They return to Australia to breed.

Arctic tern
The Arctic tern (*Sterna paradisaea*) migrates between Antarctica and breeding grounds in the Arctic and subarctic regions.

Humpback whale
Humpback whales (*Megaptera novaeangliae*) feed in the Arctic in summer, but they do not eat while at their warmer winter breeding sites.

Southern right whale
The Southern right whale (*Eubalaena australis*) spends summer just off Antarctica and migrates northward to winter breeding grounds.

Night

Copepods
Marine plankton includes countless billions of copepods, tiny crustaceans with long, bristly antennae, and nearly transparent bodies.

Scary squid
The aptly named jumbo squid (*Dosidicus gigas*) grows to at least 6.5 feet (2 m). It hunts at night and aggressively pursues tunas and other prey. Like other "flying" squids, this species can propel itself above the water to escape predators.

GATHERING TOGETHER

Many marine species gather en masse to mate, migrate, or exploit a rich food supply. At the zenith of high spring and summer tides along Southern California beaches, hordes of wriggling grunions emerge from the surf to spawn in the sand, then return to the sea. In the Caribbean, Nassau groupers once formed huge local mating aggregations—gatherings that drew enough fishermen to drive several grouper populations extinct. Food can be a huge lure for many species. After pupping and mating elsewhere, hundreds of humpbacks and other whales arrive in the Gulf of Alaska to feed on a late summer explosion of krill. Approaching autumn may bring a million or more cownose rays to the mouth of Chesapeake Bay to prepare for a long southward migration. Some sea gatherings are scientific puzzles. Scalloped hammerhead sharks are normally solitary hunters, but for unknown reasons they converge during the winter at sites such as the Straits of Florida, only to disperse again over the continental shelf in summer.

Seal mating groups
Northern elephant seals *(Mirounga angustirostris)*—named for the dangling snout of the males—gather at mid-winter at several points along the central California coast; there pregnant females give birth. The cycle begins anew as adults mate before leaving the area.

Ray roundup
In early fall, a million or more Atlantic cownose rays *(Rhinoptera bonasus)* gather at the mouth of Chesapeake Bay, then migrate together to warmer Florida waters. Pregnant females carry unborn pups until the following spring, when they are born upon the rays' return.

Animals that Gather Together		
Animal	Adaptive function	Typical season and location
Northern elephant seal (*Mirounga angustirostris*)	Mating/pupping	Winter, central California coast, USA
Horseshoe crab (*Limulus polyphemus*)	Mating/spawning	Spring, Delaware Bay, USA
Atlantic cownose ray (*Rhinoptera bonasus*)	Pre-migration	Early fall, mouth of Chesapeake Bay, USA
California grunion (*Leuresthes tenuis*)	Spawning	Spring/summer, Pacific coast, Mexico (Baja California) to central California, USA
Nassau grouper (*Epinephelus striatus*)	Spawning	Winter, Caribbean Sea
King penguins (*Aptenodytes patagonicus*)	Mating/nesting	Spring/summer, South Atlantic

GATHERING ARTHROPODS

Horseshoe crabs *(Limulus sp.)* occur in areas as distant as the Atlantic coast of North America and the Sea of Japan. At spawning season, males move close to shore. Females arrive some days later. Males attach to the egg-bearing females, which then drag the males along as they creep onto the shore. The males fertilize clusters of eggs the female deposits in a series of hollows scooped into the sand.

Female horseshoe crabs lure males in part by releasing a chemical trail of pheromones. Both sexes may also be able to visually identify potential mates.

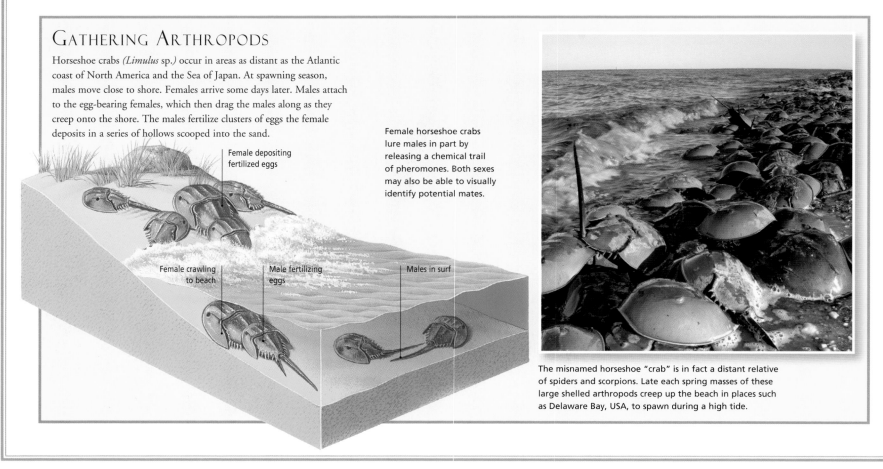

Female depositing fertilized eggs

Female crawling to beach

Male fertilizing eggs

Males in surf

The misnamed horseshoe "crab" is in fact a distant relative of spiders and scorpions. Late each spring masses of these large shelled arthropods creep up the beach in places such as Delaware Bay, USA, to spawn during a high tide.

Benefits of togetherness

When individuals of a marine species periodically gather in one location, the behavior is likely no accident. In particular, pre-migration gatherings, or those for mating, spawning, or protecting young, involve complex gene-based mechanisms for coordinating the activity of dozens, hundreds, or thousands of individuals. Such strategies improve chances that the members of a species, and the species as a whole, will survive.

King penguins
King penguins (*Aptenodytes patagonicus*) range far and wide in their usual foraging activities, but they gather into large breeding colonies.

California grunion
California grunions (*Leuresthes tenuis*) go ashore to spawn on spring and summer nights. After two weeks waves carry the young out to sea.

Naussau grouper
Multicolored male Nassau groupers (*Epinephelus striatus*) swim around a female. This triggers her egg release, which the males then try to fertilize.

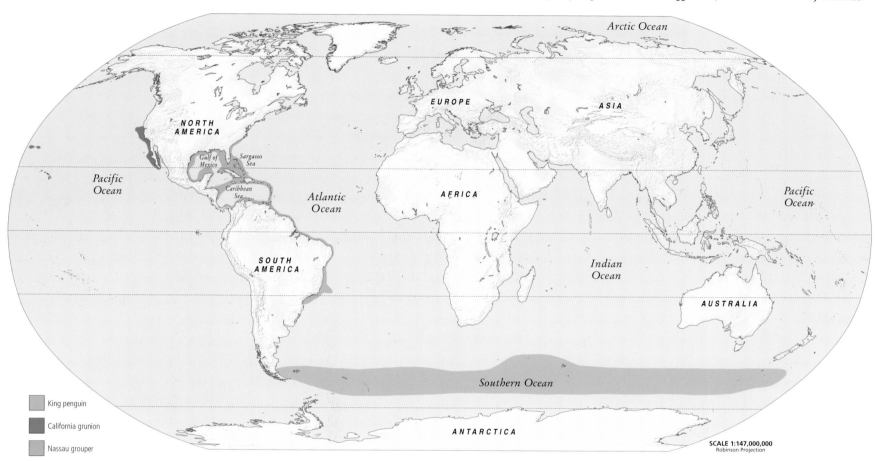

King penguin

California grunion

Nassau grouper

SCALE 1:147,000,000
Robinson Projection

RED KNOT RENDEZVOUS

Red knots (*Calidris canutus*) gather by the thousands to feed heavily before a long spring migration. A major stopover is Delaware Bay on the US Atlantic coast, where the birds' arrival tracks the spawning of horseshoe crabs. For countless generations of red knots, horseshoe crab eggs have been the key food resource fueling their migration. As human harvesting of horseshoe crabs has increased, red knot populations have been decreasing. Red knots migrate between subpolar regions of Eurasia and Canada and destinations in southern Europe, West Africa, South America, and Australia.

These red knots are but a few of the thousands that must build up their energy reserves before continuing their migratory journey.

RED KNOT MIGRATORY PATH

Staging/wintering areas

Staging areas

Wintering areas

Breeding areas

→ Migratory route

···▶ Hypothetical routes

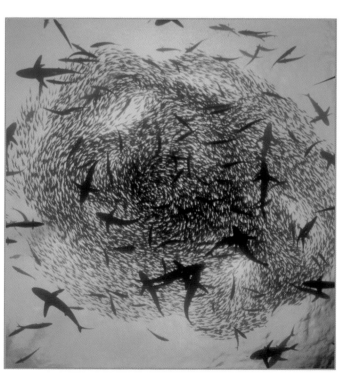

Hungry sharks
Attracted by the presence of a rich food trove—a cluster of green jacks (*Caranx sexfasciatus*) off Cocos Island, Costa Rica—silky sharks (*Carcharhinus falciformis*) converge to feed.

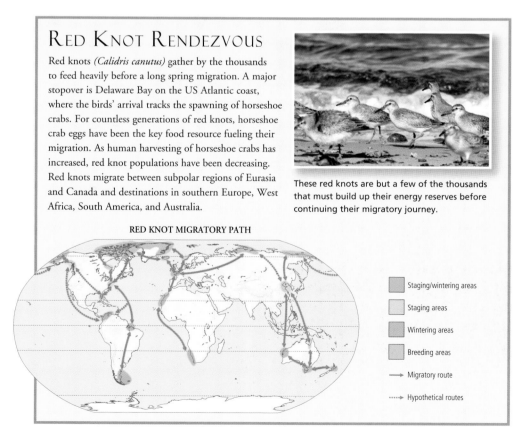

Minerals

Minerals are among the sea's premier non-living resources. Commercial salt works, where impounded seawater slowly evaporates and leaves behind salt crystals, produce more than 30 percent of the world's table salt. Magnesium also is extracted from seawater for use in manufacturing precision metal parts. Huge deposits of methane hydrates—ice-locked methane, the main component of natural gas—occur in sediments of continental shelves. Highly promising as an alternative fuel source, methane hydrates also pose environmental challenges due to methane's status as a greenhouse gas that stokes global warming. Other sought-after industrial minerals include manganese, copper, and iron in seafloor fields of fist-sized nodules at depths of 13,000–20,000 feet (4,000–6,000 m). High extraction costs may stymie efforts to exploit this rich trove for the foreseeable future. By contrast, coastal beaches, dunes, and ocean bottom are heavily mined for sand used in construction, industrial processes, and beach replenishment. Intensive sand mining now threatens numerous coastal habitats.

METHANE HYDRATE DEPOSITS

SCALE 1:317,700,000
Robinson Projection

Methane hydrates

Methane is the main component of natural gas. Methane hydrates basically consist of methane trapped in slushy ice. Large deposits have been found under several continental shelves, and geologists estimate that the amount of methane they hold totals more than twice the world's reserves of other fossil fuels. Because the hydrates are located undersea, however, recovering them and safely extracting methane may prove both difficult and costly.

Mineral movements

Sand and many other minerals enter the sea when wind and rain erode them from land-based deposits. The eroded particles may fall into the sea or be transported there by rivers. If the seabed slope is steep, heavier particles will soon settle to the bottom. If the slope is shallow, currents and wave action may move sand or other sediments some distance along the shore, a process called longshore drift.

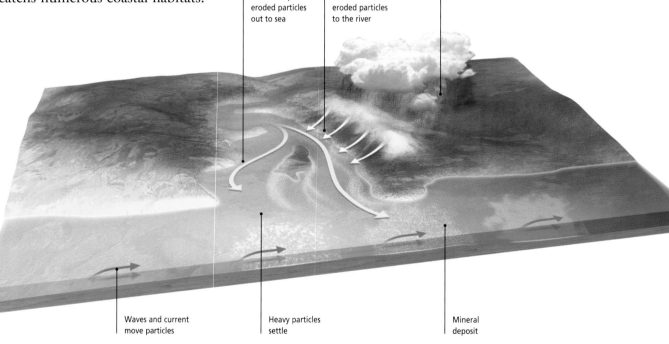

River transports eroded particles out to sea

Rain carries eroded particles to the river

Rainfall

Waves and current move particles

Heavy particles settle

Mineral deposit

Phosphate from the Sea

Earth's crust contains phosphates, which contain the mineral phosphorus used in fertilizers and other industrial chemicals. Phosphates are most accessible in land deposits. Despite this, one rich marine source is the accumulation of droppings of certain seabirds. This guano is collected and processed commercially, or used by local farmers who apply it directly to the soil—a centuries-old practice.

All plants require the mineral phosphorus to grow normally. Hence the use of phosphate-containing fertilizers on crops.

The Islas Ballestas off the coast of Peru are favored nesting sites for seabirds, making the rocky isles a major guano "mine." Scaffolding allows workers to collect the guano, which is then processed to extract phosphates.

Top Ten Phosphate Producers	
1 USA	6 South Africa
2 Russia	7 Egypt
3 China	8 Israel
4 Brazil	9 Morocco
5 Australia	10 Tunisia

Manganese-phosphorite rock

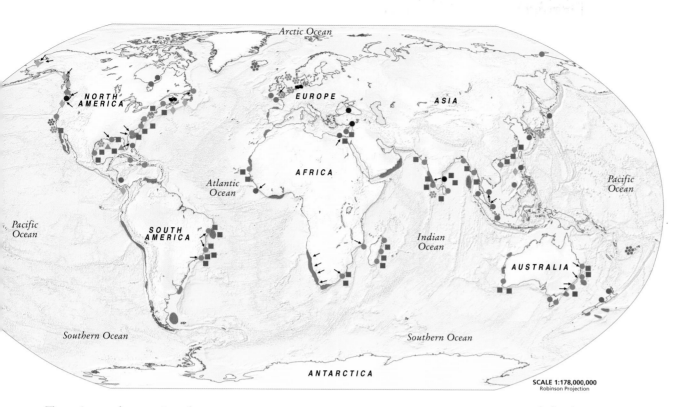

SCALE 1:178,000,000
Robinson Projection

Targeting undersea minerals

A variety of potentially valuable mineral deposits exist in deeper offshore waters in various locations around the globe. Of these, oil and gas deposits in continental shelves in locales such as the North Sea and Gulf of Mexico currently have the most commercial appeal. As land-based sources diminish, it may become economically viable to pursue other deepwater mineral resources, including phosphates and manganese nodules.

- ● iron
- ● tin
- ● chrome
- ● copper
- ● titanium
- ■ monazite
- ■ zircon

- ◆ diamond
- ◆ gold
- ✳ sand and gravel
- ✳ shell sands
- ▬ coal
- ▲ sulfur
- ▮ phosphorite
- → derivation of placer

Desalination

Fresh water moves into salt water if a semi-permeable membrane separates the two. Applying pressure to the salt water stops this flow, called osmosis. Increasing the pressure causes reverse osmosis, in which pure water flows out of the salty solution.

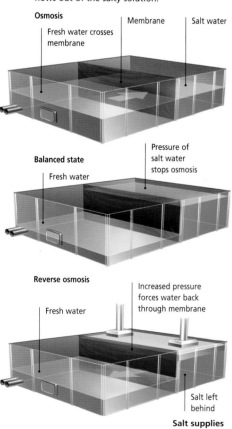

Osmosis
Fresh water crosses membrane — Membrane — Salt water

Balanced state
Fresh water — Pressure of salt water stops osmosis

Reverse osmosis
Fresh water — Increased pressure forces water back through membrane — Salt left behind

Salt supplies

Piles of sea salt—the mineral compound sodium chloride—are extracted in evaporation ponds, as shown here in Sicily. Windmills have been used to power the pumping of brackish water into the ponds since Medieval times.

MANGANESE NODULES

Lumpy nodules of manganese were first observed in the 1870s by the Challenger deep-sea expedition. The nodules lie scattered across the deep-sea floor of the world's oceans. Although not yet commercially viable because of the depths where they are located, manganese nodules are a potentially valuable source of nickel, copper, and manganese. Nodules enlarge as minerals accumulate, giving them an intricate interior structure.

Cross section

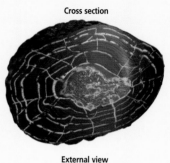

External view

Researchers are developing methods to retrieve manganese nodules from as deep as 19,500 feet (6,000 m) below the sea. By current estimates the supply of key ores in the richest Pacific Ocean nodule fields could meet human needs for 20 centuries.

NODULE INGREDIENTS

Other 40.53%
Manganese 24.2%
Iron 14%
Water 19.4%
Nickel, copper, cobalt 1.87%

On average a manganese nodule is about one-quarter manganese. Smaller amounts of other ores are valuable because the ores have such vital industrial uses.

OIL AND GAS

At dozens of sites around the globe, the seabed conceals major offshore fields of oil and natural gas. Both these fossil fuels formed over millions of years as buried, carbon-rich remains of animals and plants were compressed under accumulating rock layers. They gradually seep upward through porous rock strata until becoming trapped in pressurized pools under a hard, impermeable layer called caprock. Drilling at depths ranging from a few hundred feet to more than 34,000 feet (10,360 m) taps these pools and allows crude oil and natural gas to be piped to the surface. Extensive undersea oil and gas fields are known in the Middle East, in the North Sea, along the Gulf Coast of North America and off the east coast of South America, and the west coast of Africa. Due to the time span required for fossil fuels to form, they are finite resources that inevitably are being depleted as world demand for them grows.

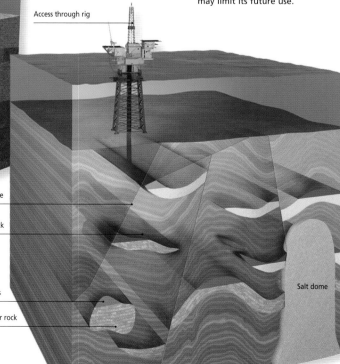

Drilling support
Oil platforms are built on steel or concrete supports that must withstand the force of waves, currents, and in some areas ice. Some rigs float while others rest atop pillars sunk into the seafloor.

Remains accumulate
Dead organisms drop to the ocean floor and are quickly covered by mud and silt. Where little or no oxygen is present, remains only partially decay. Over time the remains are trapped within thickening sediment layers.

Settling remains

Sediment layers

Controlled decay
As rock layers accumulate, organic remains trapped within them are subjected to moderate heat and increasing pressure. These conditions favor the formation of oil and gas from the buried remains.

Accumulating rock layers

Trapped organic material

Rise of fossil fuels
Once oil and gas have formed, they percolate upward through the overlying layers of rock. Both seep through porous sandstone, but eventually stop rising and pool when they reach higher, nonporous rock such as shale.

Porous rock

Impermeable rock

Rising oil and gas

Oil reserves
More than 60 percent of the world's oil reserves lie in the territory of five Middle Eastern countries. As global supplies dwindle, pressure is growing to tap other reserves.

OIL

Rest of world 37.4%
Saudi Arabia 24.9%
Iran 8.5%
Kuwait 9.2%
Iraq 10.7%
United Arab Emirates 9.3%

GAS

Rest of world 37.3%
Russia 30.7%
Iran 14.8%
Qatar 9.3%
United Arab Emirates 3.9%
Saudi Arabia 4.0%

Gas options
Russia has the richest reserves of natural gas, but environmental concerns about this diminishing and highly valuable fossil fuel may limit its future use.

Oil and gas formation

Oil and natural gas form from the buried remains of marine life that have been compressed over millions of years between rock layers. These layers form as sediments are compacted in low-oxygen conditions, which preserve carbon compounds in decaying tissues. The modern-day inland location of many oil and gas deposits is due to tectonic movements and changing sea levels during Earth's geological past.

Formation of a reservoir
The oil and gas collect in reservoir rock that is porous. The nonporous caprock above prevents the pooled fossil fuels from leaking away. Drilling then allows access to these reservoirs.

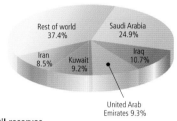

Access through rig

Fault line

Nonporous caprock

Pooled oil and gas

Reservoir rock

Salt dome

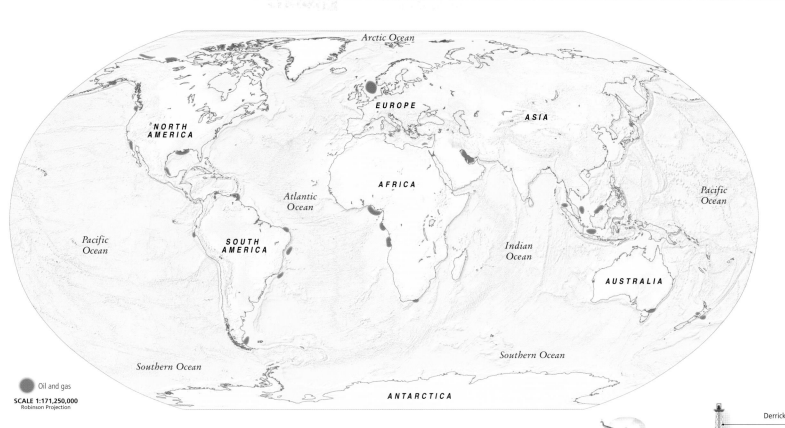

Oil and gas

SCALE 1:171,250,000
Robinson Projection

Oil and gas production

Offshore oil and gas production centers mainly in
the Middle East, the North Sea, and Central and
South America. Other important reserves have been
found along the continental shelf off Nigeria, Egypt,
and Indonesia. This map shows the most important
areas of offshore oil and gas production at present.
The multibillion-dollar oil and gas industry globally
employs hundreds of thousands of workers.

Transporting oil
Fleets of supertankers move crude oil from its
sources to refineries around the globe. Smaller
vessels carry refined petroleum products to the
market. The largest crude oil tankers transport
550,000 dead-weight tons (500,000 t) of oil,
roughly 6 million barrels.

Oil platform
Oil platforms pump out millions of barrels
of oil per day. Most stay operational for
about 25 years. Large platforms may have
living quarters for as many as 300 workers
and derricks supporting multiple drills.

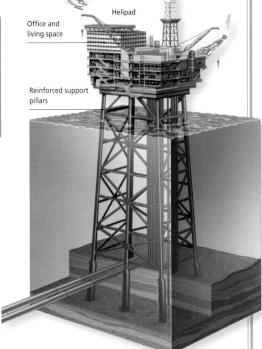

Derrick
Helipad
Office and living space
Reinforced support pillars

Top Ten Oil and Gas Consumers 2006

Country	Millions of barrels/day (combined oil and gas)	Country	Millions of barrels/day (combined oil and gas)
1 USA	20.59	6 India	2.53
2 China	7.27	7 Canada	2.22
3 Japan	5.22	8 Brazil	2.12
4 Russia	3.10	9 South Korea	2.12
5 Germany	2.63	10 Saudi Arabia	2.07

LIFE AROUND THE RIG

The submerged portions of oil platforms lure large
numbers of marine organisms, especially where the
seafloor lacks rocky surfaces that attract species
requiring a hard substrate. In such places, hard
platform supports may become home to thriving
communities including corals and arrays of other
invertebrates and fish. Platforms in warm and
temperate seas have the most diverse marine life.

PLATFORM FIELDS WITH HIGH MARINE DIVERSITY

California coast, Gulf of Mexico, Coastal Venezuela, Persian Gulf, Indo-Australia

Rigs with significant wildlife

Hydroids (*Hydrozoa* sp.),
marine invertebrates that
superficially resemble
plants, grow profusely on
the support of an oil rig
in warm waters of the
Gulf of Mexico.

Orcas, or killer whales (*Orcinus
orca*), pass by a New Zealand oil
refinery where tankers offload
crude oil to be processed.

This Green turtle (*Chelonia mydas*)
was photographed in the Gulf of
Mexico swimming around one of the
many oil platforms.

SEA POLLUTION

Pollution is a serious threat to the seas, in part because roughly 40 percent of the world's population lives within 65 miles (104 km) of an ocean. Agricultural and urban runoff routinely contaminate coastal waters with trash, pesticides, and fertilizers that cause unnatural algal blooms. Industrial discharges to the air and waterways add toxins such as polychlorinated biphenyls (PCBs) and polycyclic aromatic hydrocarbons (PAHs) that accumulate in the tissues of marine organisms and eventually become magnified through the marine food web. Massive oil spills, such as the oil released after the 2002 sinking of the tanker *Prestige* off northwestern Spain, may damage coastal ecosystems and fisheries for as long as 15 years. Coastal cities routinely discharge minimally processed sewage. Although international regulations prohibit the once-common practices of ocean dumping of radioactive wastes, municipal garbage, sewage sludge, vessel trash, industrial wastes, and hazardous dredge spoils, enforcement is difficult and violations are common.

A sea of contamination

No part of the marine world is free from pollution. Areas where this contamination is worst include the Mediterranean Sea and many seacoasts. Much coastal pollution is due to the combined effects of coastal development and marine ship traffic to and from ports. Relatively speaking, the open ocean is the least contaminated. Fortunately, improvements to oil tanker design and operation have gradually reduced marine oil spills.

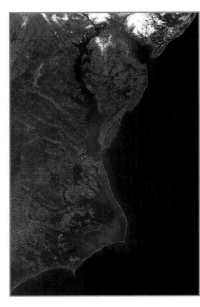

Coastal runoff
In Chesapeake Bay, the largest US estuary, runoff from farmland contains large quantities of fertilizers. This fuels the overgrowth of phytoplankton, which in turn leads to the depletion of oxygen in large "dead zones" in Bay waters.

OCEAN POLLUTION SOURCES	
Type	Source
Land-based	• Runoff—nitrogen and phosphorus from farming fertilizers and pesticides • River-borne industrial chemicals • Dumping of waste at sea • Sewage, gray water, and waste water • Radioactive waste dumping • Improper garbage disposal
Airborne	• Pollutants such as wind-borne nitrogen and sulfur compounds deposited at sea • Acid rain
Maritime transportation	• Oil pollution from tanker spills • Waste and vessel sewage from tankers, naval ships, cruise liners, and recreational boats • Oil and gas platform waste

- ◾ Severely polluted sea areas
- ◾ Less polluted sea areas
- ◾ Areas of frequent oil pollution by shipping
- ● Sites of major oil tanker spills
- ▲ Major oil rig blow-outs
- ◼ Offshore dump sites for industrial and municipal waste

Agricultural inputs
Virginia is one of several US states bordering Chesapeake Bay. Many farmers there are experimenting with methods that can help reduce the use of agricultural chemicals.

OCEAN POLLUTANTS

Land-based sources 44%
Atmospheric inputs 33%
Other 11%
Maritime transportation sources 12%

ANIMALS IN TROUBLE

Floating garbage, noxious chemicals, and other pollution all harm marine wildlife. One of the worst offenders is plastic, in the form of discarded fishing lines and nets, trash bags, bottle holders, and other debris. Oil slicks that coat seabirds or other large wildlife also take a toll. Small organisms along oil-fouled coastlines may take a double hit, because they can be killed by some kinds of clean-up efforts.

Commercial fishermen often discard or lose nets at sea. These gray snappers (*Lutjanus griseus*) suffocated when they became entangled in a floating gill net.

A plastic garbage bag wrapped around this lemon shark (*Negaprion brevirostris*) may remain for years, assuming that the entangled shark can continue to function normally. The shark could be doomed if the plastic obstructs its gills.

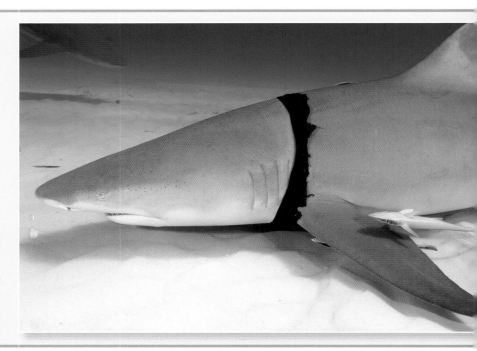

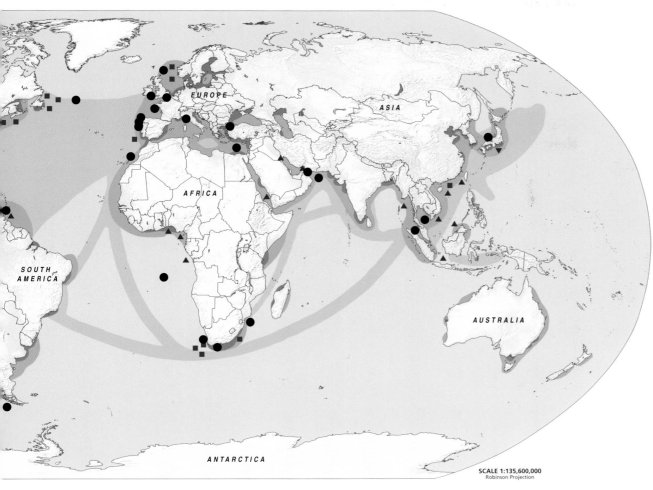

SCALE 1:135,600,000
Robinson Projection

Blooming algae
Surplus nutrients in runoff fueled this algal bloom in Everglades National Park, Florida, USA. It depleted oxygen and killed life in the waters.

Most polluted Mediterranean
Industrial and agricultural wastes make up the majority of contaminants in the heavily polluted Mediterranean Sea.

Mumbai rubbish
Debris covering this beach in Mumbai, India, provides a mother pig and her piglets with food scraps, and they leave their droppings behind.

Oil-soaked coast
The Exxon Valdez oil spill had a severe impact on Alaska's Prince William Sound. About 11,000 tons (10,000 t) of the spilled oil came ashore, affecting wildlife and fisheries along more than 300 miles (480 km) of coastline.

POLLUTION FROM OIL TANKERS/PLATFORMS		
Year	Tanker	Crude oil spilled [tons (t)]
1991	Iraqi tankers in Gulf War	up to 1.5 million (1.3 million)
1991	ABT Summer	260,000 (236,000)
1991	MT Haven	144,000 (131,000)
1988	Odyssey	132,000 (120,000)
1983	Castillo de Beliver	252,000 (229,000)
1980	Irenes Serenade	100,000 (91,000)
1979	Atlantic Empress & Aegean Captain	287,000 (260,000)
1979–80	Ixtoc I exploratory well	up to 480,000 (435,000)
1978	Amoco Cadiz	227,000 (206,000)
1972	Sea Star	115,000 (104,000)

Spill and aftermath
When the supertanker Exxon Valdez went aground in Prince William Sound, Alaska in 1989, only about one-fifth of the ship's cargo leaked from its damaged hull. Even so, clean up efforts took years, cost billions, and were only partially effective.

Shore effects
Oiled rocks and sand were blasted with hot, pressurized water. Later studies revealed the hot blasts killed many small animals.

Aerial attack
Helicopters sprayed a strong detergent on the spreading slick. The spray only helped disperse about 5 percent of the oil.

Detergent spray

Oil slick
About 30 percent of the spilled oil formed a slick on the water's surface. Currents and wave action drove most of this oil ashore.

Containment
Containment booms enclose areas of oil above and below the surface. Much of the oil evaporates, some is burned off, and some is pumped out by skimmer ships.

When oil fouls the plumage of seabirds like this duck caught in the Exxon Valdez spill, they lose body heat and cannot fly. Hundreds of thousands of affected seabirds died, as did sea otters, whales, and millions of fish.

COMMERCIAL FISHING

The sea has supplied humans with food and other essentials for at least 40,000 years. From the Arctic to the Southern Ocean, early fishermen used nets, spears, ingenious traps, hook-and-line, and even their hands. Such low-impact practices helped sustain many generations of coastal peoples. Today millions of vessels using sophisticated electronic gear trawl, longline, or set massive nets along the continental shelves and on the high seas. This industrial fishery harvests billions of tons of sea creatures valued for food or fertilizer, including tunas, anchovies, shrimps, and squid, and earns annual revenues of more than US $400 billion dollars. Millions of tons of non-target "bycatch" species are simply discarded. By recent estimates, 52 percent of marine fish populations are being harvested to the maximum sustainable limit, while another 24 percent are being dangerously overharvested. Despite efforts at international controls, a few nations still conduct "scientific" whaling even though the populations of most whale species are a mere shadow of their former numbers.

FISHING TRADITION

Peoples of the high Arctic traditionally traveled in skin-covered kayaks or larger craft called umiaks. They used woven nets and hook-and-line methods to catch fish, while seals, walrus, and the occasional whale were taken with spears or harpoons. Although some Inuit still use traditional methods, others employ motorized vessels and use a harpoon cannon or rifle to kill large prey, such as narwhals, beluga whales, and other species.

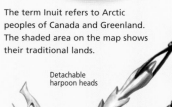

An Inuit fisherman may wait many hours at holes cut in the ice for Arctic char and other coveted fish species. This man is using a time-honored Inuit spear-fishing technique.

The term Inuit refers to Arctic peoples of Canada and Greenland. The shaded area on the map shows their traditional lands.

Knife used in preparing food

Detachable harpoon heads

Harpoon head

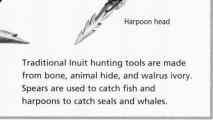

Fishing spear

Traditional Inuit hunting tools are made from bone, animal hide, and walrus ivory. Spears are used to catch fish and harpoons to catch seals and whales.

Main fisheries

Fishing operations annually capture hundreds of millions of metric tons of fish used for human food, animal feed and fertilizers. Fisheries are spread around the global sea, but nearly 50 percent of this intensive harvesting occurs in different parts of the Pacific Ocean. Three nations—China, Peru, and the USA—account for nearly one-third of all catches. Nations neighboring the Indian Ocean and North Atlantic are other major producers.

	Greater than 20 million tons (18 million tonnes)
	10–20 million tons (9–18 million tonnes)
	5–10 million tons (4.5–9 million tonnes)
	2–5 million tons (1.8–4.5 million tonnes)
	Less than 2 million tons (1.8 million tonnes)
—	Boundary of major fishing areas
10 (9)	Production, tons (tonnes)

Open sea fishing
The deck of this commercial trawler is awash with Pacific cod caught off the coast of Alaska. Following an unsustainable 430 percent increase in the number of Pacific cod taken in recent years, the fishery today is more carefully regulated.

Fish to market
A Tokyo fish market features arrays of freshly caught tunas. Japan and other Asian nations operate roughly 70 percent of the world's motorized fishing vessels. These craft range from small powerboats to the high-tech vessels of industrial fishing fleets.

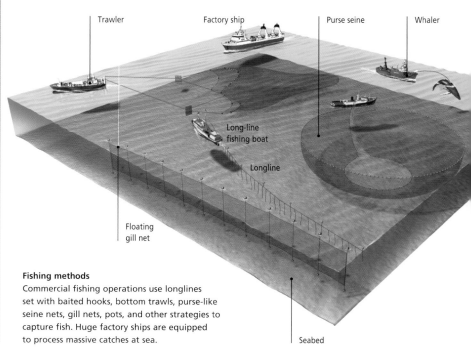

Trawler

Factory ship

Purse seine

Whaler

Long-line fishing boat

Longline

Floating gill net

Seabed

Fishing methods
Commercial fishing operations use longlines set with baited hooks, bottom trawls, purse-like seine nets, gill nets, pots, and other strategies to capture fish. Huge factory ships are equipped to process massive catches at sea.

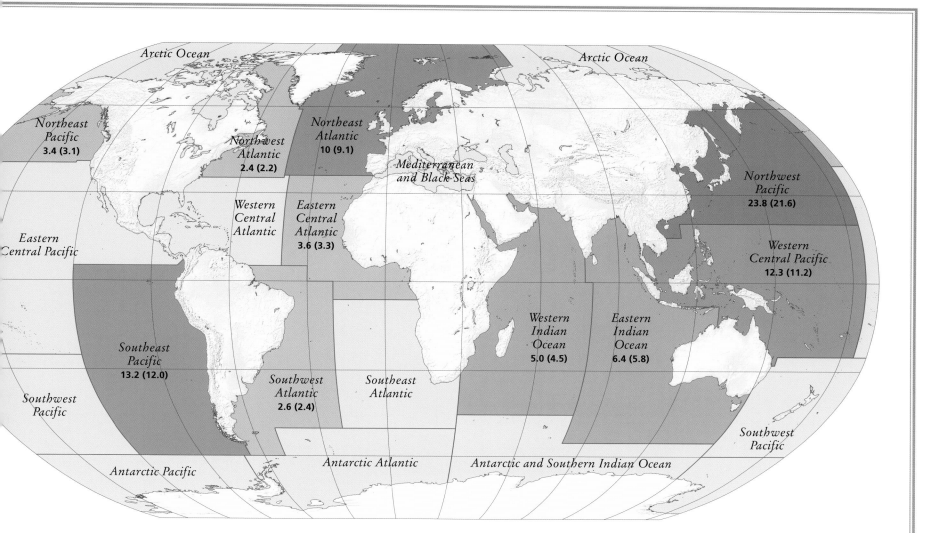

Northeast
Pacific
3.4 (3.1)

Northwest
Atlantic
2.4 (2.2)

Northeast
Atlantic
10 (9.1)

*Mediterranean
and Black Seas*

Northwest
Pacific
23.8 (21.6)

Eastern
Central Pacific

Western
Central
Atlantic

Eastern
Central
Atlantic
3.6 (3.3)

Western
Central Pacific
12.3 (11.2)

Western
Indian
Ocean
5.0 (4.5)

Eastern
Indian
Ocean
6.4 (5.8)

Southeast
Pacific
13.2 (12.0)

Southwest
Atlantic
2.6 (2.4)

Southeast
Atlantic

Southwest
Pacific

Southwest
Pacific

Arctic Ocean — Arctic Ocean

Antarctic Pacific — Antarctic Atlantic — Antarctic and Southern Indian Ocean

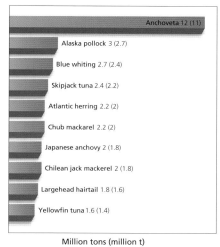

Anchoveta 12 (11)
Alaska pollock 3 (2.7)
Blue whiting 2.7 (2.4)
Skipjack tuna 2.4 (2.2)
Atlantic herring 2.2 (2)
Chub mackarel 2.2 (2)
Japanese anchovy 2 (1.8)
Chilean jack mackerel 2 (1.8)
Largehead hairtail 1.8 (1.6)
Yellowfin tuna 1.6 (1.4)

Million tons (million t)

Major commercial species, 2004
By weight the Peruvian anchovy (anchoveta) outstrips all other commercially caught wild fish. Other fish targeted by marine fisheries include tunas, and blue whiting, the latter a common ingredient in fish meal.

Target: lobsters
A lobster boat heads out into the western North Atlantic where baited pots will be set. In recent years catches of wild lobsters have begun to decline while consumer demand has risen.

Shrimping
Spot prawns are the catch in this small pot set in the cold waters of British Columbia, Canada. The majority of wild shrimp are caught with specialized trawl nets that rake in millions of tons annually.

WHALING

In the 20th century populations of many whale species fell as whaling fleets used spotter planes to locate animals and processed catches at sea on factory ships. The International Whaling Commission introduced protection for blue, gray and humpback whales in 1965. In 1985 an international moratorium banned nearly all whaling.

In Norway, Japan, and several other countries, whale meat is a prized delicacy. This photograph shows whale meat in a Norwegian market.

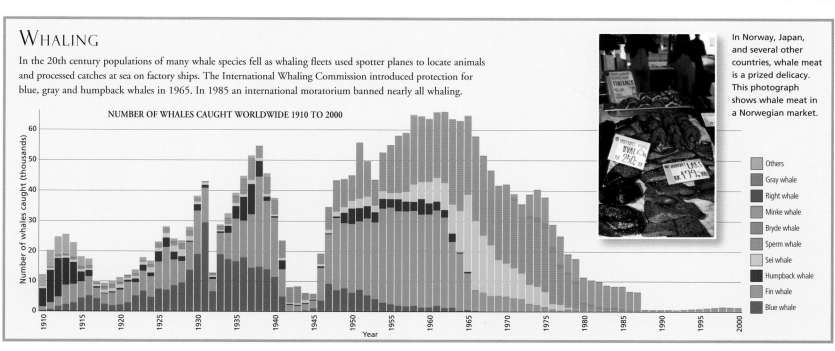

NUMBER OF WHALES CAUGHT WORLDWIDE 1910 TO 2000

Number of whales caught (thousands)

Year

Others, Gray whale, Right whale, Minke whale, Bryde whale, Sperm whale, Sei whale, Humpback whale, Fin whale, Blue whale

THREATENED SEA LIFE

Certain ocean areas and species have been hard-hit by aggressive fisheries, coastal development, pollution, and environmental changes due to global warming. Pollution, coral bleaching, and fishing with explosives have helped place coral reefs in the Caribbean and Indo-Pacific into the critically endangered category. Some scientists estimate that populations of vital reef predators such as sharks have declined as much as 50 to 90 percent. Development and oxygen-depleting nutrient pollution seriously threaten many estuaries that are major nursery grounds for many young fish and shrimp. The United Nations estimates that more than 20 percent of mangrove estuaries have been destroyed in recent years. Leatherbacks, hawksbills, and all other sea turtles are endangered, in part because humans consume their eggs and meat or use turtle shells for ornaments. Overfishing has decimated stocks of bluefin tunas, billfish, and shark species such as the sand tiger, and unrelenting whaling has nearly eradicated the blue whale, the largest animal ever to have existed on Earth.

On the brink

Scores of marine animals are listed as vulnerable, endangered, or critically endangered by the International Union for the Conservation of Nature (IUCN). Four of the five species pictured here are critically endangered, meaning that their numbers are so few that they may be on the brink of extinction. Human activities, including overharvesting and habitat destruction, have been the key factors placing these species in peril.

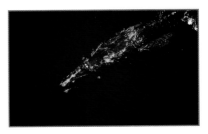

Northern right whale
Heavy whaling from the late 1840s to the mid-1880s decimated populations of the Northern right whale (*Eubalaena glacialis*).

MOST ENDANGERED SHARKS
1 Ganges shark (*Glyphis gangeticus*)
2 Striped smoothhound (*Mustelis fasciatus*)
3 Pondicherry shark (*Carcharhinus hemiodon*)
4 Daggernose shark (*Isogomphodon oxyrhynchus*)
5 Angel shark (*Squatina squatina*)
6 Dumb gulper shark (*Centrophorus harrissoni*)
7 Borneo shark (*Carcharhinus borneensis*)
8 New Guinea river shark (*Glyphis* sp.)
9 Speartooth shark (*Glyphis glyphis*)
10 Narrownose smoothhound (*Mustelis schmitti*)
11 Smoothtooth blacktip (*Carcharhinus leiodon*)
12 Whitefin topeshark (*Hemitriakis leucopeript*)
13 Bizant river shark (*Glyphis* sp.)
14 Smoothback angel shark (*Squatina oculata*)
15 Sawback angel shark (*Squatina aculeata*)

THREATENED ANIMALS

- North Atlantic right whale
- Hawksbill turtle
- Smalltooth sawfish
- Mediterranean monk seal
- Goliath grouper

SCALE 1:137,000,000
Robinson Projection

ACIDIFICATION

Increasing atmospheric carbon dioxide is a major phenomenon in global warming and climate change. As the level of carbon dioxide rises, related chemical reactions may be making the ocean more acidic. This change in turn can reduce the amount of calcium carbonate available to form the shells and skeletons of organisms such as corals, mollusks, and crustaceans. Concerned scientists are tracking shifts in acidification and monitoring their impacts.

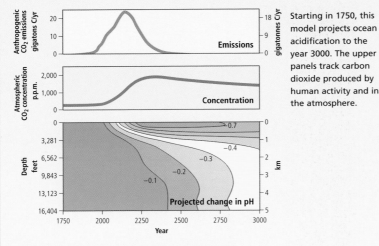

Starting in 1750, this model projects ocean acidification to the year 3000. The upper panels track carbon dioxide produced by human activity and in the atmosphere.

In the diagrams below, red marks ocean depths where too little calcium carbonate is (or will be) available for use by marine invertebrates.

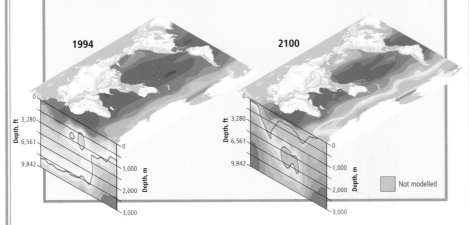

1994   2100

Not modelled

Shark mortality

South Africa, Australia, the USA, and Mediterranean nations all protect great white sharks (*Carcharodon carcharias*) in their waters. This 15-foot (4.6-m) specimen may have died when it tried to take fish hooked on a longline.

Death by finning

Fisheries for shark fins are destructive and wasteful. The fins are used in a luxury soup consumed in some Asian cultures. Typically, once fins are sliced off, the living shark is thrown back into the sea where it drowns.

Hawksbill turtle
Hawksbill (*Eretmochelys imbricata*) populations have been depleted by human consumption of its eggs and use of its shell for ornaments.

Smalltooth sawfish
Numbers of this tropical ray (*Pristis pectinata*) have perished in nets set for other species. Its habitat has been destroyed by development.

Mediterranean monk seal
Killing by fishermen, disturbed colony sites, and entanglement in fishing nets are some causes for this species (*Monachus monachus*) decline.

Goliath grouper
The grouper (*Epinephelus itajara*) is critically endangered due to intensive fishing pressure on its habitats and its slow rate of reproduction.

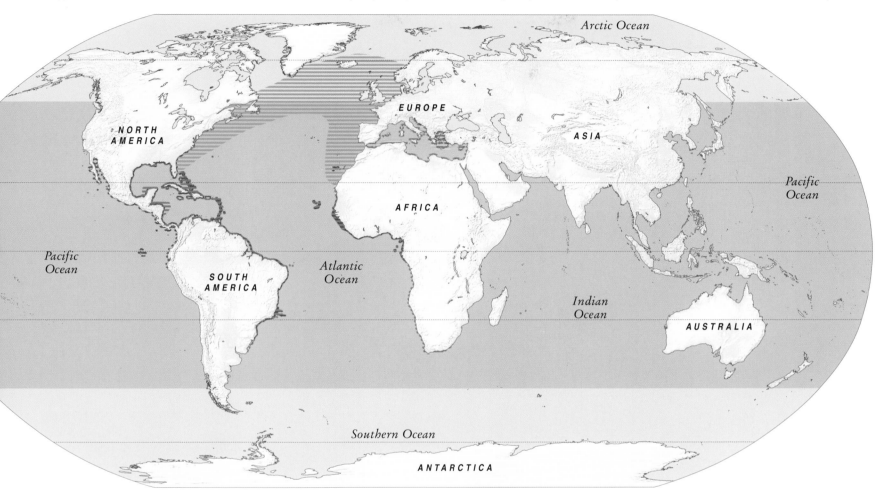

Ghost nets
Caught in an abandoned, drifting "ghost net," this endangered green sea turtle (*Chelonia mydas*) was unable to surface and breathe. Ghost nets probably also kill large numbers of sharks, which must swim unfettered in order to breathe.

Lethal bycatch
Lured by longline bait, sea turtles are sometimes taken as accidental bycatch on commercial longlines set for fish. Unless released in good condition the turtle will suffocate.

Death by dynamite
In some tropical regions fishermen use the highly destructive practice of dynamiting to "harvest" reef fish. This harmful practice is illegal, but unfortunately common.

EXTINCT MARINE ANIMALS

Caribbean monk seal
This small, inquisitive seal (*Monachus tropicalis*), native to the Caribbean and Gulf of Mexico, was sought after for its oil. In 1952 it was declared extinct.

Steller's sea cow
This immense 26-foot (7.9-m) long marine mammal, the steller sea cow (*Hydrodamalis gigas*) was hunted to extinction in less than three decades after it was discovered in 1741.

Great auk
The great auk (*Pinguinus impennis*) was flightless and therefore an easy target for hunters. It was last seen in Newfoundland, Canada, in 1852.

CONSERVATION OF THE SEAS

Until the mid-1800s the sea's bounty seemed inexhaustible, but by the early 1900s some northern waters were depleted of once vast stocks of cod, haddock, and oysters. Advances in fishing technology and storage allowed commercial fishers to pursue catches ever farther from shore, but by the 1970s overfishing and destruction of marine habitats began to be serious global concerns. In 1972 the United Nations Educational, Scientific and Cultural Organization (UNESCO) began its World Heritage program that now includes dozens of undersea sites around the globe. Today, governmental agencies and private organizations including the International Union for the Conservation of Nature (IUCN) and World Wildlife Fund work to help conserve marine habitats through scientific research, fisheries management, and public education. Major sanctuaries include marine reserves such as Palmyra Atoll, Kingman Reef, and Rose Atoll, a set of central Pacific islands that form the world's largest protected marine area.

Monitoring reef health
Using a digital camera, researchers photograph seaweed growing on a Hawaiian reef. These algae are an important part of the reef ecosystem. Long-term study of the sites allows scientists to monitor their health and track potential changes.

Shark tagging
This porbeagle shark (Lamna nasus) is being measured prior to being tagged and released back into the sea. Tagging studies allow marine scientists to gather data about shark migration and information on the ecology of populations.

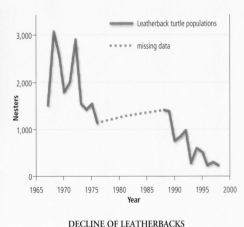

Sustainable salmon
Sustainability is a major goal of the carefully managed Alaska salmon fishery, in which small vessels are the norm. This boat's purse seine encloses a load of chum (dog salmon), one of five species caught in Alaska waters.

Turtle excluders
When shrimp trawl nets are equipped with turtle excluder devices (TEDs) like those shown here, sea turtles and large fish inadvertently caught in the nets are shunted back out through an opening in the device.

LEATHERBACKS

🕐 Leatherback sea turtles (Dermochelys coriacea) have a thick, leathery skin instead of hard scutes and grow to about 7 feet (2 m). They range through much of the global sea, with nesting beaches concentrated in the tropics and subtropics. The largest of living marine reptiles, leatherbacks are critically endangered due mainly to intensive human consumption of their eggs and meat. Conservation efforts focus on halting and possibly reversing the decline.

LEATHERBACK DISTRIBUTION

Satellite tracking allows researchers to monitor a leatherback's diving behavior and travel patterns through the ocean. The satellite tag, attached to a harness, feeds information to a satellite that transfers the data to a receiver on land.

Numbers painted onto a sea turtle's back allow scientists to identify it after it is released back into the wild.

Leatherback turtle populations

missing data

Nesters

1965 1970 1975 1980 1985 1990 1995 2000
Year

DECLINE OF LEATHERBACKS

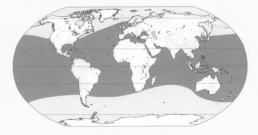

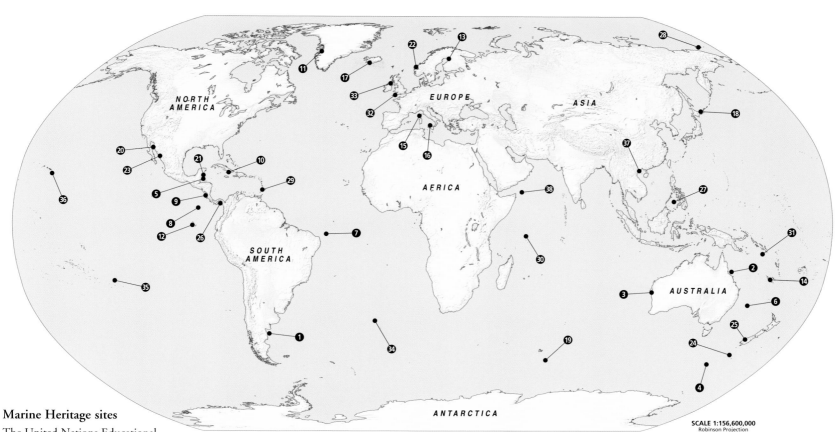

SCALE 1:156,600,000
Robinson Projection

Marine Heritage sites

The United Nations Educational, Scientific and Cultural Organization (UNESCO) designates protected Marine Heritage sites in coastal areas around the globe. The sites are selected for their outstanding natural and/or cultural significance. Site personnel receive training and support for state-of-the-science management methods to counter damage to the world's marine environments.

UNESCO MARINE HERITAGE SITES

1 Península Valdés, Argentina
2 Great Barrier Reef, Australia
3 Shark Bay, Australia
4 Macquarie Island, Australia
5 Belize Barrier Reef Reserve System
6 Lord Howe Island Group, Australia
7 Brazilian Atlantic Islands
8 Cocos Island National Park, Costa Rica
9 Area de Conservacion, Guanacaste, Costa Rica
10 Desembarco de Granma National Park, Cuba

11 Ilulissat Ice Fjord, Denmark
12 Galapagos Islands, Ecuador
13 High Coast/Kvarken Archipelago, Finland & Sweden
14 The lagoons of New Caledonia
15 Gulf of Porto, Corsica
16 Isole Aolie (Aeolian Islands), Italy
17 Surtsey, Iceland
18 Shiretoko, Hokkaido, Japan
19 MacDonald and Heard Islands, Australia

20 Gulf of California, Mexico, Islands, and Protected Areas
21 Sian Ka'an, Mexico
22 West Norwegian Fjords, Norway
23 El Vizcaino Whale Sanctuary, Mexico
24 New Zealand Sub-Antarctic Islands
25 Tewahipounamu, Southwest New Zealand
26 Coiba National Park, Panama
27 Tubbataha Reef Marine Park, Philippines
28 Natural System of Wrangel Island Reserve, Russian Federation

29 Pitons Management Area, St. Lucia
30 Aldabra Atoll, Seychelles
31 East Rennell, Solomon Islands
32 Dorset & East Devon Coast, UK
33 Giants Causeway and Causeway Coast, UK
34 Gough and Inaccessible Islands, UK
35 Henderson Island, UK
36 Hawaii Volcanoes National Park, Hawaii, USA
37 Ha Long Bay, Vietnam
38 Socotra Archipelago, Yemen

Great Barrier Reef
The Great Barrier Reef of Australia is the world's largest coral reef system. It consists of hundreds of islands and nearly 3,000 separate reefs.

Giant's Causeway
The Giant's Causeway, located on the coast of Northern Ireland, consists of more than 4,000 basalt blocks formed by volcanic activity.

Ha Long Bay
The shimmering seawaters of Ha Long Bay in Vietnam encompass several thousand intriguingly shaped limestone islands.

Cocos Islands
The world-famous coral reef of Cocos Island, Costa Rica, is renowned for its sea life including whale sharks and hammerhead sharks.

MANATEES

Manatees (*Trichechus manatus latirostris*) are classified (with dugongs) as sirenians. Genetic studies suggest that elephants are the group's closest living relatives. Two of the three recognized species—the West Indian manatee and the West African manatee—spend time in salt water. All manatee populations are small and under threat. Manatees are known for lolling in tropical estuaries, rivers, and coastal waters where they feed on submerged grasses.

MANATEE DISTRIBUTION

Manatees have a blunt head and snout, short flippers used for slow swimming, and a flattened, rounded tail.

This researcher is attaching a satellite tracking device to a young Florida manatee before releasing it at a wildlife refuge.

Because manatees live mainly in the shallows, collisions with watercraft are common. In Florida boats cause up to 40 percent of manatee deaths.

BOAT SPEED KILLS

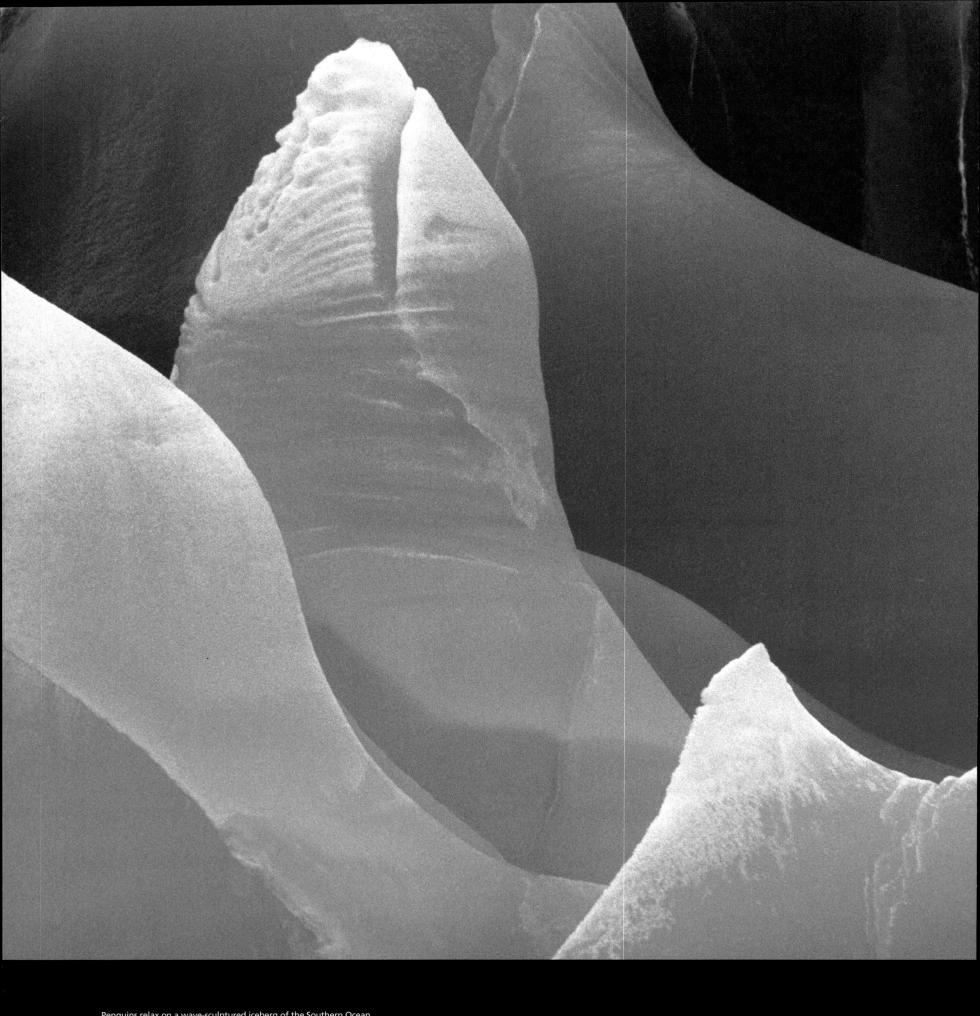

Penguins relax on a wave-sculptured iceberg of the Southern Ocean. Ice covers both polar oceans in winter, melting and breaking up in spring to release nutrients and surface food. On this annual bonanza depend the fish, seals, whales, and seabirds abundant in polar oceans both north and south. Icebergs provide sanctuary away from land for penguins and other seabirds.

POLAR OCEANS

ARCTIC OCEAN

During the 16th and 17th centuries, ship-borne explorers heading northward from Europe on early spring voyages soon found themselves among sea ice. Floes and towering, castle-like icebergs pressed dangerously around their ships, drifting steadily south from a seemingly endless reservoir located far to the north under Arctos, the pole star. Was there an Arctic Ocean, and could it be crossed to reach the wealth of China and the Indies? Penetrating the fringe seas east and west of Greenland, early Dutch and British explorers brought home tales of unimaginable cold and hardship. Those that headed northeast toward Russia, favored by warm currents from the north Atlantic Ocean, skirted the Siberian coast and became the first Europeans to enter the Arctic Ocean itself. The "Northeast Passage" to China evaded them, but traders who followed brought home cargoes of whale oil, baleen, walrus ivory, polar bear and reindeer skins, and later valuable furs from Siberia. The ocean was first crossed by Nansen's ship *Fram* in 1893-96.

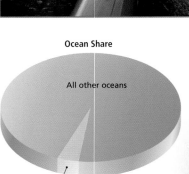

Oil pipeline
Ice investing the northern shores of Alaska in winter makes year-round shipping impracticable. Oil drilled at Prudhoe Bay travels south instead by pipeline to Valdez, an ice-free port on the Pacific Ocean shore. The Trans-Alaska pipeline, which is 800 miles (1,280 km) long, was completed in 1977.

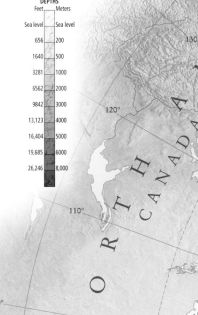

BATHYMETRIC DEPTHS

Feet	Meters
Sea level	Sea level
656	200
1640	500
3281	1000
6562	2000
9842	3000
13,123	4000
16,404	5000
19,685	6000
26,246	8,000

Ocean Share

All other oceans

Arctic Ocean
5.4 million sq miles
(14.1 million km²)
4%

THE FACTS

Area	5.4 million square miles (14.1 million km²)
Average depth	4,690 feet (1,430 m)
Maximum depth	18,455 feet (5,625 m)
Maximum width	2,000 miles (3,200 km)
Maximum length	3,100 miles (5,000 km)

NATURAL RESOURCES

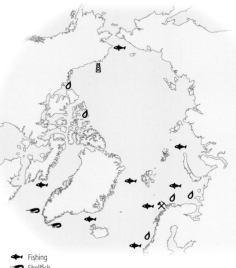

➤ Fishing
➤ Shellfish
✕ Mining
⛽ Oil production
⬧ Gas production

There are rich fisheries in the Barents, Greenland, and Bering seas. Seals are still hunted commercially throughout the Arctic: whales are hunted off Norway, and Inuit communities take small numbers of whales and seals locally. Northern Siberia and Alaska have huge reserves of oil, coal, and gas.

Walrus herd
Walrus *(Odobenus rosmarus)* feed mainly on clams, which they seek in the mud of the nearshore seabed, using their whiskers as sensors and their tusks as rakes. Many thousands of walruses have been killed commercially for the solid ivory in their tusks, and for their tough leather hides.

Murmansk
Though north of the Arctic Circle, the port of Murmansk on Kola Peninsula remains ice-free throughout the year, warmed by waters of the North Atlantic Drift. Founded in 1916, it now has a population of more than 300,000. It is an important center for Arctic shipping.

NORTH CANADA

Queen Maud Gulf

King William Island

Hudson Bay Southampton Island

Melville Peninsula

Coats Island

Mansel Island

Foxe Basin

Foxe Peninsula

Prince Charles Island

Hudson Strait

Baffin Island

Ungava Bay

Cape Chidley

Davis Strait

Labrador Sea

Nuuk

Labrador Basin

140°
130°
120°
110°
100°
90°
80°
70°
60°
50°

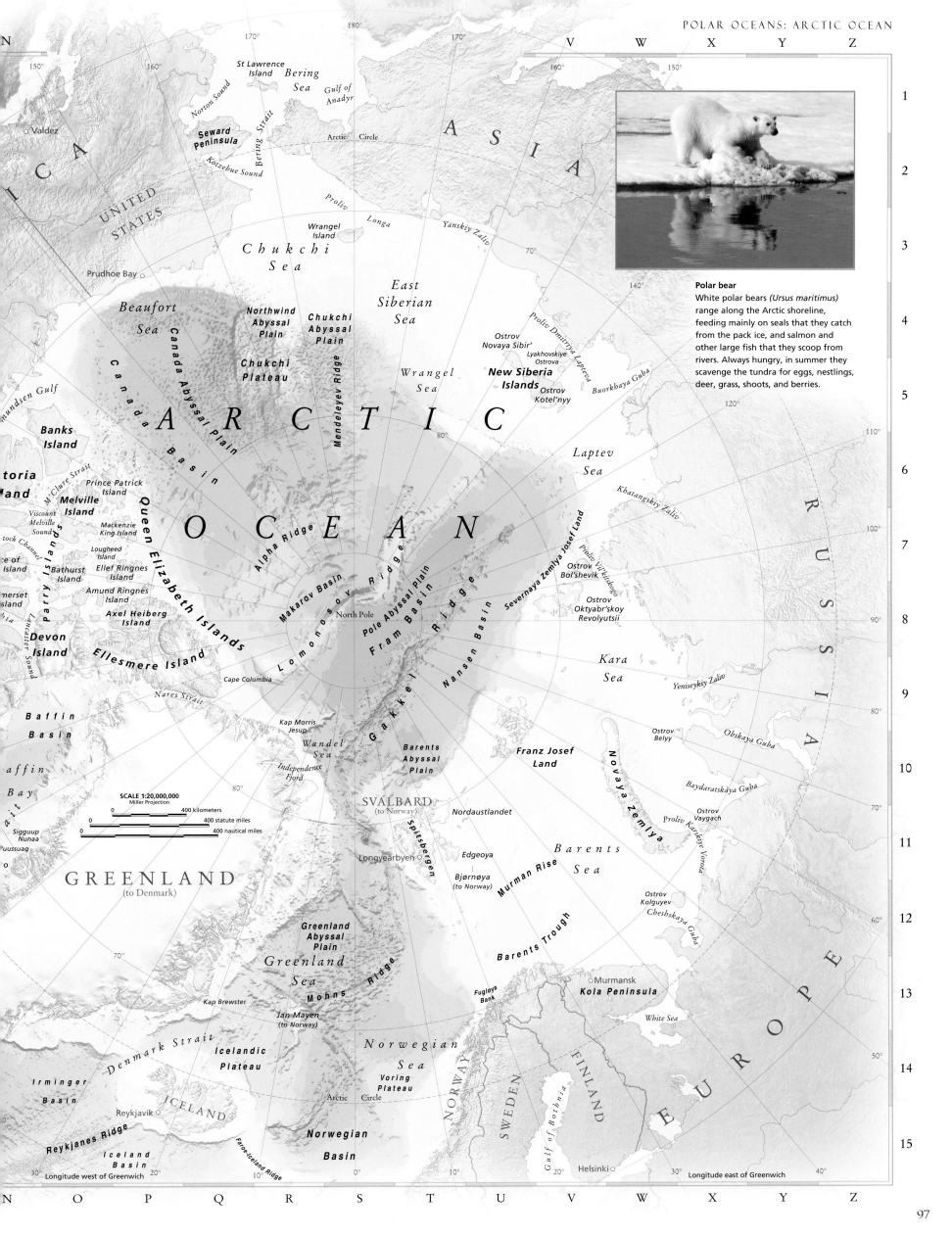

Polar bear
White polar bears *(Ursus maritimus)* range along the Arctic shoreline, feeding mainly on seals that they catch from the pack ice, and salmon and other large fish that they scoop from rivers. Always hungry, in summer they scavenge the tundra for eggs, nestlings, deer, grass, shoots, and berries.

EAST OF GREENLAND

Latitude for latitude this is by far the mildest sector of the Arctic. Except for the east coast of Greenland itself, the seas and coasts east of Greenland are warmed throughout the year by surface waters of the North Atlantic Drift—the northernmost branch of the Gulf Stream—which extends far into the Kara Sea. Without the North Atlantic Drift Britain, Iceland, and Norway would be as cold in winter as Labrador and Newfoundland; Archangel and Murmansk would be ice-bound for several months each year. The admixture of cold and warm currents brings fertility to the surface waters of these Arctic fringe seas. Generations of whalers, sealers, and fishermen have braved ice and foul weather to exploit their riches; deep-sea fishing for cod and prawns still brings prosperity to most of the neighboring countries. Seabed gas and oil have been exploited, and command continuing interest as reserves elsewhere are exhausted.

Hammerfest, Norway
Since the 16th century North Europeans have exploited the huge stocks of cod, herring, and other fish of cold North Atlantic and Arctic fringe waters. Today commercial fishing boats, like these in Hammerfest, Norway, continue to hunt for reduced stocks, working within scientifically-managed limits.

Kittiwakes
Crags and cliffs of hundreds of rocky islands provide breeding space, and the cold oceans provide rich feeding grounds, for these kittiwakes (*Rissa* sp.) and many other species of seabirds. This group has been foraging among the broken ice and open water in front of an active glacier.

Greenland shark
Up to 21 feet (7 m) long, Greenland sharks (*Somniosus microcephalus*) live in both shallow and deep water along the Greenland coast, usually close to the seabed, where they feed on other fish. Inuit hunters harpoon them for their meat, oil, and scaly sandpaper skin.

Surface currents
Strong surface currents leave the polar basin, carrying streams of old sea ice and icebergs southward between Greenland, Svalbard, and the Siberian islands, and blocking and chilling harbors along the coasts. Warm currents from the North Atlantic keep the shores of Iceland and Norway relatively ice-free.

→ East Greenland Current
→ East Spitsbergen Current
→ Irminger Current
→ Norwegian Atlantic Current

GREENLAND

Narsarsuaq
Daneborg
Ammassalik
Kap Farvel
Ittoqqortoormiit
Kap Brewster

Irminger
Basin

Greenland–Iceland Rise

Denmark Strait

Spar Fracture Zone

Jan Mayen Fracture Zone

Kolbeinsey Ridge

Jan Mayen

Icelandic Plateau

Jan Mayen Ridge

Reykjanes Ridge

Arctic Circle

★ REYKJAVÍK
ICELAND
Vík

Aegir Ridge

Faroe–Iceland Ridge

Norwegian Sea

Faroe Islands

Faroe–Shetland Trough

Ålesund

Shetland Islands

North Sea

Berg

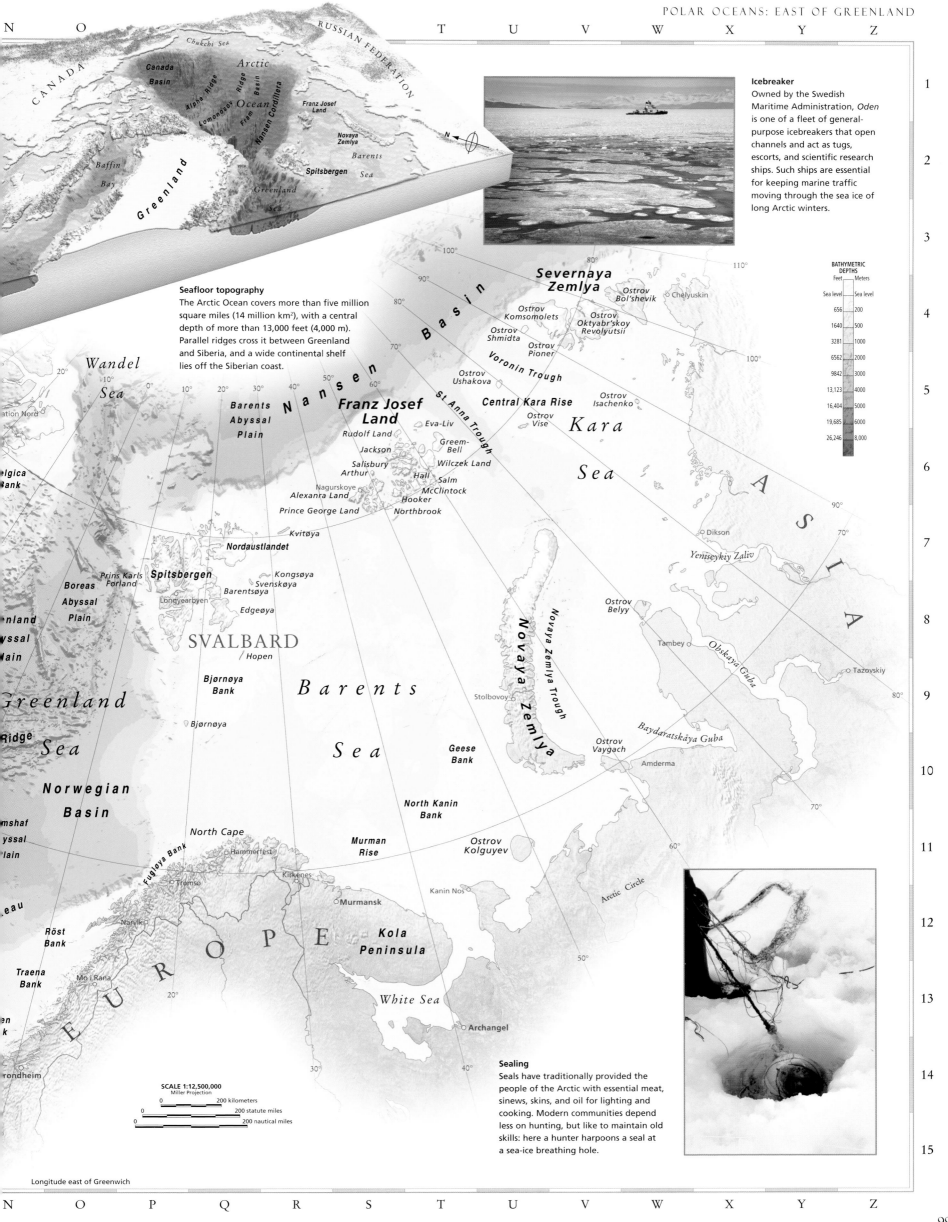

RUSSIAN FEDERATION

CANADA

Chukchi Sea

Canada
Basin

Arctic
Ocean

Alpha Ridge

Lomonosov Ridge

Franz Josef
Land

Fram
Basin

Nansen Cordillera

Novaya
Zemlya

Baffin
Bay

Greenland

Barents
Sea

Spitsbergen

N

Greenland
Sea

Icebreaker
Owned by the Swedish
Maritime Administration, *Oden*
is one of a fleet of general-
purpose icebreakers that open
channels and act as tugs,
escorts, and scientific research
ships. Such ships are essential
for keeping marine traffic
moving through the sea ice of
long Arctic winters.

Seafloor topography
The Arctic Ocean covers more than five million
square miles (14 million km²), with a central
depth of more than 13,000 feet (4,000 m).
Parallel ridges cross it between Greenland
and Siberia, and a wide continental shelf
lies off the Siberian coast.

BATHYMETRIC DEPTHS	
Feet	Meters
Sea level	Sea level
656	200
1640	500
3281	1000
6562	2000
9842	3000
13,123	4000
16,404	5000
19,685	6000
26,246	8,000

Severnaya
Zemlya

Ostrov
Bol'shevik

Chelyuskin

Ostrov
Komsomolets

Ostrov
Oktyabr'skoy
Revolyutsii

Ostrov
Shmidta

Ostrov
Pioner

Voronin Trough

Nansen Basin

St Anna Trough

Ostrov
Ushakova

Central Kara Rise

Ostrov
Isachenko

*Wandel
Sea*

*Barents
Abyssal
Plain*

Nansen

**Franz Josef
Land**

Eva-Liv

Ostrov
Vise

*Kara
Sea*

ASIA

Rudolf Land

Greem-
Bell

Jackson

Salisbury

Arthur

Wilczek Land

Hall

Salm

McClintock

Nagurskoye

Alexanra Land

Hooker

Prince George Land

Northbrook

Dikson

Kvitøya

Nordaustlandet

Yeniseykiy Zaliv

*Boreas
Abyssal
Plain*

Prins Karls
Forland

Spitsbergen

Kongsøya

Svenskøya

Longyearbyen

Barentsøya

Ostrov
Belyy

Edgeøya

Novaya Zemlya Trough

Tambey

Obskaya Guba

Tazovskiy

Greenland

SVALBARD

Hopen

Sea

Ridge

Barents

Stolbovoy

Novaya Zemlya

Baydaratskaya Guba

Bjørnøya
Bank

Bjørnøya

Sea

Geese
Bank

Ostrov
Vaygach

Amderma

*Norwegian
Basin*

North Kanin
Bank

North Cape

Fugløya Bank

Murman
Rise

Ostrov
Kolguyev

Arctic Circle

Hammerfest

Tromsø

Kirkenes

Kanin Nos

EUROPE

Narvik

Murmansk

Röst
Bank

**Kola
Peninsula**

Traena
Bank

Mo i Rana

White Sea

Trondheim

Archangel

SCALE 1:12,500,000
Miller Projection

0   200 kilometers
0   200 statute miles
0   200 nautical miles

Sealing
Seals have traditionally provided the
people of the Arctic with essential meat,
sinews, skins, and oil for lighting and
cooking. Modern communities depend
less on hunting, but like to maintain old
skills: here a hunter harpoons a seal at
a sea-ice breathing hole.

Longitude east of Greenwich

NORTHWEST PASSAGES

When geographers thought it likely that an ocean surrounded the North Pole, the search for the shortest sea route to China and the Indies began. Explorers sailing northward from Europe found concentrated ice off Svalbard. Sailing northeastward brought them little farther than northern Russia's Kola Peninsula. Exploration to the northwest was more promising: pioneering voyages by Davis, Baffin, and Hudson in the late 16th and early 17th centuries took them as far as Baffin Bay—to the gateway of this ice-bound archipelago forming the northeast corner of North America. The search was resumed in the late 18th and early 19th centuries, from Baffin Bay westward through the maze of islands and waterways. While Davis Strait and Baffin Bay became hunting grounds for British, Dutch, and German whalers, naval expeditions explored the archipelago right through to the Bering Sea. Not until the early 20th century was the passage completed in a single voyage, by the Norwegian explorer Roald Amundsen.

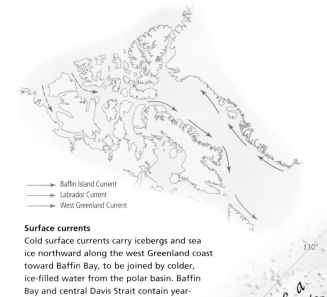

→ Baffin Island Current
→ Labrador Current
→ West Greenland Current

Surface currents
Cold surface currents carry icebergs and sea ice northward along the west Greenland coast toward Baffin Bay, to be joined by colder, ice-filled water from the polar basin. Baffin Bay and central Davis Strait contain year-round ice that drifts south with the Baffin Island and Labrador currents.

Beaufort Sea

Queen

Prince Patrick Island   Macke King Is

Lands End

P

Eglinton Island

Cape Prince Alfred

70°

Cape Bathurst

o Ikaahuk

Banks Island

McClure Strait

Melv Isla

Visc Met Sor

Stef Isl

Thesiger Bay

Prince of Wales Strait

Passage Point

Prince Albert Peninsula

Amundsen Gulf

130°

Paulatuk o

o Uluqsaqtuuq

Prince Albert Sound

Storkerso Peninsul

Arctic archipelago
Satellite imagery shows the complex of islands and ice-strewn channels of the Canadian Arctic archipelago. Here at the western end are Banks Island (left) and Victoria Island (center), separated from the Canadian mainland (bottom) by Amundsen Gulf, one of the western entrances to the Northwest Passages.

120°

Wollaston Peninsula

Victoria Island

Collinson Peninsula

Kugluktuk o

Coronation Gulf

o Cambridge

Drifting icebergs
Icebergs and pack ice drift south constantly from the Arctic. Remnants like these may reach shipping lanes, where they can become a danger to shipping. *Titanic* in 1912 was lost to an iceberg from Davis Strait. Satellite monitoring now reduces the risk considerably.

o Umingmaktok

C

Queen Gu

110°

Bathurst o Inlet

Whaling
North European ships, particularly German, Dutch, and British, hunted Arctic whales from the 17th to the 20th century, bringing home blubber for oil and baleen ("whalebone") for corset stays. Harpooning a 40-foot (12-m) whale from an open boat was a hazardous business.

N O P Q R S T U V W X Y Z

SCALE 1:10,000,000
Miller Projection

0   200 kilometers
0   200 statute miles
0   200 nautical miles

Lincoln Sea

Alert

Elizabeth Islands

Sverdrup Channel

Nansen Sound

Ellesmere Island

Nares Strait

Peary Channel

Axel Heiberg Island

Ellef Ringnes Island

Amund Ringnes Island

Kane Basin

Smith Sound

G R E E N L A N D

Cornwall Island

Graham Island

Thule

Bathurst Island

Grise Fiord

Ummannaq

Cornwallis Island

Jones Sound

Devon Island

Resolute Bay

Parry Channel

Nuussuaq

Baffin Bay

Lancaster Sound

Somerset Island

Prince of Wales Island

Prince Regent Inlet

Bylot Island

Borden Peninsula

Brodeur Peninsula

Kangersuatsiaq

70°

Disko

Ilulissat

Qeqertarsuaq

Boothia Peninsula

Gulf of Boothia

Baffin Island

William sland

Haven

Committee Bay

Rowley Island

Home Bay

Davis Strait

Kangerlussuaq

Parry Bay

D A

Melville Peninsula

Prince Charles Island

Air Force Island

Qikiqtarjuaq

Cumberland Peninsula

Repulse Bay

Foxe Basin

Cape Dorchester

Bowman Bay

Cumberland Sound

Cape Mercy

NUUK

Narsasuaq

Paamiut

60°

Vansittart Island

Foxe Peninsula

Hall Peninsula

Lemieux Islands

Iqaluit

Southampton Island

Foxe Channel

Cape Dorset

Mill Island

Meta Incognita Peninsula

Frobisher Bay

Loks Land

Salisbury Island

Nottingham Island

Big Island

Resolution Island

Labrador Sea

Hudson Strait

Cape Labrador

Killiniq

INUIT CULTURE AND COMMUNITIES

Inuit, formerly called Eskimos, are the coastal people indigenous to the western Arctic. Traditionally they lived in small communities from Bering Strait to East Greenland, making seasonal nomadic movements. Today Inuit are more likely to be housed in settlements, with government-sponsored schools and medical facilities. Under their respective national governments they have increasing political self-determination.

In the vast, Arctic landscape there are few natural landmarks. This inukshuk, carefully constructed from local rocks, is a signpost or indicator of direction for travelers.

BATHYMETRIC DEPTHS

Feet	Meters
Sea level	Sea level
656	200
1640	500
3281	1000
6562	2000
9842	3000
13,123	4000
16,404	5000
19,685	6000
26,246	8,000

Harp seal
A seal of the Arctic and north Atlantic pack ice, the harp seal *(Phoca groenlandica)* is so-called from a characteristic harp-shaped dorsal patch of dark fur. This female, hunting for fish, has come up for air. Thousands of harp seal pups have been killed commercially each year for their white natal fur.

SOUTHERN OCEAN

Some call it the Antarctic Ocean, but Capt. James Cook, RN, the explorer who first defined it in the 1770s, called it the Southern Ocean. A ring-shaped ocean, its northern oceanographic limit is the Antarctic Convergence or Polar Front, where cold waters spreading north from Antarctica pass beneath warmer subtropical waters. Its southern limit is Antarctica itself. Persistent westerly winds drive surface waters eastward, except immediately around the continent where westward-flowing surface currents prevail. It is a deep ocean, dropping steeply from Antarctica to a mean depth of 14,750 feet (4,500 m). Of the total area, a high proportion is frozen over every winter, pack ice sometimes extending as far north as the Antarctic Convergence in the Pacific and Indian ocean sectors. In summer the ice edge retreats, but pack ice persists in many coastal areas. It is a permanent feature in the Weddell and Ross seas, the two great bights between East and West Antarctica.

Crabeater seals
Crabeater seals (Lobodon carcinophagus) breed on Antarctic pack ice. They feed on shoals of tiny shrimps that swarm in Antarctic waters in summer, filtering them through their trilobed teeth. Here a group surfaces to breathe off the west coast of the Antarctic Peninsula.

THE FACTS	
Area	7.8 million square miles (20.3 million km²)
Average depth	14,750 feet (4,500 m)
Maximum depth	24,032 feet (7,325 m)
Maximum width	1,700 miles (2,700 km)
Maximum length	13,400 miles (21,500 km)

Ocean Share

All other oceans

Southern Ocean
7.8 million sq miles
(20.3 million km²) 6%

NATURAL RESOURCES

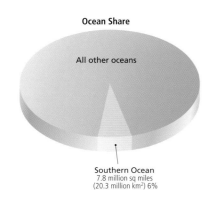

Fishing
Tourism

POLYNYAS: ICE-FREE POCKETS

In both polar oceans, particular areas called polynas remain ice-free even in mid-winter. They may be formed either by strong winds blowing freshly-formed ice away, or by water at temperatures above freezing point upwelling from below. Either way they are important to wildlife, allowing whales and seals to breathe and birds to feed throughout the year.

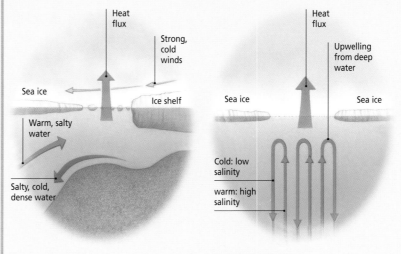

Heat flux
Strong, cold winds
Sea ice
Ice shelf
Warm, salty water
Salty, cold, dense water

Heat flux
Upwelling from deep water
Sea ice
Sea ice
Cold: low salinity
warm: high salinity

Wind-formed polynyas
These occur where strong downslope winds from land keep thin, newly-formed sea ice moving, sweeping it seaward and allowing relatively warm water to come up from below.

Upwelling polynyas
These occur on the open sea or channels at points where, for a variety of reasons, relatively warm vertical currents erode sea ice as fast as it forms. The result is persistent open water even in winter.

Natural resources
The Southern Ocean has no exploited seabed minerals, and mineral prospecting and development are prohibited within the area of the Antarctic Treaty (south of 60°S). Past industries have been based on a wealth of fur seals and whales: currently the region's resources support deep-sea fishing and tourism.

Russian Orthodox chapel
On a hilltop behind the Russian Bellingshausen Station, on King George Island, South Shetland Islands, stands this miniature Russian Orthodox church. Unusual but not unique: a neighboring Chilean station has a Catholic chapel, a bank, a hospital, and a supermarket.

FALKLAND ISLANDS

SOUTH AMERICA
ARGENTINA

Falkland Islands

Tierra del Fuego

Punta Arenas

CHILE

Mornington Abyssal Plain

Southe

BATHYMETRIC DEPTHS
Feet — Meters
Sea level — Sea level
656 — 200
1640 — 500
3281 — 1000
6562 — 2000
9842 — 3000
13,123 — 4000
16,404 — 5000
19,685 — 6000
26,246 — 8,000

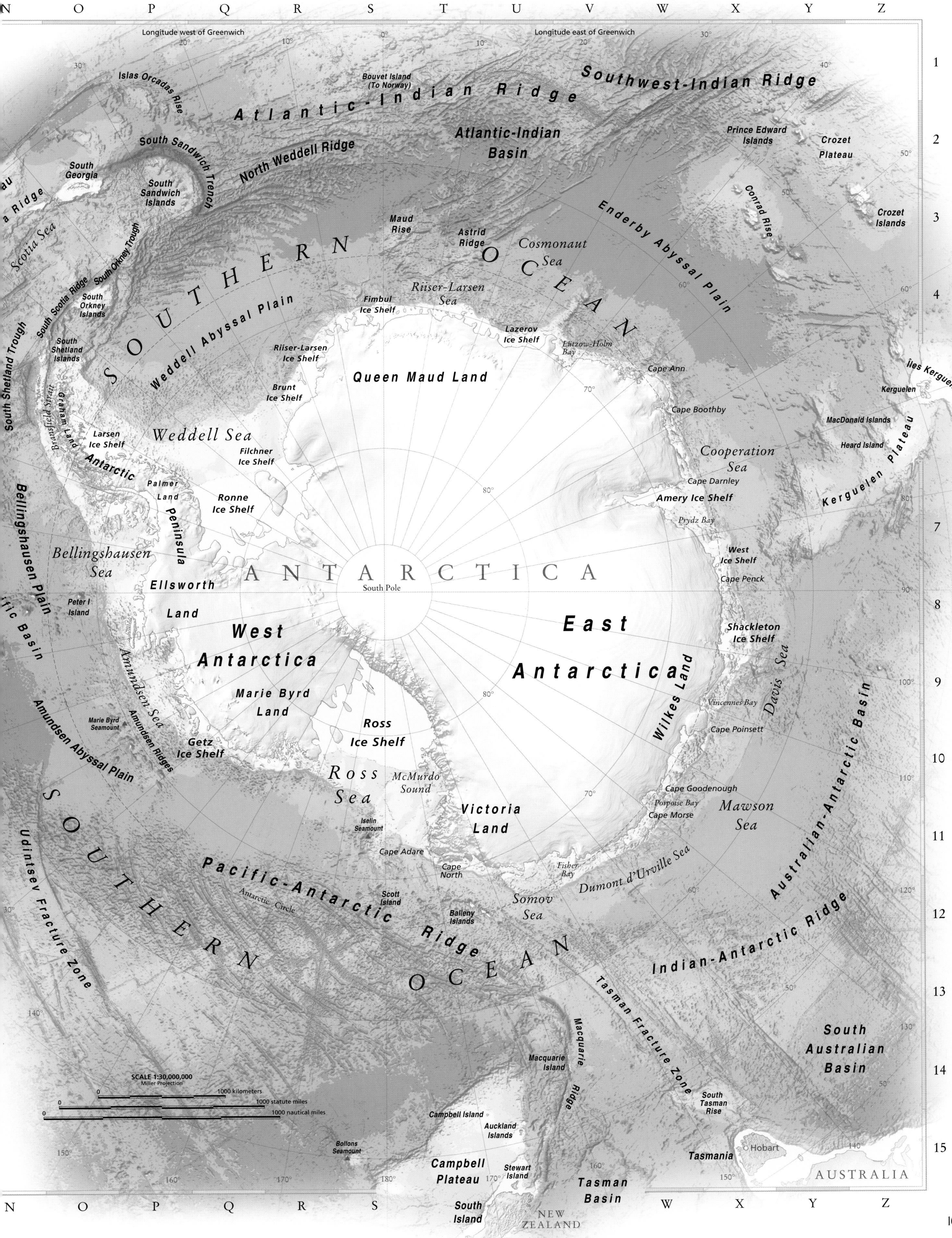

N O P Q R S T U V W X Y Z

Longitude west of Greenwich   Longitude east of Greenwich

1

Islas Orcadas Rise

Bouvet Island
(To Norway)

Southwest-Indian Ridge

Atlantic-Indian Ridge

Prince Edward
Islands

Crozet
Plateau

2

South Sandwich Trench

North Weddell Ridge

Atlantic-Indian
Basin

Conrad Rise

Crozet
Islands

South Georgia

South
Sandwich
Islands

SOUTHERN

Maud
Rise

Astrid
Ridge

Cosmonaut
Sea

Enderby Abyssal Plain

3

a Ridge

Scotia Sea

South Scotia Ridge

South Orkney Trough

Riiser-Larsen
Sea

OCEAN

4

South
Orkney
Islands

South Shetland Trough

Riiser-Larsen
Ice Shelf

Fimbul
Ice Shelf

Lazerov
Ice Shelf

Lützow-Holm
Bay

Îles Kerguelen

Weddell Abyssal Plain

South
Shetland
Islands

Brunt
Ice Shelf

Queen Maud Land

Cape Ann

Kerguelen

Bransfield Strait

Graham Land

Larsen
Ice Shelf

Weddell Sea

Filchner
Ice Shelf

Cape Boothby

MacDonald Islands

Heard Island

Bellingshausen Plain

Antarctic

Palmer
Land

Ronne
Ice Shelf

Cooperation
Sea

Kerguelen Plateau

Peninsula

Cape Darnley

Amery Ice Shelf

7

ific Basin

Bellingshausen
Sea

Ellsworth
Land

ANTARCTICA

South Pole

Prydz Bay

West
Ice Shelf

Peter I
Island

West
Antarctica

East
Antarctica

Cape Penck

8

Shackleton
Ice Shelf

Marie Byrd
Land

Wilkes Land

Vincennes Bay

Davis
Sea

Australian-Antarctic Basin

9

Amundsen Abyssal Plain

Marie Byrd
Seamount

Amundsen Sea

Amundsen Ridges

Getz
Ice Shelf

Ross
Ice Shelf

Cape Poinsett

10

Ross
Sea

McMurdo
Sound

Cape Goodenough

Porpoise Bay

Cape Morse

Mawson
Sea

SOUTHERN

Iselin
Seamount

Victoria
Land

11

Cape Adare

Cape
North

Fisher
Bay

Dumont d'Urville Sea

Indian-Antarctic Ridge

Udintsev Fracture Zone

Pacific-Antarctic

Antarctic Circle

Scott
Island

Somov
Sea

12

OCEAN

Balleny
Islands

Tasman Fracture Zone

Ridge

13

South
Australian
Basin

14

SCALE 1:30,000,000
Miller Projection

Macquarie
Island

Macquarie
Ridge

South
Tasman
Rise

0   1000 kilometers

0   1000 statute miles

0   1000 nautical miles

Campbell Island

Auckland
Islands

Tasmania

Hobart

15

Bollons
Seamount

Campbell
Plateau

Stewart
Island

Tasman
Basin

AUSTRALIA

South
Island

NEW
ZEALAND

N O P Q R S W X Y Z

103

ANTARCTIC PENINSULA

The Antarctic Peninsula and the islands of the Scotia Arc form stepping stones between South America and West Antarctica—a path first traced by early 19th-century sealers, and now followed each summer by thousands of cruise ship tourists. Geologically the peninsula is a southern extension of the Andes, heavily glaciated as the southern Andes formerly were, and invested with pack ice for several months each year. Climatically and biologically it forms a separate province, the Maritime Antarctic. It is much warmer year-round than continental Antarctica and has richer vegetation. The Weddell Sea, east of the peninsula, is renowned for its circulating pack ice that caught and destroyed Shackleton's expedition ship *Endurance*. Accessibility made the peninsula the most favored sector of Antarctica for early 20th-century exploration and the starting region for Antarctic whaling. Currently it is favored by more than 20 nations for research stations that give them access to membership of the Antarctic Treaty, and thus a political stake in Antarctica itself.

Cruise ships
Tens of thousands of tourists now visit Antarctica each summer, most of them on cruise ships that, like this one, land their passengers at penguin colonies and other points of interest. Bigger ships carrying more than 500 passengers cruise the scenic waterways but make no landings.

Peninsula scenery
While more than 95 percent of Antarctica's coastal scenery is ice cliffs, with no mountains visible, the west coast of the Antarctic Peninsula features spectacular mountains, islands, and channels, that in recent years have made it a major tourist attraction. Piedmont ice cliffs and glaciers line the shores.

Drifting icebergs
Icebergs breaking from Antarctic glaciers and ice shelves drift around the continent with the pack ice, taking several years to melt and crumble. Tourist visitors delight in their infinite variety. Scientists use satellite imagery to follow their progress, gaining information about sea currents and climatic variation.

Argentine station
The peninsula sector, which is more accessible than the rest of Antarctica through its longer summer period, supports the scientific research stations of many nations. The Argentine station, Esperanza, (above) is a small community with comfortable facilities for overwintering scientists and their families.

Fur seals
From their discovery in the late 18th century, fur-seal (*Arctocephalus gazella*) colonies brought northern hemisphere sealers to the Antarctic Peninsula. Hundreds of thousands of seals were killed for their skins. Sealers explored the islands and channels, recording many geographical discoveries throughout the region.

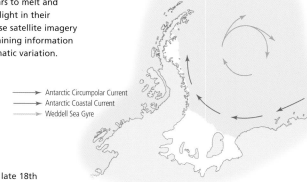

→ Antarctic Circumpolar Current
→ Antarctic Coastal Current
→ Weddell Sea Gyre

Surface currents
The predominantly westward-flowing Antarctic Coastal Current, encountering the eastern shore of the peninsula, fills the Weddell Sea with a massive, persistent gyre of multi-year sea ice. This rotates southward along the Coats Land coast, and packs northward-moving masses of ice tightly against the peninsula flank.

Farwell Island

Thurston Island

Abbot Ice Shelf

Eights Coast

Sherman Island

King Peninsula

Pine Island Bay

Walgreen Coast

90°

100°

110°

A

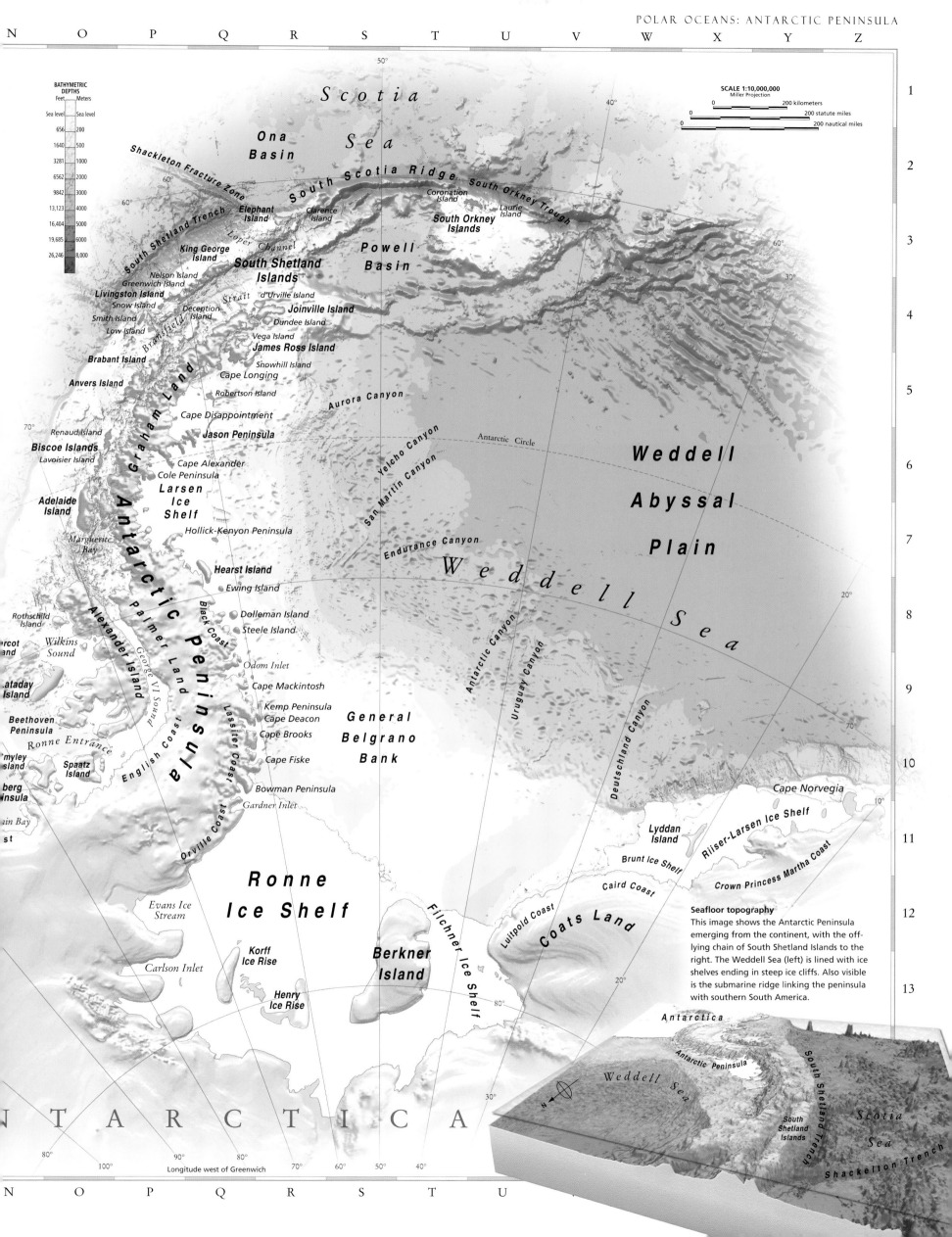

Seafloor topography
This image shows the Antarctic Peninsula emerging from the continent, with the off-lying chain of South Shetland Islands to the right. The Weddell Sea (left) is lined with ice shelves ending in steep ice cliffs. Also visible is the submarine ridge linking the peninsula with southern South America.

Ross Sea

One of two great embayments in the flanks of Antarctica, the Ross Sea was discovered by Capt. James Clark Ross, RN, on a Royal Navy expedition of 1841. Despite its high latitude, circulation of pack ice within the Ross Sea allows ships of minimal icebreaking capacity to reach 78°S, making it a gateway for land expeditions to reach the South Pole. The southern limit of the sea is the Ross Ice Shelf, a huge floating sheet of glacier ice that descends from the high plateau of central Antarctica and terminates in a continuous ice cliff 500 miles (800 km) long. Land-based expeditions led by Scott, Shackleton, Amundsen, Borchgrevink, Byrd, and others made use of the gateway to explore inland, in particular to reach the south geographic and magnetic poles. McMurdo Sound is currently the site of McMurdo Station, Antarctica's largest township. Its population varies from about 250 in winter to 1,200 in summer.

Shackleton's team
Ernest Shackleton (centre left) and three companions in 1908-09 discovered a route from McMurdo Sound, in the southwestern Ross Sea, via Beardmore Glacier to the South Pole. The route is today used by US tractor trains to replenish Amundsen-Scott, the permanent US South Pole station.

Emperor penguins
Largest of all living penguins, emperor penguins (*Aptenodytes forsteri*) live in Antarctic coastal colonies as far south as Cape Crozier, Ross Island, incubating their single eggs on the sea ice in winter, and rearing their chicks through early spring. Fewer than 50 colonies are known around the continent.

Ice cliffs
On the southern flank of Ross Island, Windless Bight's heavily-glaciated cliffs face the Ross Ice Shelf. It was named by a party from Scott's Terra Nova expedition of 1910–13, who found it an oasis of calm on their otherwise storm-ridden journey to Cape Crozier.

McMurdo Station

McMurdo Station was established by the United States in 1955 as the logistical base from which Amundsen-Scott (South Pole) and other Antarctic stations and camps could be established and re-supplied. Currently involving some 90 buildings, it is a township with laboratories, workshops, garaging, fuel stores, airstrips, shops, and accommodation for more than 1,000 support staff and scientists.

Symbol of the past. Erected in 1902, this hut was an emergency depot for Scott's expedition ship *Discovery*, which lay frozen in close by. Solitary for half a century, it stands on the edge of McMurdo Station, Antarctica's largest and busiest community

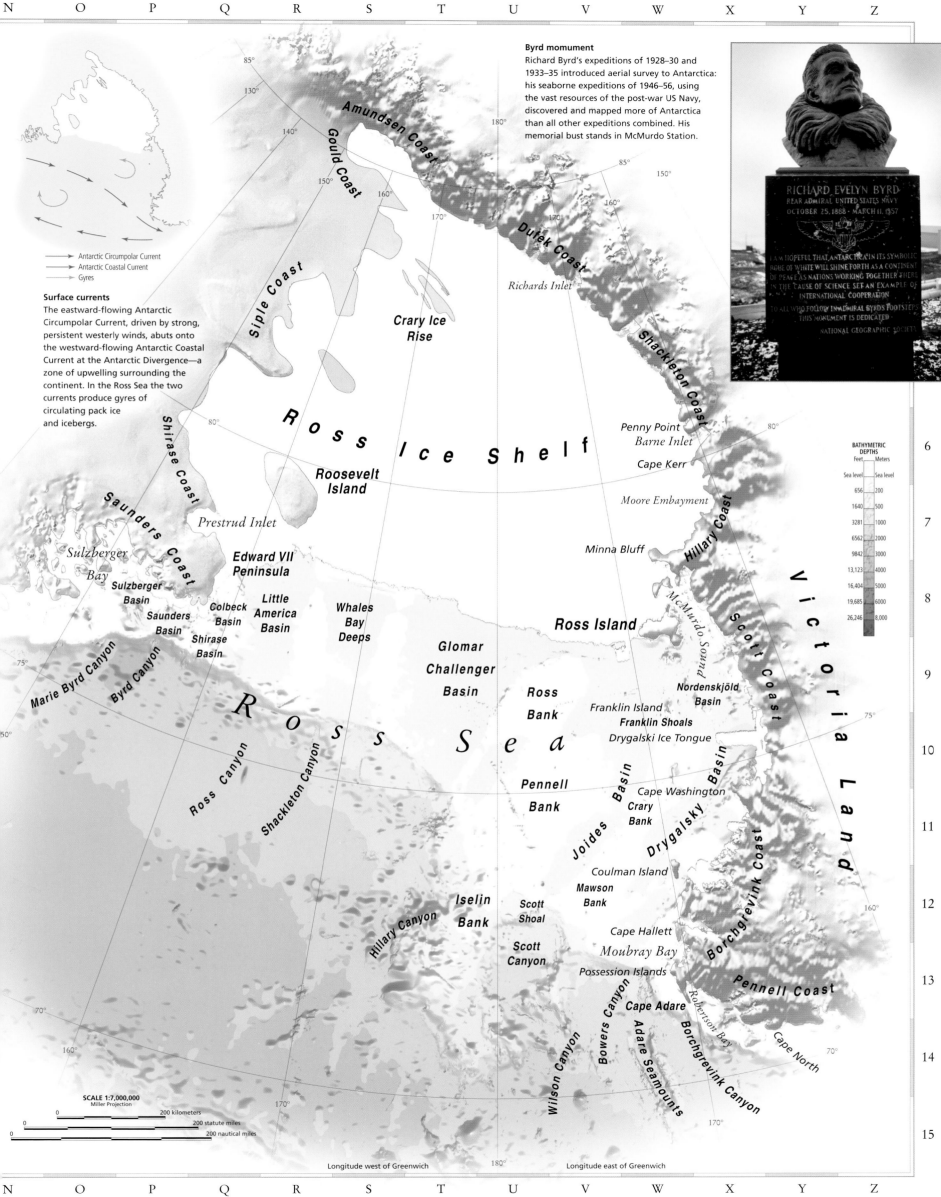

85°
130°
140°
150°
160°
170°

Byrd momument
Richard Byrd's expeditions of 1928–30 and
1933–35 introduced aerial survey to Antarctica:
his seaborne expeditions of 1946–56, using
the vast resources of the post-war US Navy,
discovered and mapped more of Antarctica
than all other expeditions combined. His
memorial bust stands in McMurdo Station.

RICHARD EVELYN BYRD
REAR ADMIRAL UNITED STATES NAVY
OCTOBER 25, 1888 · MARCH 11, 1957

I AM HOPEFUL THAT ANTARCTICA IN ITS SYMBOLIC
ROBE OF WHITE WILL SHINE FORTH AS A CONTINENT
OF PEACE AS NATIONS WORKING TOGETHER THERE
IN THE CAUSE OF SCIENCE SET AN EXAMPLE OF
INTERNATIONAL COOPERATION
TO ALL WHO FOLLOW IN ADMIRAL BYRDS FOOTSTEPS
THIS MONUMENT IS DEDICATED
NATIONAL GEOGRAPHIC SOCIETY

Amundsen Coast
Gould Coast
85°
150°
160°
Duiek Coast
170°
Richards Inlet
Shackleton Coast

Antarctic Circumpolar Current
Antarctic Coastal Current
Gyres

Surface currents
The eastward-flowing Antarctic
Circumpolar Current, driven by strong,
persistent westerly winds, abuts onto
the westward-flowing Antarctic Coastal
Current at the Antarctic Divergence—a
zone of upwelling surrounding the
continent. In the Ross Sea the two
currents produce gyres of
circulating pack ice
and icebergs.

Crary Ice
Rise

Penny Point
Barne Inlet
Cape Kerr
80°

R o s s   I c e   S h e l f

80°

Moore Embayment

**BATHYMETRIC
DEPTHS**
Feet   Meters

6

Siple Coast

Shirase Coast

Roosevelt
Island

Prestrud Inlet

Hillary Coast

Minna Bluff

Sea level   Sea level
656   200
1640   500
3281   1000
6562   2000
9842   3000
13,123   4000
16,404   5000
19,685   6000
26,246   8,000

7

8

Saunders Coast

*Sulzberger
Bay*

**Edward VII
Peninsula**

Little
America
Basin

Whales
Bay
Deeps

Ross Island

Scott Coast
McMurdo Sound

V i c t o r i a   L a n d

Sulzberger
Basin

Colbeck
Basin
Saunders
Basin
Shirase
Basin

**Glomar
Challenger
Basin**

Nordenskjöld
Basin

9

**Ross
Bank**

Franklin Island
Franklin Shoals
Drygalski Ice Tongue

75°

75°

50°

Marie Byrd Canyon

Byrd Canyon

R o s s

S e a

Ross Canyon

Shackleton Canyon

**Pennell
Bank**

Joides Basin

Cape Washington
Crary
Bank

Drygalsky Basin

Borchgrevink Coast

10

11

Coulman Island

Mawson
Bank

Iselin
Bank

Hillary Canyon

Scott
Shoal

Scott
Canyon

Cape Hallett
Moubray Bay

Possession Islands

Pennell Coast

12

13

70°

160°

Wilson Canyon

Bowers Canyon

Adare Seamounts

Cape Adare

Robertson Bay

Borchgrevink Canyon

Cape North

70°

14

SCALE 1:7,000,000
Miller Projection

0   200 kilometers
0   200 statute miles
0   200 nautical miles

170°

180°

Longitude west of Greenwich

Longitude east of Greenwich

15

The rugged shoreline of southern Cape Breton Island, part of the
Canadian province of Nova Scotia, experiences frequent coastal fog.
The north Atlantic Ocean to the south and east, and the Gulf of
St Lawrence to the north and west, both have a considerable influence
on the weather here. Whale watching for pilot whales *(Globicephala
melas)* has become key to the island's economy.

ATLANTIC OCEAN

ATLANTIC OCEAN

The Atlantic is the world's second largest ocean, covering approximately one-fifth of Earth's surface. It is also a relatively young ocean having been formed about 150 million years ago, and it is still growing. Seafloor spreading from the mid-Atlantic ridge widens it by approximately an inch (25 mm) each year. Many of the world's great rivers drain into it. On its north and south American margins there are the St Lawrence, the Mississippi, the Orinoco, the Amazon, the Uruguay and the Parana; on the west African coasts the Congo and Niger flow; and the northeast Atlantic has inputs from the Loire, the Rhine, the Elbe, and the great rivers draining into the Mediterranean, Black, and Baltic seas. The broad, stable continental shelves around its margins have been a source of wealth for many centuries, sustaining abundant fisheries (though many have now collapsed) and, more recently, yielding oil and gas.

THE FACTS

Area	29.7 million square miles (76.8 million km²)
Average depth	11,827 feet (3,605 m)
Maximum depth	28,231 feet (8,605 m)
Maximum width	4,900 miles (7,900 km)
Maximum length	8,770 miles (14,120 km)
Coastline length	69,510 miles (111,866 km)

Ocean Share

All other oceans

Atlantic Ocean
29.7 million sq miles
(76.8 million km²)
23%

Great barracuda
Great barracuda (*Sphyraena barracuda*) are found throughout the tropical and subtropical Atlantic, shoaling as juveniles but usually solitary as adults. They are ambush predators that prey on everything from anchovy to jacks. Adults can reach 6 feet (2 m) in length and bite large prey species in half.

SCALE 1:50,000,000
Miller Projection

1500 kilometers
1500 statute miles
1500 nautical miles

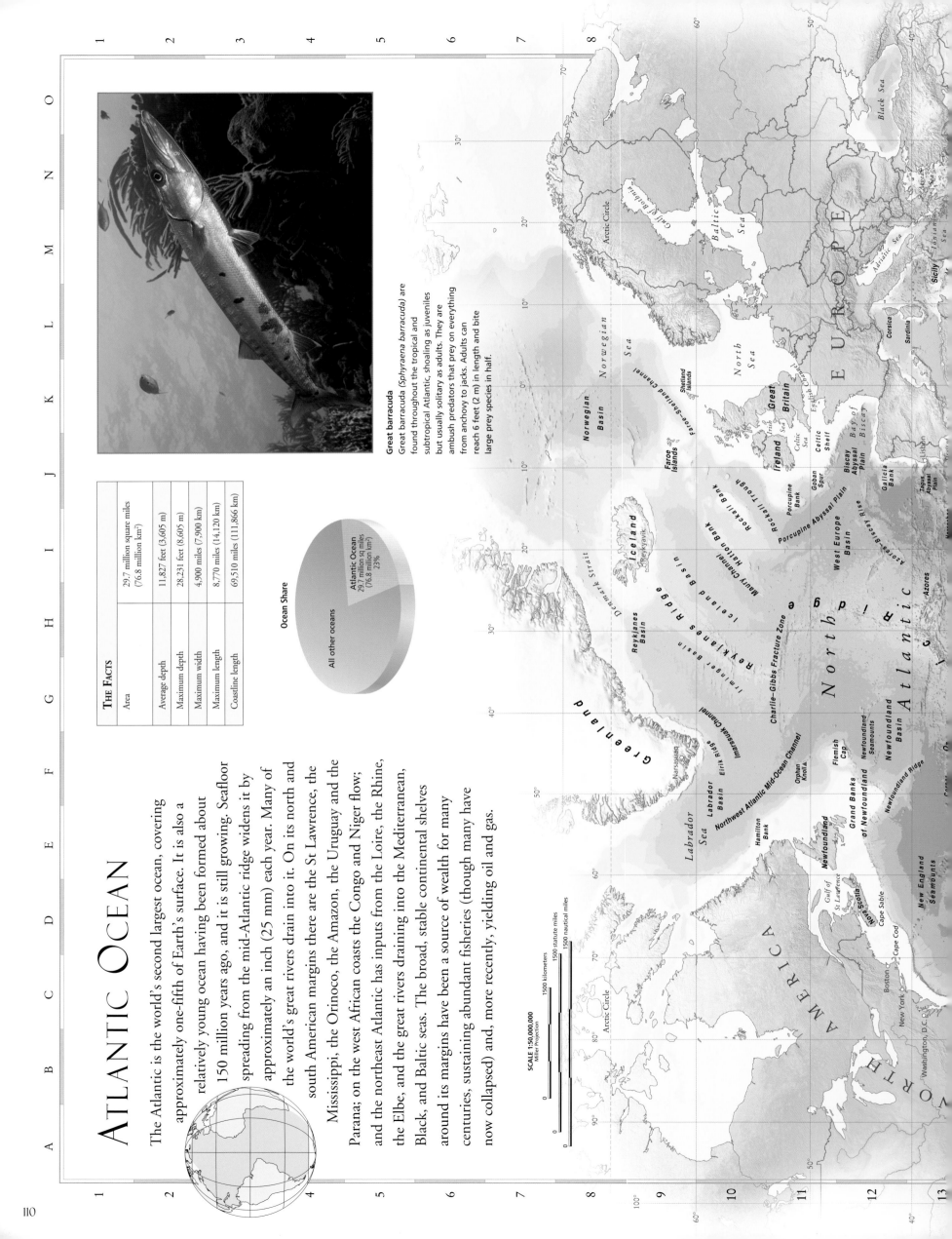

NORTHERN ATLANTIC OCEAN

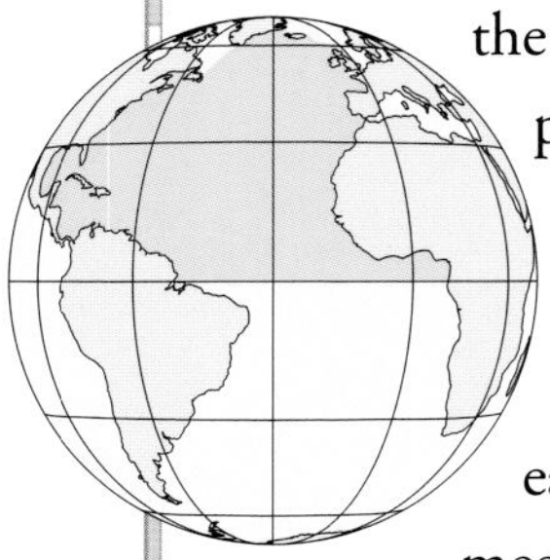

The circulation of the water masses of the North Atlantic shapes the climate of adjacent landmasses. The Coriolis effect, produced by Earth's rotation, causes the water in the North Atlantic to circulate clockwise. This has the effect of causing warm water from the Gulf of Mexico and the Caribbean to be carried northward along the east coast of North America as the Gulf Stream. It meets the cold waters of the Labrador Current off Newfoundland, giving rise to the notorious fogs of the Grand Banks. Some of the warmer water continues eastward as the North Atlantic Drift that creates the relatively warm and wet climate of northwest Europe. The eventual cooling and sinking of the North Atlantic Drift water forms a deep water mass known as North Atlantic bottom water and helps to drive the "Ocean Conveyor" system of deep water currents that connect the world's oceans.

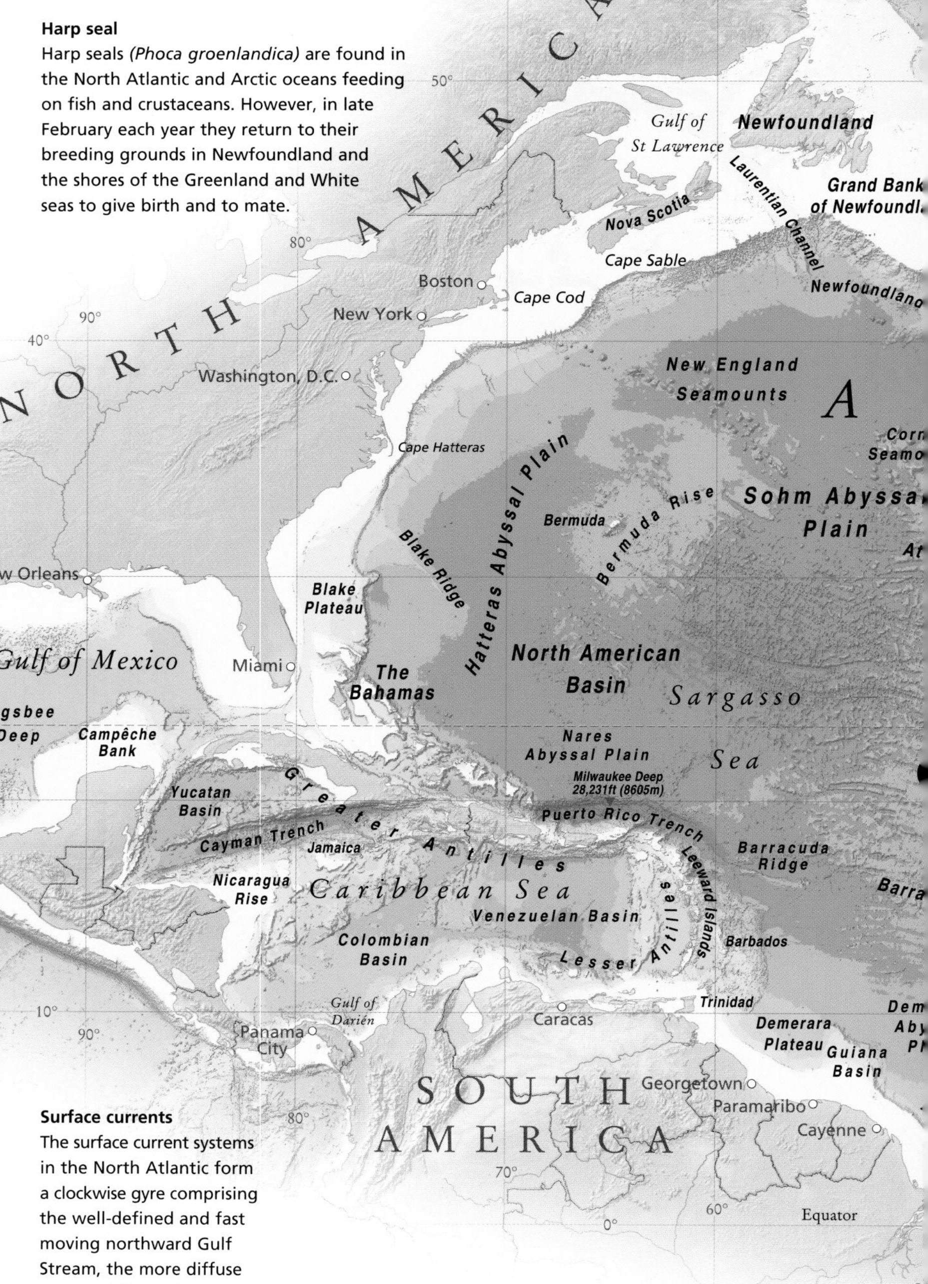

BATHYMETRIC DEPTHS

Feet	Meters
Sea level	Sea level
656	200
1640	500
3281	1000
6562	2000
9842	3000
13,123	4000
16,404	5000
19,685	6000
26,246	8,000

Harp seal
Harp seals *(Phoca groenlandica)* are found in the North Atlantic and Arctic oceans feeding on fish and crustaceans. However, in late February each year they return to their breeding grounds in Newfoundland and the shores of the Greenland and White seas to give birth and to mate.

NATURAL RESOURCES

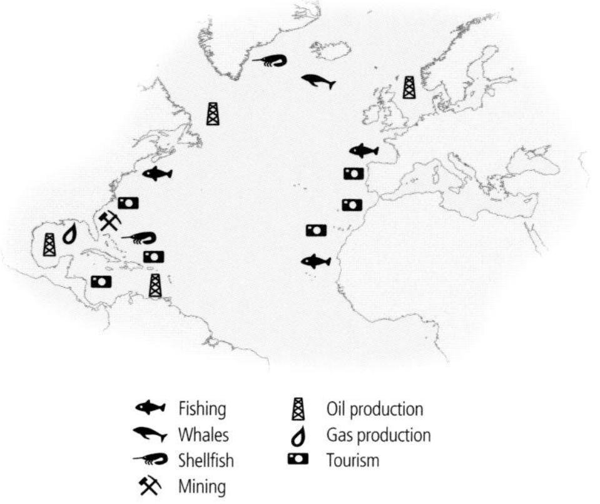

- ✈ Fishing
- ➤ Whales
- ➤ Shellfish
- ✕ Mining
- ⚒ Oil production
- ♦ Gas production
- ▣ Tourism

Hermit crab
Hermit crabs, such this species, *(Dardanus calidus)* from the Canary Islands, are found from the shoreline to the depths. Unlike other crustaceans they have a soft abdomen, which they protect by living in discarded shells. They move to larger shells as they grow.

Sea pen
Sea pens are formed by groups of polyps that feed by capturing food particles suspended in the water. The species shown here *(Pennatula phosphorea)* is biolumin-escent. It emits blue-green light if disturbed.

Surface currents
The surface current systems in the North Atlantic form a clockwise gyre comprising the well-defined and fast moving northward Gulf Stream, the more diffuse eastward North Atlantic Drift, the cold southward Canary Current, and the westward North Equatorial Current, which completes the loop.

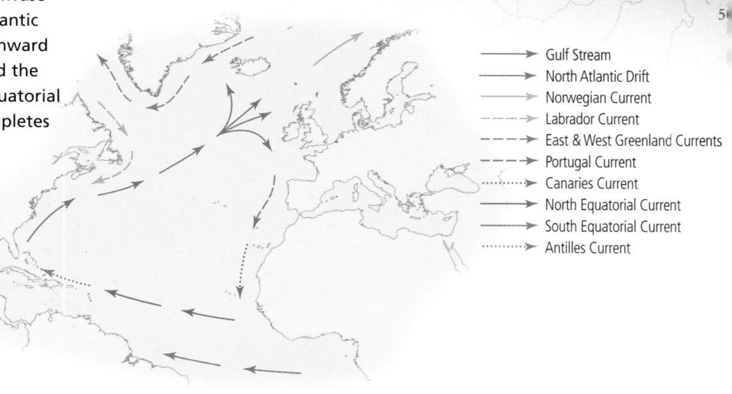

- → Gulf Stream
- → North Atlantic Drift
- → Norwegian Current
- — Labrador Current
- ─ ─ East & West Greenland Currents
- → Portugal Current
- ⋯ Canaries Current
- → North Equatorial Current
- → South Equatorial Current
- ⋯ Antilles Current

Labrador Sea

Labrador Basin

Northwest

Hamilton Bank

NORTH AMERICA

Gulf of St Lawrence

Newfoundland

Nova Scotia

Laurentian Channel

Grand Bank of Newfoundl.

Cape Sable

Newfoundl.

Boston

Cape Cod

New York

New England Seamounts

Washington, D.C.

A

Cape Hatteras

Corn. Seamo.

Bermuda

Bermuda Rise

Sohm Abyssa. Plain

New Orleans

Blake Ridge

Hatteras Abyssal Plain

North American Basin

At.

Blake Plateau

Sargasso

Gulf of Mexico

Miami

The Bahamas

Sigsbee Deep

Campêche Bank

Nares Abyssal Plain

Sea

Milwaukee Deep 28,231ft (8605m)

Yucatan Basin

Greater Antilles

Puerto Rico Trench

Barracuda Ridge

Cayman Trench

Jamaica

Leeward Islands

Barra.

Nicaragua Rise

Caribbean Sea

Venezuelan Basin

Barbados

Colombian Basin

Lesser Ant.

Trinidad

Demerara Plateau

Dem. Aby. Pl.

Gulf of Darién

Caracas

Guiana Basin

Panama City

SOUTH AMERICA

Georgetown

Paramaribo

Cayenne

Equator

N O P Q R S T U V W X Y Z

Longitude west of Greenwich   Longitude east of Greenwich

40°   30°   20°   10°   0°   10°

70°

1

Greenland

Arctic Circle

Kolbeinsey Ridge
Denmark Strait
Icelandic Plateau
Jan Mayen Fracture Zone
Norwegian Basin

Norwegian Sea

Arctic Circle

30°

2

Greenland–Iceland Rise
Iceland
Reykyavik
Aegir Ridge

Gulf of Bothnia

Irminger Basin
Reykjanes Ridge
Iceland–Faeroe Rise
Faroe Islands
Faroe–Shetland Channel
Shetland Islands

Helsinki
Gulf of Finland
St Petersburg

60°

3

Iceland Basin
Maury Channel
Hatton Bank
Rockall Plateau
Rockall Bank
Rockall Trough
Hebridean Shelf
Norwegian Deep

Oslo
Stockholm
Baltic Sea

Charlie–Gibbs Fracture Zone
East Thulean Rise
Porcupine Abyssal Plain
Porcupine Bank

North Sea
Skagerrak
Copenhagen
Amsterdam

40°

4

Mid-

Atlantic

Ocean Channel

Ireland
Irish Sea
Great Britain
Celtic Sea
London
English Channel
Celtic Shelf

EUROPE

50°

5

West Europe Basin
Goban Spur
Biscay Abyssal Plain
Bay of Biscay

Azores–Biscay Rise

Galicia Bank
Iberian Abyssal Plain

Adriatic Sea
Rome
Black Sea

Newfoundland Seamounts
Kurchatov Fracture Zone
Azores

Barcelona
Corsica
Sardinia

Istanbul

40°

Newfoundland Basin

Lisbon
Tagus Abyssal Plain
Straits of Gibraltar

Sicily
Aegean Sea
Ionian Sea
Athens
Crete
Cyprus

ASIA

Oceanographer Fracture Zone
Monaco Basin
Horseshoe Seamounts
Ampere Seamount
Madeira Ridge

Tunis
Mediterranean Sea

40°

Cruiser Seamount
Madeira
Dacia Seamount

Rabat
Tripoli

Cairo

30°

40°

Great Meteor Bank
Canary Islands
Saharan Seamounts
Tropic Seamount

Red Sea

9

Tropic of Cancer

30°

Cape Verde Abyssal Plain
Cape Verde Plateau

20°

10

Cape Verde Islands
Cap Vert
Dakar

AFRICA

30°

SCALE 1:40,000,000
Miller Projection

0   1000 kilometers
0   1000 statute miles
0   1000 nautical miles

Gambia Abyssal Plain

11

Vema Fracture Zone

10°

Doldrums Fracture Zone

Sierra Leone Rise
Sierra Leone Basin

Accra
Lagos
Niger Cone

20°

Seafloor topography
The New England seamounts are a chain of 20 extinct underwater volcanoes, 620 miles (1,000 km) long, that lies between the coast of Massachusetts and the Bermuda Rise. They were formed 80 to 100 million years ago and today are home to rich communities of marine organisms.

Four North Fracture Zone
Ceara Ridge
São Pedro e São Paulo
Saint Paul Fracture Zone
Gulf of Guinea
São Tomé

12

Ceara Abyssal Plain
Romanche Gap
Guinea Basin

Equator

0°

10°

Fernando de Noronha

30°

Cape Cod

13

Lobster
North Atlantic lobsters, (Homarus americanus) such as this juvenile, are a valuable commercial shellfish species. However, decades of overfishing of wild stocks has depleted their numbers and in many places hatcheries have been established in an attempt to boost stocks.

Hatteras Abyssal Plain
New England Seamounts
Atlantic Ocean

N

Bermuda
Bermuda Rise

Nashville Seamount

Sohm Abyssal Plain

N O P Q R S T U V

NORTH SEA

The North Sea is a semi-enclosed arm of the North Atlantic, with most ocean water flowing in through the north-western opening between Scotland and Norway and smaller volumes through the English Channel and the Strait of Dover. There are also substantial freshwater inputs from major rivers such as the Rhine. The margins of the North Sea comprise one of the most diverse coastal regions in the world, with a great variety of habitats (fjords, estuaries, deltas, banks, beaches, sandbanks and mudflats, marshes, rocks, and islands). Its coastal margins are also heavily populated and vulnerable to catastrophic flooding caused by storm surges that cause water levels to rise dramatically as winter storms and tides force water southward into the narrowing southern North Sea. Its once-abundant fish stocks, particularly cod and herring, have been seriously over-fished and the oil and gas fields that were first exploited in the 1970s are becoming exhausted.

THE FACTS	
Area	222,100 square miles (570,200 km²)
Average depth	308 feet (94 m)
Maximum depth	2,165 feet (660 m)
Maximum width	373 miles (600 km)
Maximum length	621 miles (100 km)

OIL DRILLING

The broad continental shelf of the North Atlantic that includes the North Sea contains large reserves of oil and gas. The first offshore wells were drilled in 1964 and commercial extraction began in the 1970s, but intense storms in the region make it a difficult working environment. The peak of production has now passed and many rigs are being decommissioned.

The worldwide outcry against the proposed deep-water dumping of a decommissioned North Sea rig in the 1990s forced oil companies to scrap all old rigs on land.

Atlantic puffin
Atlantic puffins (*Fratercula arctica*) feed on small fish that they catch just below the water's surface. In the breeding season both parents bring fish in their beaks to feed their chick. Sixty percent of the world's Atlantic puffins breed in Iceland.

Cliff erosion
Soft sandstone, exposed to the force of North Atlantic waves on the west coast of the Orkney Islands, erodes rapidly, causing the formation of sea stacks and rugged cliff faces.

Coastal flooding
The low-lying coasts of the Netherlands and the east coast of England are vulnerable to flooding. In winter the funneling effect of the North Sea from north to south, high spring tides and strong northerly winds heap up the water in the southern North Sea.

Hamburg Harbor
For centuries Hamburg has been the hub of sea-borne trade between central Europe and the rest of the world, firstly as one of the main Hanseatic league ports, in the 19th century as a major trans-Atlantic port, and now as a modern container port.

Surface currents
The main surface currents in the North Sea move counterclockwise, generally following the coastlines of the surrounding land with oceanic inputs to the north and south. There are also smaller surface currents that carry less dense low salinity coastal water offshore and saltier water inshore.

→ Inflow from Baltic Sea
→ Oceanic inflow
--→ Wind and tide-driven circulation

Longitude west of Greenwich   Longitude east of Greenwich

Norwegian Sea

Storegga

Tampen

Viking Bank

Norwegian Deep

Herma Ness
Unst
Yell
Fetlar
Whalsay
Shetland Islands
Mainland
Bressay
Foula
Fitful Head
Sumburgh Head

Hebridean Shelf

Fair Isle

Papa Westray
Westray
Rousay
Nth Ronaldsay
Sanday
Stronsay
Shapinsay
Orkney Islands
Holy Island
Mainland
Scapa Flow
Hoy
South Ronaldsay
Pentland Firth
Duncansby Head

Cape Wrath
Noss Head
e Minch
Dornoch Firth
Tarbat Ness
Moray Firth
Buchan Ness

SCOTLAND
Aberdeen
Girdle Ness
Dundee
Fife Ness
Firth of Forth

Glasgow
★ Edinburgh

Arran
Firth of Clyde

UNITED

Solway Firth

Isle of Man

Irish Sea

KINGDOM

Liverpool

Kingston upon Hull

ENGLAND

LONDON ▣

English Channel

Beachy Head
Calais
Strait of Dover

BELGIUM

FRANCE

North Sea

Devils Hole

Great Fisher Bank

Jutland Bank

NORWAY

Bergen

Skagerrak

Jylland

DENMARK

Odense
Fyn

Kieler Bucht
Kiel

Helgoländer Bucht

Hamburg

GERMANY

Dogger Bank

Waddeneilanden
Texel
Waddenzee
IJsselmeer

★ **AMSTERDAM**

NETHERLANDS

Rotterdam

Oslofjorden

Ancient site
Skara Brae on mainland Orkney is a Neolithic settlement that was occupied between 3100 and 2500 BC. In 1850 a storm revealed the site, and excavations between 1928 and 1930 uncovered 10 houses built from flagstones naturally eroded from the rocky shore.

Storm barrier
On the night of January 31, 1953 a storm surge killed nearly two thousand people in the Netherlands, United Kingdom, and Belgium. In response, the Dutch government set up the massive sea defence building program known as the 'Delta Works' to prevent another tragedy.

SCALE 1:8,000,000
Miller Projection

0   200 kilometers
0   200 statute miles
0   200 nautical miles

BATHYMETRIC DEPTHS	
Feet	Meters
Sea level	Sea level
656	200
1640	500
3281	1000
6562	2000
9842	3000
13,123	4000
16,404	5000
19,685	6000
26,246	8000

NATURAL RESOURCES

- Fishing
- Shellfish
- Oil production
- Gas production
- Tourism

BALTIC SEA

The Baltic is the world's largest body of brackish water, with marine species found in the saltier waters at the western end, and species that are intolerant of any salt in the fresh water at the eastern end where there are significant river inputs. The circulation of water in the Baltic is complex, with irregular inflows of salt water from the North Sea entering approximately every 10 years. The salt water enters via the Danish straits and slowly mixes with the brackish waters of the central part of the Baltic. There is also a permanent surface current carrying brackish water out into the North Sea. Within the Baltic there is a general counterclockwise circulation of water. The Baltic occupies a basin that was created by glacial erosion and since the removal of the ice sheet the land around and beneath the Baltic has been rising because of post-glacial rebound, making the sea smaller and shallower. In the last cenury the whole area has risen by at least four inches (100 mm) and the inner part of the Gulf of Bothnia will rise above sea level within the next 250 years.

THE FACTS	
Area	163,000 square miles (422,200 km²)
Average depth	180 feet (55 m)
Maximum depth	1,380 feet (421 km)
Maximum width	324 miles (540 km)
Maximum length	795 miles (1,280 km)

Gulf of Finland
Fast ice, attached to the shoreline, develops first, and then thinner more mobile pack or rafter ice forms in open water. This satellite image shows the pack ice, driven by the wind into fast ice, piling up into ridges up to 50 feet (15 m) high.

Helsinki archipelago
The Finnish capital, Helsinki, is approximately midway along an archipelago of more than 300 small islands that lies parallel to the Finnish mainland. The archipelago was created by a post-glacial rise in sea level that left the tops of coastal hills as islands.

Kiel Canal
The Kiel Canal was begun in 1887 and completed in 1895. Its construction was driven by the wish of the German navy and merchant shipping interests to have a direct link between the North Sea and the German Baltic ports, avoiding the need to sail around Denmark.

Ice floes
Baltic sea ice usually starts to form in the northern end of the Gulf of Bothnia in mid-November and extends south and westwards so that the open waters of Bothnian Bay are frozen by February. The Gulf of Finland and the Gulf of Riga are frozen by early January.

Surface currents
Apart from the well-defined outflow of brackish water through the Danish straits there is no clearly defined pattern of surface currents within the Baltic. Local surface currents are generated by prevailing winds and by the outflows of the larger rivers that discharge into the Baltic.

→ Outflow through Danish straits
→ Riverine inputs

NATURAL RESOURCES

🐟 Fishing
📷 Tourism

Longitude east of Greenwich

Arctic Circle

*Bottenviken
(Bay of Bothnia)*

Hailuoto

SCALE 1:10,000,000
Miller Projection

0 _____ 200 kilometers

0 _____ 200 statute miles

0 _____ 200 nautical miles

Gulf of Bothnia

Ångesön

Raippaluoto

FINLAND

Gräsö

Åland

Ålands Hav

Turku

HELSINKI ✳

Gulf of Finland

St Petersburg

ORWAY

✳ OSLO

SWEDEN

STOCKHOLM ●

*Gotland
Basin*

Hiiumaa

Saaremaa

Muhu

Kolga
laht

Purekkari neem

*Narva
Bay*

✳ TALLINN

Vormsi

Väinameri

Soela Väin

Abruka

Kihnu

Pärnu
laht

ESTONIA

RUSSIAN
FEDERATION

gerrak

Orust
Tjörn

Gotska Sandön

Fårösund

Gotland

Irbe Strait

Ruhnu

*Gulf
of
Riga*

LATVIA

Gothenburg

Baltic Sea

Laesø

Kattegat

Anholt

Öland

RĪGA ✳

Liepāja

ENMARK

COPENHAGEN ✳

Sjaelland

Hanöbukten

Klaipéda

LITHUANIA

F y n

Malmö

Bornholm

Lolland

Fakse Bugt

Falster

MØn

Gulf of
Gdańsk

Kaliningrad

RUSSIAN
FEDERATION

Kiel

Zatoka
Pomorska

Gdańsk

WIND FARMS

Shallow coastal waters are good sites for wind farms because of the winds produced by convection created by the differential heating of land and sea each day. Wind speeds in these zones share the characteristics of both onshore and offshore wind, depending on the prevailing wind direction. However, there are concerns that wind farms pose a hazard to migratory birds where they are built along flyways.

GERMANY

POLAND

BATHYMETRIC
DEPTHS

Feet	Meters
Sea level	Sea level
656	200
1640	500
3281	1000
6562	2000
9842	3000
13,123	4000
16,404	5000
19,685	6000
26,246	8,000

Stockholm

Stockholm is sometimes known as the "Venice of the North" as the city stands on 14 islands connected by more than 50 bridges, with ocean-going vessels able to dock in the centre of the city. Stockholm is part of an archipelago with some 24,000 islands.

GULF OF ST LAWRENCE

The Gulf of St Lawrence is considered to be the world's largest estuary, where the fresh water of the Great Lakes meets North Atlantic seawater. The size and shape of the gulf make it similar to an inland sea. It has a distinct ecosystem, characterized by partial isolation from the North Atlantic, a large freshwater runoff from the land, a deep trough running along its length, seasonal ice, the presence of a cold intermediate layer, shallow depths, and high biological productivity and diversity. The deep submarine trough, the Laurentian Channel, is a crucial component to the biology of the gulf as it brings in cold, nutrient-rich Atlantic water that slowly mixes and enriches the less dense overlying waters. The distinct qualities of the physical and biological components of the gulf combine to create its unique environment and its fishing grounds are an important regional economic asset. In the 1990s overfishing caused the collapse of cod and redfish stocks; the contribution of fishing to the regional economy is now maintained by the shellfish catch.

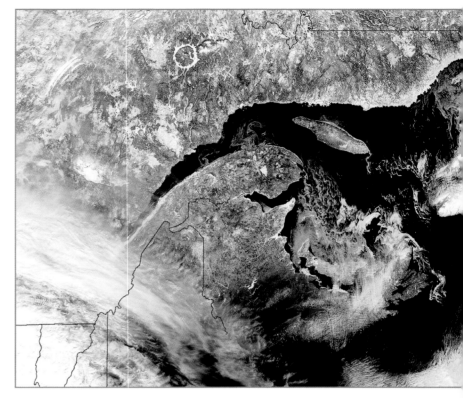

Gulf structure
The St Lawrence River flows northeastward, entering the gulf either side of Anticosti Island. The round shape in the upper middle of the image is Reservoir Manicouagan, which is a lake that now occupies a meteoric impact crater that was created 214 million years ago.

Navigation
Within the Gulf of St Lawrence the complex currents, numerous small islands, and the formation of winter ice are major hazards to navigation. The control of shipping movements and the provision of buoys, lighthouses, and other navigational aids are the responsibility of the Canadian Coast Guard.

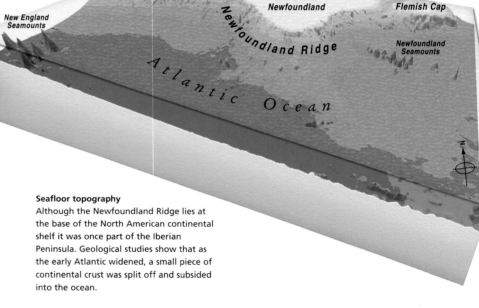

Seafloor topography
Although the Newfoundland Ridge lies at the base of the North American continental shelf it was once part of the Iberian Peninsula. Geological studies show that as the early Atlantic widened, a small piece of continental crust was split off and subsided into the ocean.

Surface currents
Each spring, as the winter snows melt, the increased fresh water flows into the gulf from the St Lawrence River, the Saguenay River, and other rivers along the shores. This produces a low-salinity, higher-temperature surface layer of water that begins to flow toward the Atlantic Ocean.

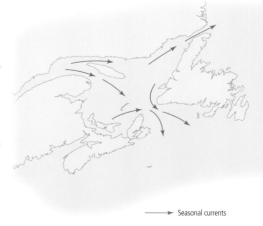

→ Seasonal currents

N O P Q R S T U V W X Y Z

1
2
3
4
5
6
7
8
9
10
11
12
13
14
15

Longitude east of Greenwich
55°
65°
60°

Labrador

Sea

Belle Isle

Strait of Belle Isle

Cape Bauld

Grey Islands

White Bay

CANADA
QUÉBEC

Îles de Mingan
Détroit de Jacques-Cartier
Pointe de l'Ouest
Île d'Anticosti
Détroit d'Honguedo
Pointe de l'Est

50°

Notre Dame Bay

Fogo Island

NEWFOUNDLAND AND
LABRADOR
Newfoundland

Bonavista Bay

St Lawrence

Péninsule de Gaspé
Cap Gaspé

Gulf of

St Lawrence

Cape St George

Trinity Bay

Conception Bay

Chaleur Bay
Miscou Island
Île Lamèque

NEW

Îles de la Madeleine
Île Brion
Île de l'Est

Cabot Strait

St John's

BRUNSWICK
Miramichi Bay

Île du Harve Aubert

St Paul Island

Cabot Strait

Miquelon

Fortune Bay

Avalon Peninsula

PRINCE EDWARD
ISLAND
Prince Edward Island
Charlottetown

Cape North

Cape Breton Island

Laurentian Channel

ST-PIERRE and MIQUELON (to France)
St-Pierre
ST-PIERRE

Placentia Bay

St Mary's Bay

Northumberland Strait
St Georges Bay

Grand Banks of Newfoundland

Chignecto Bay
Minas Basin

NOVA SCOTIA

Strait of Canso
Cape Canso

45°

Grand Manan Island
Bay of Fundy
Minas Channel

Halifax

Atlantic

55°

Long Island

Ocean

Gulf of Maine

Sable Island

Cape Sable Island

60°

SCALE 1:8,000,000
Miller Projection
200 kilometers
200 statute miles
200 nautical miles

BATHYMETRIC DEPTHS
Feet | Meters

Feet	Meters
Sea level	Sea level
656	200
1640	500
3281	1000
6562	2000
9842	3000
13,123	4000
16,404	5000
19,685	6000
26,246	8,000

BARNACLES

Despite their appearance these goose or stalked barnacles are filter-feeding crustaceans. They begin life as larvae living in the water column but they will eventually settle on the surface of any floating object. Goose barnacles, unlike other encrusting barnacles, rely on external water movements, rather than the use of feathery limbs, known as cirri, to generate a feeding current.

NATURAL RESOURCES

Fishing
Whales
Tourism

Great cormorant
The great cormorant (*Phalacrocorax carbo*) is found throughout the world, with a sub-species that inhabits estuaries around the North Atlantic. In North America the only breeding colonies are found in the Canadian maritime provinces, with most found around the shores of the Gulf of St Lawrence.

N O P Q R S T U V W X Y Z

GULF OF MEXICO

The Gulf of Mexico is the ninth largest body of water on the planet and occupies a roughly circular basin whose formation continues to be the subject of geological debate. Seawater from the Caribbean Sea enters the gulf through the Yucatan Strait, circulates clockwise as the Loop Current, and exits through the Straits of Florida eventually forming the Gulf Stream. Portions of the Loop Current often break away forming eddies or gyres which affect regional current patterns. The gulf also receives huge volumes of fresh water from the river systems that drain into it, the largest being the Mississippi. However, excessive amounts of nutrients brought down by the rivers have caused algal blooms that create anoxic "dead zones" when they die. The wide continental margins of the gulf also contain large amounts of oil and gas that contribute a quarter of the United States' gas production and one-eighth of its oil production. In 2008 production was more than a million barrels of oil per day.

Mississippi Delta
This satellite image shows the algal blooms created by the upwelling of cold, nutrient-rich bottom water, caused by the plume of fresh water discharged from the Mississippi Delta. This river water does not fully mix with the surrounding seawater until it passes through the Straits of Florida.

Hurricane damage
Hurricane Katrina entered the Gulf of Mexico at the end of August 2005 and, although once it made its first landfall wind speeds dropped to 125 mph (205 km/h), it not only caused wind damage but also created a storm surge 20 feet (6 m) high, flooding nearly 80 percent of the city.

Giant grouper
The giant grouper (*Epinephelus itajara*) is found in the Gulf of Mexico. However, this species is classified by the International Union for Conservation of Nature (IUCN) as critically endangered throughout its range. Its slow growth, low reproductive rate, and spawning behavior have made it especially susceptible to overfishing.

Algal blooms
Red tides, or "harmful algal blooms," in the Gulf of Mexico were first described by Spanish explorers in the 1530s and are mainly caused by *Gymnodinium breve*, a dinoflagellate. This organism produces powerful neurotoxins that cause fish-kills on a large scale and contaminate all forms of edible shellfish.

HURRICANES

Hurricanes, such as Katrina that devastated the Gulf Coast in 2005, form over warm tropical waters as rotating clusters of thunderstorms. The storm system spins faster as it moves away from the equator and the winds within increase in speed. Once the wind speed is above 74 miles per hour (120 km/h) it officially becomes a hurricane if it is in North America or the Caribbean.

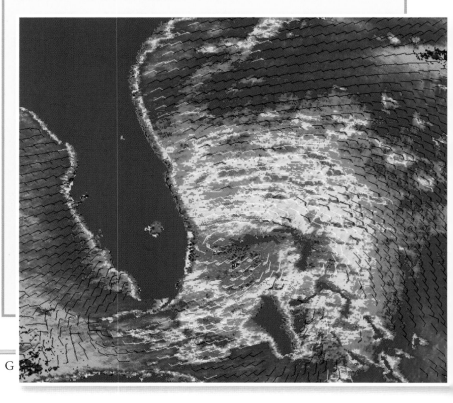

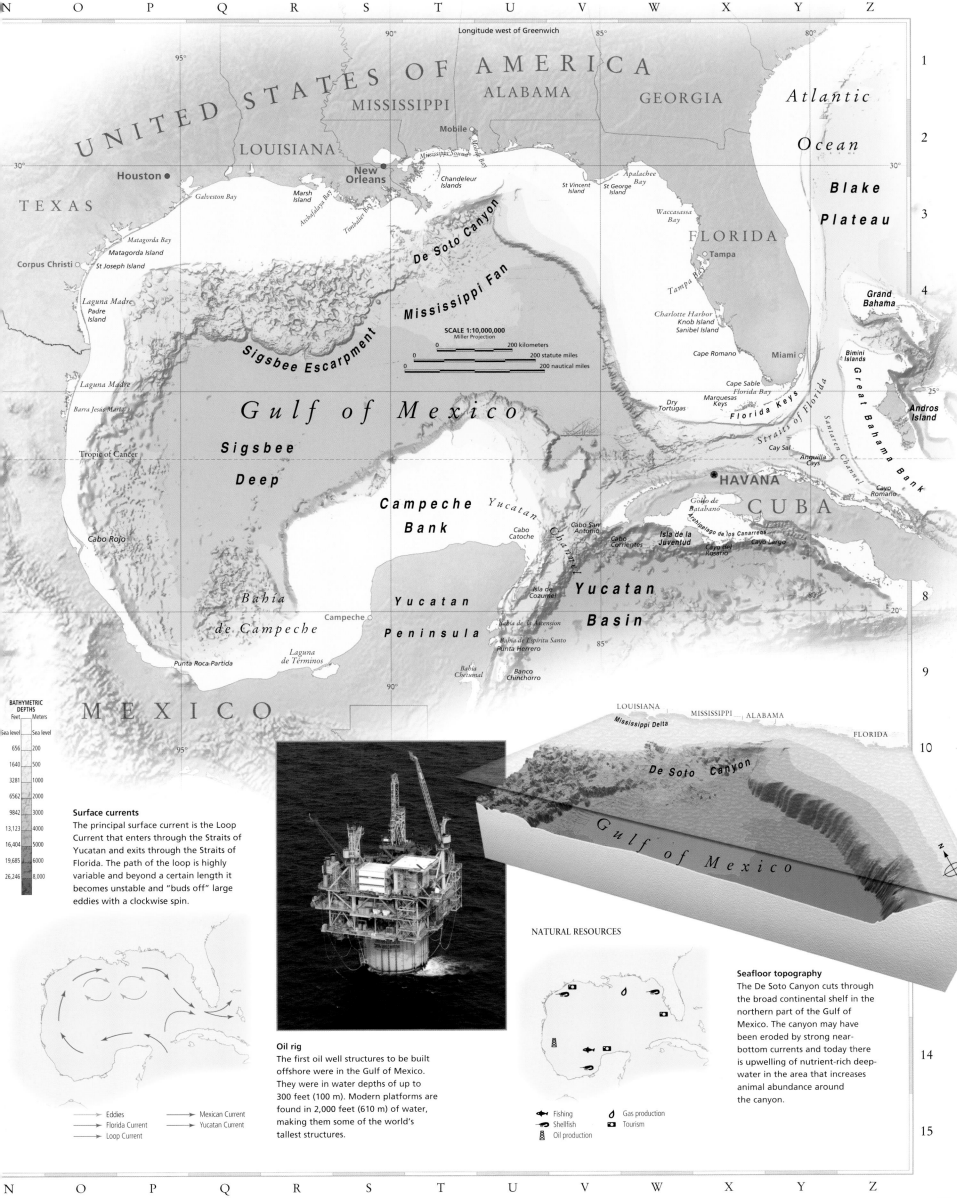

Longitude west of Greenwich

UNITED STATES OF AMERICA

MISSISSIPPI   ALABAMA   GEORGIA

Atlantic

Ocean

Blake

Plateau

Mobile

LOUISIANA

New Orleans

Mississippi Sound

Mobile Bay

Chandeleur Islands

TEXAS

Houston

Galveston Bay

Marsh Island

Archafalaya Bay

Timbalier B.

St Vincent Island

St George Island

Apalachee Bay

FLORIDA

Matagorda Bay

Matagorda Island

De Soto Canyon

Waccasassa Bay

Corpus Christi

St Joseph Island

Mississippi Fan

Tampa

Laguna Madre

Padre Island

Sigsbee Escarpment

SCALE 1:10,000,000
Miller Projection

0   200 kilometers

0   200 statute miles

0   200 nautical miles

Charlotte Harbor

Knob Island

Sanibel Island

Grand
Bahama

Laguna Madre

Gulf of Mexico

Cape Romano

Bimini Islands

Barra Jesús María

Tropic of Cancer

Sigsbee

Deep

Cape Sable

Florida Bay

Dry Tortugas

Marquesas Keys

Florida Keys

Straits of Florida

Cay Sal

Santaren Channel

Great Bahama Bank

Andros
Island

Cabo Rojo

Campeche

Bank

Yucatan

Cabo San Antonio

Cabo Catoche

Channel

Cabo Corrientes

HAVANA

Golfo de Batabanó

Archipelago de los Canarreos

Isla de la Juventud

Cayo del Rosario

Cayo Largo

Anguilla Cays

Cayo Romano

CUBA

Bahía

de Campeche

Campeche

Yucatan

Peninsula

Isla de Cozumel

Yucatan

Basin

Bahía de la Ascensión

Bahía de Espíritu Santo

Punta Herrero

Punta Roca Partida

Laguna de Términos

Bahía Chetumal

Banco Chinchorro

MEXICO

LOUISIANA   MISSISSIPPI   ALABAMA

FLORIDA

Mississippi Delta

Surface currents

The principal surface current is the Loop Current that enters through the Straits of Yucatan and exits through the Straits of Florida. The path of the loop is highly variable and beyond a certain length it becomes unstable and "buds off" large eddies with a clockwise spin.

De Soto Canyon

Gulf of Mexico

N

BATHYMETRIC DEPTHS

Feet	Meters
Sea level	Sea level
656	200
1640	500
3281	1000
6562	2000
9842	3000
13,123	4000
16,404	5000
19,685	6000
26,246	8,000

Eddies →   Mexican Current →

Florida Current →   Yucatan Current →

Loop Current →

Oil rig

The first oil well structures to be built offshore were in the Gulf of Mexico. They were in water depths of up to 300 feet (100 m). Modern platforms are found in 2,000 feet (610 m) of water, making them some of the world's tallest structures.

NATURAL RESOURCES

🐟 Fishing   🛢 Gas production

🦐 Shellfish   🏖 Tourism

🛢 Oil production

Seafloor topography

The De Soto Canyon cuts through the broad continental shelf in the northern part of the Gulf of Mexico. The canyon may have been eroded by strong near-bottom currents and today there is upwelling of nutrient-rich deep-water in the area that increases animal abundance around the canyon.

CARIBBEAN SEA

The Caribbean Sea is a relatively shallow sea that occupies two main basins separated by a broad, submarine plateau. However, there are deep trenches such as the Cayman Trench that runs between Cuba and Jamaica and which contains the Caribbean's deepest point. The Caribbean Sea has a counterclockwise current that brings in Atlantic water between the Lesser Antilles. Once in the Caribbean the water is warmed, and exits via the Yucatan Channel, where it eventually forms the Gulf Stream. The waters of the Caribbean are clear, warm and less salty than the Atlantic and the basin has a very low tidal range. These conditions are ideal for reef-building corals and the Caribbean has nine percent of the world's coral reefs that help attract tourists, who make a major contribution to the regional economy. Volcanic activity and earthquakes are common in the Caribbean, as are destructive hurricanes that gain energy from the warm water.

THE FACTS	
Area	1.1 million square miles (2.7 million km²)
Average depth	8,685 feet (2,647 m)
Maximum depth	25,218 feet (7,686 m)
Maximum width	840 miles (1,400 km)
Maximum length	1,678 miles (2,700 km)

Schooling barracuda
Juvenile barracuda (Sphyraena barracuda) are frequently found in large schools. They are reputed to be good eating but there is an increasing problem with the toxin from the alga Ciguatera that causes severe food poisoning and which accumulates in the barracudas' muscles.

Yucatan coast
The "Temple of the Winds" at Tulum on the Yucatan Peninsula was built by the Mayans to act as a lookout and hurricane warning. As a hurricane approaches the strong winds blow across a hole in the top of the structure, producing a loud warning note.

Surface currents
Water from the equatorial Atlantic is carried by the North Equatorial, North Brazil, and Guiana currents between the Antilles to become the Caribbean Current. This carries large amounts of water northwestward, eventually entering the Gulf of Mexico and becoming part of the Yucatan Current.

→ Caribbean Current
→ Eddy
→ Guiana Current
→ Yucatan Current

BATHYMETRIC DEPTHS

Feet	Meters
Sea level	Sea level
656	200
1640	500
3281	1000
6562	2000
9842	3000
13,123	4000
16,404	5000
19,685	6000
26,246	8,000

Campeche Bank

HAVANA

Golfo de Batabanó

Cabo Catoche

Cabo San Antonio

Cabo Corrientes

Isla de la Juventud

Archipiélago de los Canarreos

Cayo Largo

Cancún

Yucatan Peninsula

Tulum

Isla de Cozumel

Yucatan Basin

CAYMAN ISLANDS

Little

Bahía de la Ascensión

Bahía de Espíritu Santo

GEORGE TOWN

Grand Cayman

Chetumal

Banco Chinchorro

Misteriosa Bank

Rosario Bank

Cayman

Belize

BELIZE

Turneffe Islands

Rosa Ba

Isla de Utila

Islas de la Bahía

Isla de Guanaja

Isla de Roatán

Nicaragua Rise

Golfo de Honduras

GUATEMALA

La Ceiba

Cabo Camarón

Punta Patuca

Cabo Gracias á Dios

HONDURAS

South Cay
Cayos Miskitos

EL SALVADOR

Golfo de Fonseca
Punta Cosigüina

NICARAGUA

Isla de Providencia

Mosquito Coast

Punta de Perlas

Islas del Maíz

Isla de San And

Pacific

Cabo Santa Elena

Punta del Mono

Bahía de San Juan del Norte

COSTA RICA

Limón

Cabo Blanco

Golfo de los Mosquitos

Bahía de Coronado

Punta San Pedro

PANAM

Golfo Dulce

Punta Burica

Golfo de Chiriquí

Pen de A

Isla Coiba

Golfo de Montijo

Pun Marí

Ocean

MEXICO

Yucatan Channel

Tropic of Cancer

Straits of Fl

Cay

Archi

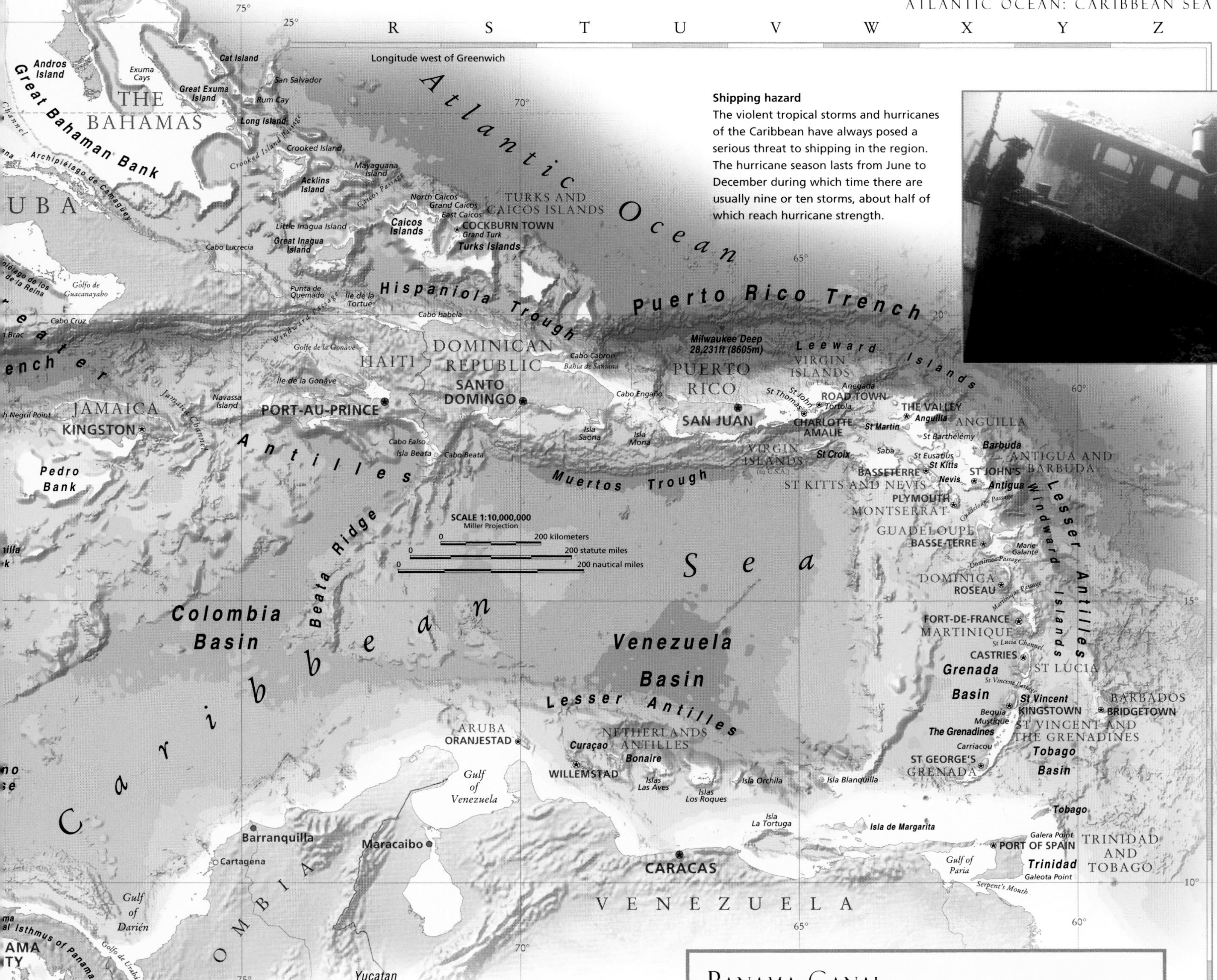

Longitude west of Greenwich

Map labels

THE BAHAMAS

Andros Island
Great Bahaman Bank
Exuma Cays
Great Exuma Island
Cat Island
San Salvador
Long Island
Rum Cay
Crooked Island
Crooked Island Passage
Acklins Island
Mayaguana Island
Little Inagua Island
North Caicos
Grand Caicos
East Caicos
Caicos Islands
TURKS AND CAICOS ISLANDS
COCKBURN TOWN
Grand Turk
Turks Islands
Great Inagua Island

CUBA
Archipiélago de Camagüey
Golfo de la Reina
Cabo Lucrecia
Cabo Cruz
Brac

Atlantic Ocean

Hispaniola Trough
Puerto Rico Trench
Windward Passage
Punta de Quemado
Île de la Tortue
Cabo Isabela
HAITI
DOMINICAN REPUBLIC
SANTO DOMINGO
Cabo Cabron
Bahía de Samaná
Golfe de la Gonâve
Île de la Gonâve
PORT-AU-PRINCE
Navassa Island
Cabo Engaño
Milwaukee Deep 28,231ft (8605m)
PUERTO RICO
SAN JUAN
Isla Saona
Isla Mona
Cabo Falso
Isla Beata
Cabo Beata

JAMAICA
Negril Point
KINGSTON
Pedro Bank

Greater Antilles

VIRGIN ISLANDS
St Thomas
St John
ROAD TOWN
Tortola
Anegada
VIRGIN ISLANDS (to U.S.A.)
CHARLOTTE AMALIE
St Croix
Leeward Islands
Saba
St Eustatius
St Kitts
Nevis
BASSETERRE
ST KITTS AND NEVIS
PLYMOUTH
MONTSERRAT
St Martin
Anguilla
ANGUILLA
THE VALLEY
St Barthélemy
Barbuda
ANTIGUA AND BARBUDA
ST JOHN'S
Antigua
Guadeloupe Passage
GUADELOUPE
BASSE-TERRE
Marie-Galante
DOMINICA
ROSEAU
Dominica Passage
Martinique Passage
FORT-DE-FRANCE
MARTINIQUE
St Lucia Channel
CASTRIES
ST LUCIA
St Vincent Passage
Grenada Basin
St Vincent
KINGSTOWN
Bequia
Mustique
The Grenadines
ST VINCENT AND THE GRENADINES
Carriacou
ST GEORGE'S
GRENADA
Grenada
BARBADOS
BRIDGETOWN
Tobago
Tobago Basin

Muertos Trough
Antilles
Beata Ridge
Colombia Basin
Venezuela Basin
Lesser Antilles
Windward Antilles
Lesser Antilles

Caribbean Sea

ARUBA
ORANJESTAD
Curaçao
NETHERLANDS ANTILLES
Bonaire
WILLEMSTAD
Islas Las Aves
Islas Los Roques
Isla Orchila
Isla Blanquilla
Isla La Tortuga
Isla de Margarita
Gulf of Venezuela
Barranquilla
Maracaibo
Cartagena
CARACAS
Tobago
Galera Point
PORT OF SPAIN
Trinidad
TRINIDAD AND TOBAGO
Gulf of Paria
Geloata Point
Serpent's Mouth

COLOMBIA
Gulf of Darién
Gulf of Uraba
Isthmus of Panama
PANAMA CITY

VENEZUELA

Scale
SCALE 1:10,000,000
Miller Projection
0   200 kilometers
0   200 statute miles
0   200 nautical miles

Shipping hazard

The violent tropical storms and hurricanes of the Caribbean have always posed a serious threat to shipping in the region. The hurricane season lasts from June to December during which time there are usually nine or ten storms, about half of which reach hurricane strength.

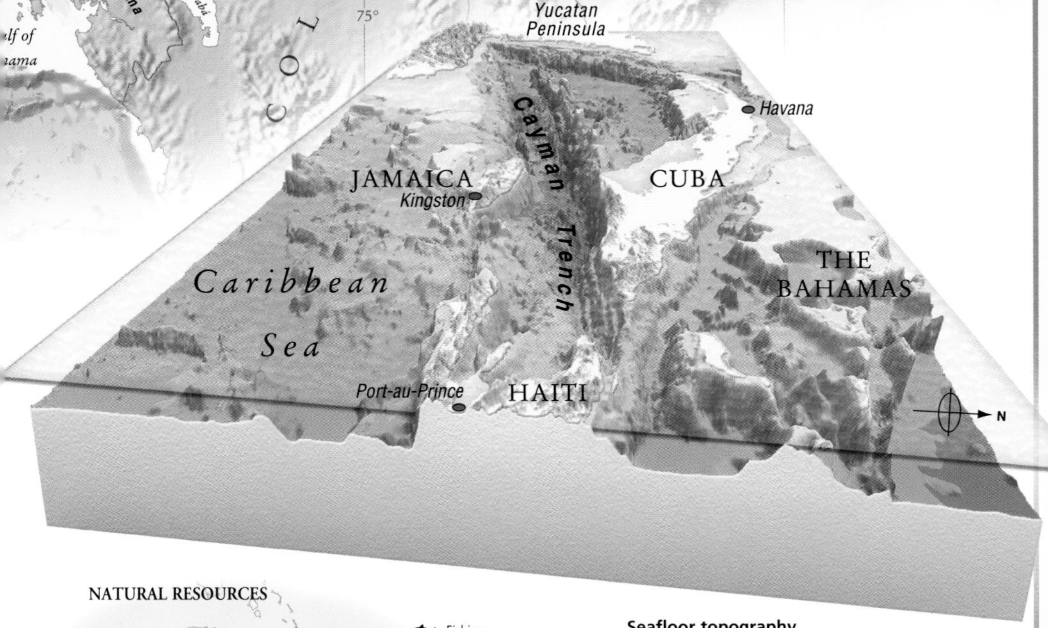

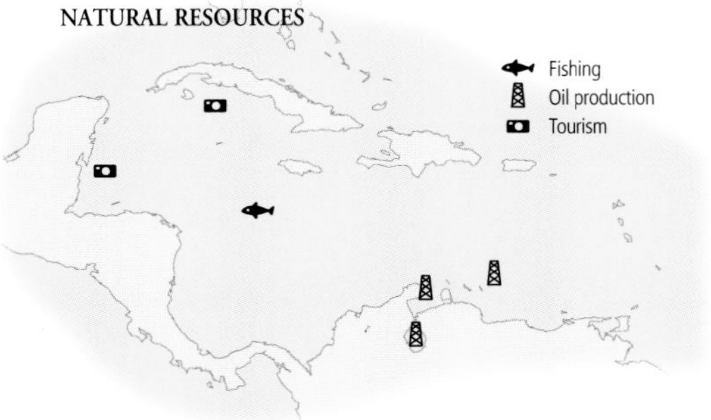

PANAMA CANAL

The Panama Canal is a shortcut for shipping between the Atlantic and Pacific oceans. Construction began in 1880 under French control but disease and natural hazards caused its abandonment. The canal was eventually finished in 1914, after United States army engineers and doctors had eradicated the malaria and yellow fever that killed most of the 27,500 workers who died during the canal's construction.

Seafloor topography

The Cayman Trench between Jamaica and the Cayman Islands marks the boundary between the North American and Caribbean tectonic plates. Plans are underway for a team of scientists from the United Kingdom, to use a remotely-operated underwater vehicle to map the unexplored system of faults and underwater volcanic vents.

Seafloor topography map labels

Yucatan Peninsula
Havana
CUBA
THE BAHAMAS
JAMAICA
Kingston
Cayman Trench
Caribbean Sea
Port-au-Prince
HAITI
N

NATURAL RESOURCES

- Fishing
- Oil production
- Tourism

123

SARGASSO SEA

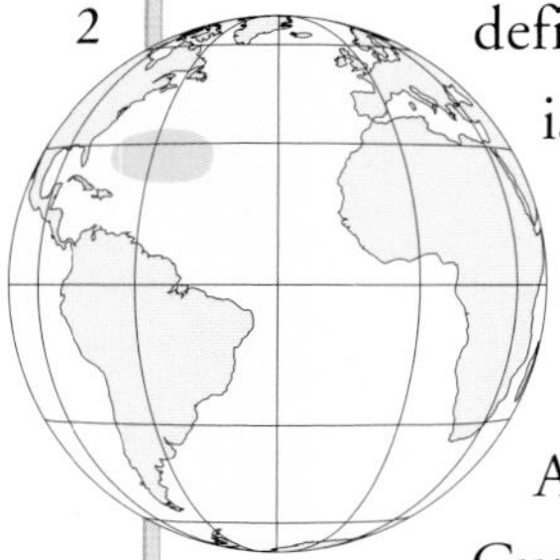

The Sargasso Sea is unusual in that it does not have limits defined by coasts or other geographic features. Instead, it is an area of the Atlantic Ocean characterized by large, floating, masses of brown sargassum seaweed that accumulate there. The sea is at the center of the North Atlantic Gyre, a group of clockwise north-Atlantic currents—the Gulf Stream, North Atlantic Current, Canary Current, and North Equatorial Current—which form a single, closed-circulation cell. This circulation causes everything that floats to become concentrated in the center of the gyre. Central gyres, such as the Sargasso Sea, have no local nutrient supply but studies have shown that Gulf Stream eddies can transport nutrient-rich waters into the Sargasso. A number of animals have co-evolved with the sargassum, taking on its brown-yellow coloration and living their entire lives in its camouflage. Also, the juveniles of some species make use of the weed as protection.

Sargassum crab
The ends of the fifth pair of legs of the sargassum crab (*Portunus* sp.) are modified into paddles so that it is able to swim between clumps of sargassum weed. The mottled shell is an effective camouflage when the crab is covered by strands of weed.

THE FACTS	
Area	1.4 million square miles (3.75 million km²)
Average depth	16,405 feet (5000 m)
Maximum depth	21,005 feet (6,402 m)
Maximum width	994 miles (1,600 km)
Maximum length	1,864 miles (3,000 km)

Gulf Stream
The Gulf Stream, shown in this satellite image in red, is known as "the river in the ocean." It is Earth's fastest moving ocean current, flowing at two to five miles per hour (3 to 8 km/h).

THE MYSTERIOUS LIVES OF EELS

The most famous inhabitants of the Sargasso Sea are not permanent residents. The European eel (*Anguilla anguilla*) and the American eel (*Anguilla rostrata*), delicacies in Europe and America, spawn here. The juvenile eels then migrate into the rivers of North America and Europe.

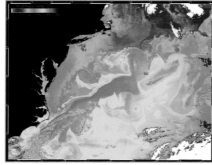

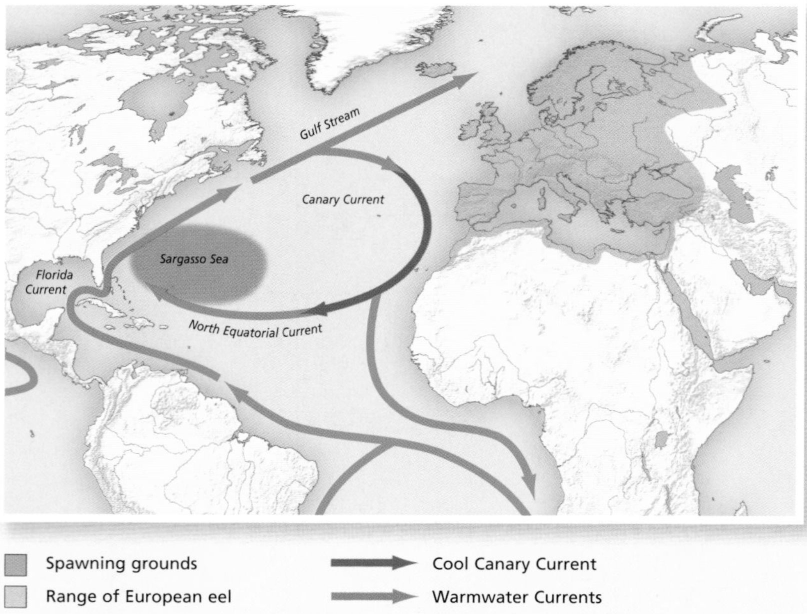

Parallel lives
The lifecycle of the European eel and its relative, the American eel, takes decades and up to 7,000 miles (11,250 km) to complete.

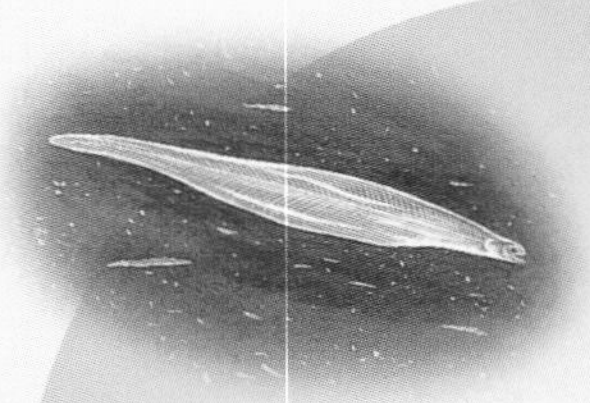

1. The journey starts
European eels spawn in the Sargasso Sea. The leaflike larvae drift on Gulf Stream currents for up to three years.

2. See-through change
Larvae metamorphose into juveniles, known as glass eels, when they arrive on European coasts, then mature into yellow eels.

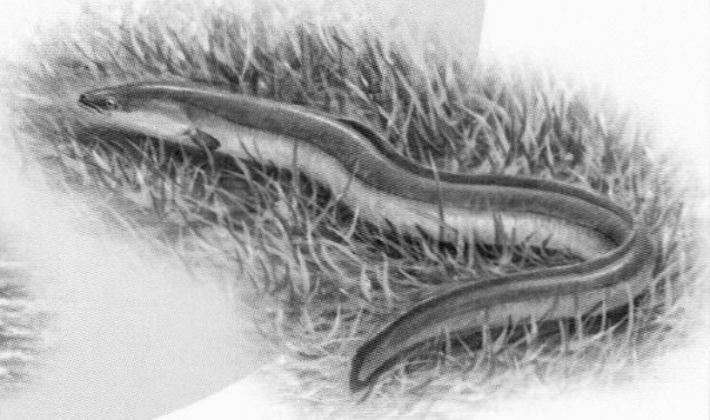

3. Long lives
Yellow eels spend 6–20 years in fresh water. At maturity they become silver eels.

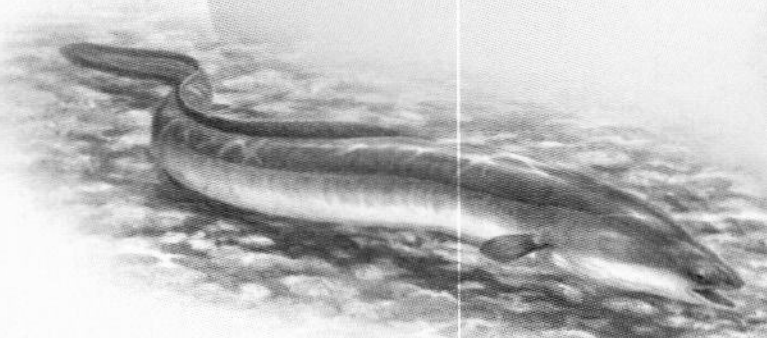

4. Mature migration
Adult eels make their way downriver to the Atlantic Ocean to return to their birthplace. They spawn once and die.

Map labels: Gulf Stream, Canary Current, Sargasso Sea, Florida Current, North Equatorial Current

Legend:
- Spawning grounds
- Range of European eel
- Cool Canary Current
- Warmwater Currents

Map labels (main map): UNITED STATES OF AMERICA, Hatteras Island, Cape Hatteras, Hatteras Canyon, Onslow Bay, Cape Fear, Long Bay, Port Royal Sound, Blake–Bahama Ridge, Blake Ridge, Blake Escarpment, Bahama Ridge, Cape Canaveral, Grand Bahama, THE BAHAMAS, Great Abaco, Miami, Eleuthera, Bimini Islands, New Providence, NASSAU, Andros Island, Cat Island, San Salvador, Florida Keys, Santaren Channel, Exuma Cays, Great Exuma Island, Rum Cay, Long Island, Straits of Florida, Anguilla Cays, Great Bahaman Bank, Crooked Island, Acklins Island, HAVANA, Little Inagua Island, Great Inagua Island, CUBA, PORT-AU-PRINCE, Windward Passage

N O P Q R S T U V W X Y Z

70°   65°   60°   55° Longitude west of Greenwich   50°   45°   40°

New England
Seamounts

Sohm

Corner
Seamount

Atlantic

Abyssal

Plain

Hayes Fracture Zone

Bermuda

Bermuda ★ HAMILTON
BERMUDA

Ocean

Atlantis   Fracture

Rise

Zone

atteras

byssal

S a r g a s s o

Plain

Researcher
Seamount

S e a

Kane   Fracture

SCALE 1:15,000,000
Miller Projection

0   400 kilometers

0   400 statute miles

0   400 nautical miles

Zone

Tropic of Cancer

Vema
Gap

Nares

Deep

URKS AND
COS ISLANDS

CKBURN TOWN
s Islands

aniola   Puerto Rico Trench

MINICAN
PUBLIC

Milwaukee Deep
28,231ft (8605m)   SAN JUAN

VIRGIN
ISLANDS

SANTO
DOMINGO

PUERTO
RICO   65°

Atlantic

70°

BATHYMETRIC
DEPTHS
Feet   Meters

Bermuda
Hamilton

Ocean

ea level   Sea level

656   200

1640   500

3281   1000

Bermuda
Rise

6562   2000

9842   3000

13,123   4000

Hatteras
Abyssal
Plain

16,404   6000

19,685   6000

26,246   8,000

Seafloor topography

The Bermuda Rise is a broad topographic
swelling that rises above the surrounding
seafloor of the western subtropical Atlantic.
Some geologists believe it was formed by a
rising plume of magma but others now
believe it was formed by activity at the
edge of tectonic plates.

Sargassum refuge

Sargassum, a brown seaweed, is covered
with gas-filled, grape-shaped floats. This
enables the plant to live on the ocean's
surface. It provides a floating refuge for
invertebrates and fish, such as these
planehead filefish (*Stephanolepis hispidus*).

1.   slope water   2.   slope
water

Gulf Stream

Sargasso
water

Sargasso
water

Gulf Stream

NATURAL RESOURCES

The Gulf Stream rings

As it flows, the Gulf Stream develops meanders
that may bud off from the main current as warm-
or cold-water eddies, depending on whether the
meander cuts off to the north or south of the
stream. These eddies, or rings, can trap nutrient-
rich water and transport it into the
center of the Sargasso Sea.

3.   slope water   4.   slope water

Gulf   Stream

slope
water

Gulf Stream

Gulf stream
slope
water

Sargasso
water

Sargasso
water

Sargasso
water

Fishing

Shellfish

Tourism

N O P Q R S T U V W X Y Z

BAY OF BISCAY

The Bay of Biscay is a semi-enclosed area of the northeast Atlantic that contains a wider than usual portion of continental shelf. This has made the bay relatively shallow and this, combined with the prevailing westerly winds that bring in waves that have traveled across most of the Atlantic, often makes its waters exceptionally stormy and rough. These waters have claimed countless vessels over the centuries. Circulation patterns within the bay are highly seasonal. From October to March, during winter season, a seasonal current flows along the slope of the continental shelf and this is known as the Navidad Current, so-called because it is present through the Christmas period. The Navidad Current flows eastward, along the north coast of Spain, and is an extension of the northward Portugal countercurrent. Where the current encounters irregularities on the continental slope, such as the Santander Canyon, it generates eddies, meanders, and warm-water lenses.

THE FACTS	
Area	86,000 square miles (223,000 km²)
Average depth	7,874 feet (2,400 m)
Maximum depth	15,525 feet (4,735 m)
Maximum width	342 miles (550 km)
Maximum length	317 miles (510 km)

Shipwrecks
Despite modern navigation aids and accurate weather forecasting the Bay of Biscay still claims ships and lives. Storms develop quickly throughout the year, though these are fiercest and most frequent during the winter months when westerly winds whip up the waves into a cauldron of churning water.

Quiet inlet
Pont Goulphar is one of the numerous secluded inlets along the southwest coast of Brittany. The inlet and the surrounding rugged cliffs inspired the Impressionist painter Claude Monet to produce a series of famous seascapes. The area continues to attract large numbers of summer visitors.

Porbeagle
Porbeagle sharks (Lamna nasus) are probably the most numerous of the large sharks in the Bay of Biscay, though overfishing in past decades has severely depleted their numbers in the North Atlantic and the species is listed as vulnerable by the International Union for Conservation of Nature (IUCN).

Gannet
The northern gannet (Morus bassanus) is the largest seabird in the North Atlantic, having a wingspan of up to six feet (2 m). Adults of the species are seen throughout the Bay of Biscay although they breed farther north.

La Rochelle Harbor
There has been a port at La Rochelle since the 10th century. Although always prosperous, as the most westerly Atlantic port in France the port also became strategically important in the 18th century when trade with French possessions in the New World expanded.

Surface currents
The surface currents of the Bay of Biscay have a clockwise circulation that is linked to the clockwise surface circulation pattern in the main part of the North Atlantic. In addition, there are strong coastal currents driven by the high tidal range within the bay.

→ Inshore tidal movement
→ North Atlantic Drift
→ Seasonal Navidad Current
→ Surface circulation

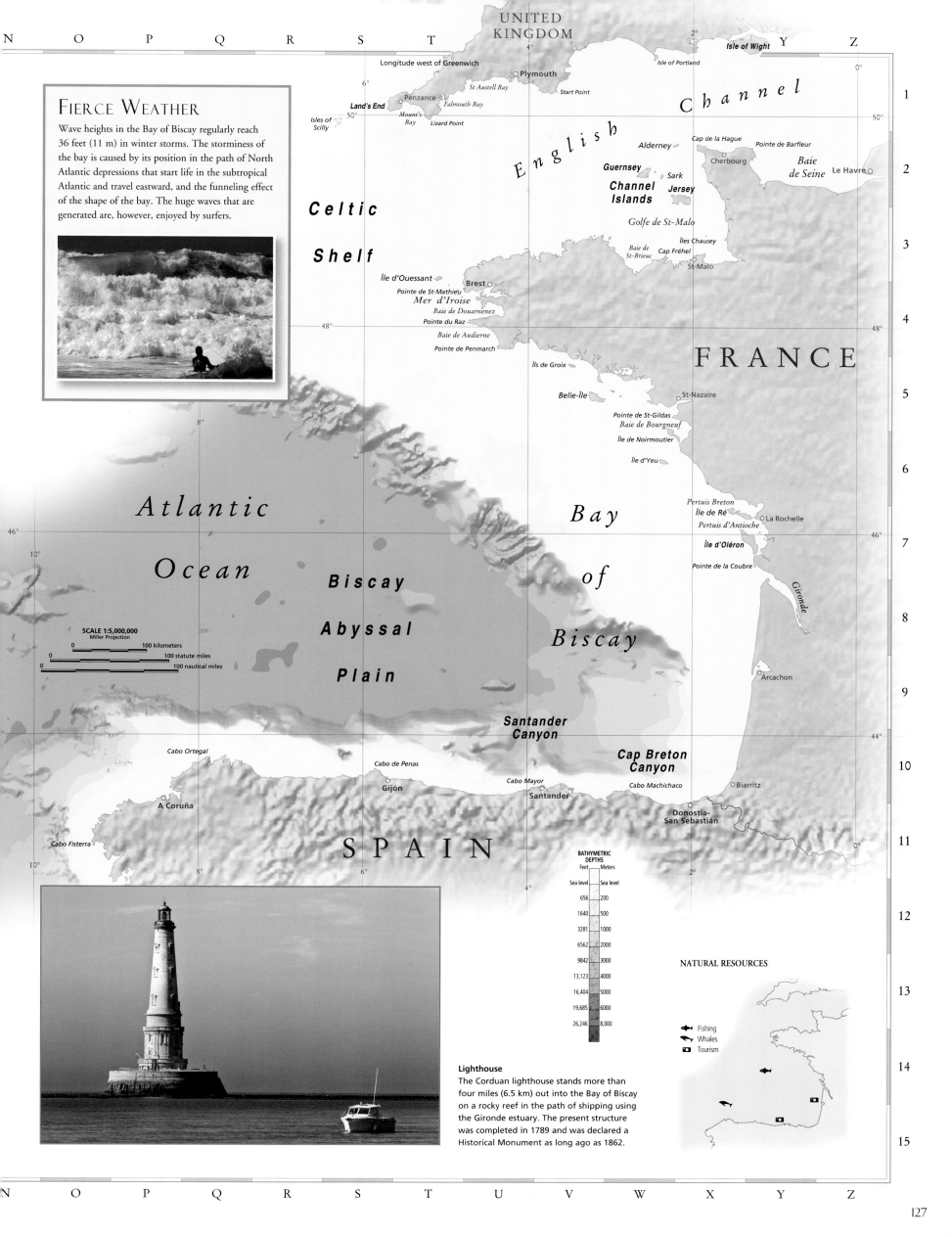

Fierce Weather

Wave heights in the Bay of Biscay regularly reach 36 feet (11 m) in winter storms. The storminess of the bay is caused by its position in the path of North Atlantic depressions that start life in the subtropical Atlantic and travel eastward, and the funneling effect of the shape of the bay. The huge waves that are generated are, however, enjoyed by surfers.

Lighthouse
The Corduan lighthouse stands more than four miles (6.5 km) out into the Bay of Biscay on a rocky reef in the path of shipping using the Gironde estuary. The present structure was completed in 1789 and was declared a Historical Monument as long ago as 1862.

SCALE 1:5,000,000
Miller Projection

0 ___ 100 kilometers
0 ___ 100 statute miles
0 ___ 100 nautical miles

BATHYMETRIC DEPTHS

Feet	Meters
Sea level	Sea level
656	200
1640	500
3281	1000
6562	2000
9842	3000
13,123	4000
16,404	5000
19,685	6000
26,246	8,000

NATURAL RESOURCES

Fishing
Whales
Tourism

Map labels

English Channel
Celtic Shelf
Atlantic Ocean
Biscay Abyssal Plain
Bay of Biscay
FRANCE
SPAIN

Isle of Wight, Plymouth, St Austell Bay, Start Point, Isle of Portland, Penzance, Falmouth Bay, Land's End, Lizard Point, Mount's Bay, Isles of Scilly, Longitude west of Greenwich
Alderney, Cap de la Hague, Pointe de Barfleur, Cherbourg, Baie de Seine, Le Havre, Guernsey, Sark, Jersey, Channel Islands, Golfe de St-Malo, Îles Chausey, Cap Fréhel, St-Malo, Baie de St-Brieuc
Île d'Ouessant, Pointe de St-Mathieu, Brest, Mer d'Iroise, Baie de Douarnenez, Pointe du Raz, Baie de Audierne, Pointe de Penmarch
Îls de Groix, Belle-Île, St-Nazaire, Pointe de St-Gildas, Baie de Bourgneuf, Île de Noirmoutier, Île d'Yeu
Pertuis Breton, Île de Ré, La Rochelle, Pertuis d'Antioche, Île d'Oléron, Pointe de la Coubre, Gironde, Arcachon
Cabo Ortegal, Cabo de Penas, Cabo Mayor, Santander Canyon, Cap Breton Canyon, Gijón, Cabo Machichaco, Biarritz, A Coruña, Santander, Donostia-San Sebastián, Cabo Fisterra

MEDITERRANEAN SEA

The Mediterranean Sea's only link with the Atlantic is through the Strait of Gibraltar, where dense salty Mediterranean water flows out beneath less dense Atlantic water. As a consequence, the tidal range in the Mediterranean is short and the circulation patterns are driven by evaporation and freshwater inputs. High evaporation in the eastern half causes the water level to decrease and salinity to increase eastward. This draws relatively low-salinity water from the Atlantic across the basin; it warms and becomes saltier as it travels east, then sinks in the region of the Levant and circulates westward, to exit at the Strait of Gibraltar. The Mediterranean Sea is largely populated by species that have entered via the Strait of Gibraltar and adapted to warmer more saline water than the Atlantic. However, since the opening of the Suez Canal in 1869 Red Sea species have begun to colonize the eastern Mediterranean.

THE FACTS	
Area	959,210 square miles (2,484,342 km²)
Average depth	4,920 feet (1,500 m)
Maximum depth	16,897 feet (5,150 m)
Maximum width	497 miles (800 km)
Maximum length	1,250 miles (2,000 km)

City of Venice
Venice stands on 118 small islands within a saltwater lagoon bounded by the mouths of the River Piave to the north and the River Po to the south. During the Middle Ages and the Renaissance Venice was the dominant political and military power in the Mediterranean.

SCALE 1:15,000,000
Miller Projection

Aegean Sea
The Aegean Sea is an embayment of the Mediterranean separating the Greek and Turkish mainlands. It was known to the Greeks as "Archipelago" referring to the large number of islands within it, though the term is now used to refer to island groups throughout the world.

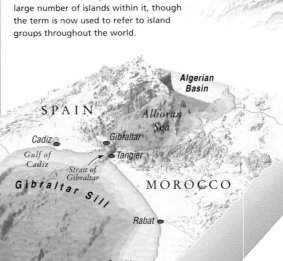

Surface currents
Surface circulation of the Mediterranean consists of separate counterclockwise movements of the water in each of the two basins. The complexity of the northern coastline and of the numerous islands generates many small eddies and other local currents that contribute to the general surface circulation.

Seafloor topography
The Strait of Gibraltar is the only natural connection between the Mediterranean Sea and the world ocean. It is 36 miles (58 km) long and narrows to 8 miles (13 km). Depths in the strait range between 980 and 3,000 feet (300 and 900 m).

→ Atlantic surface inflow
→ Surface circulation

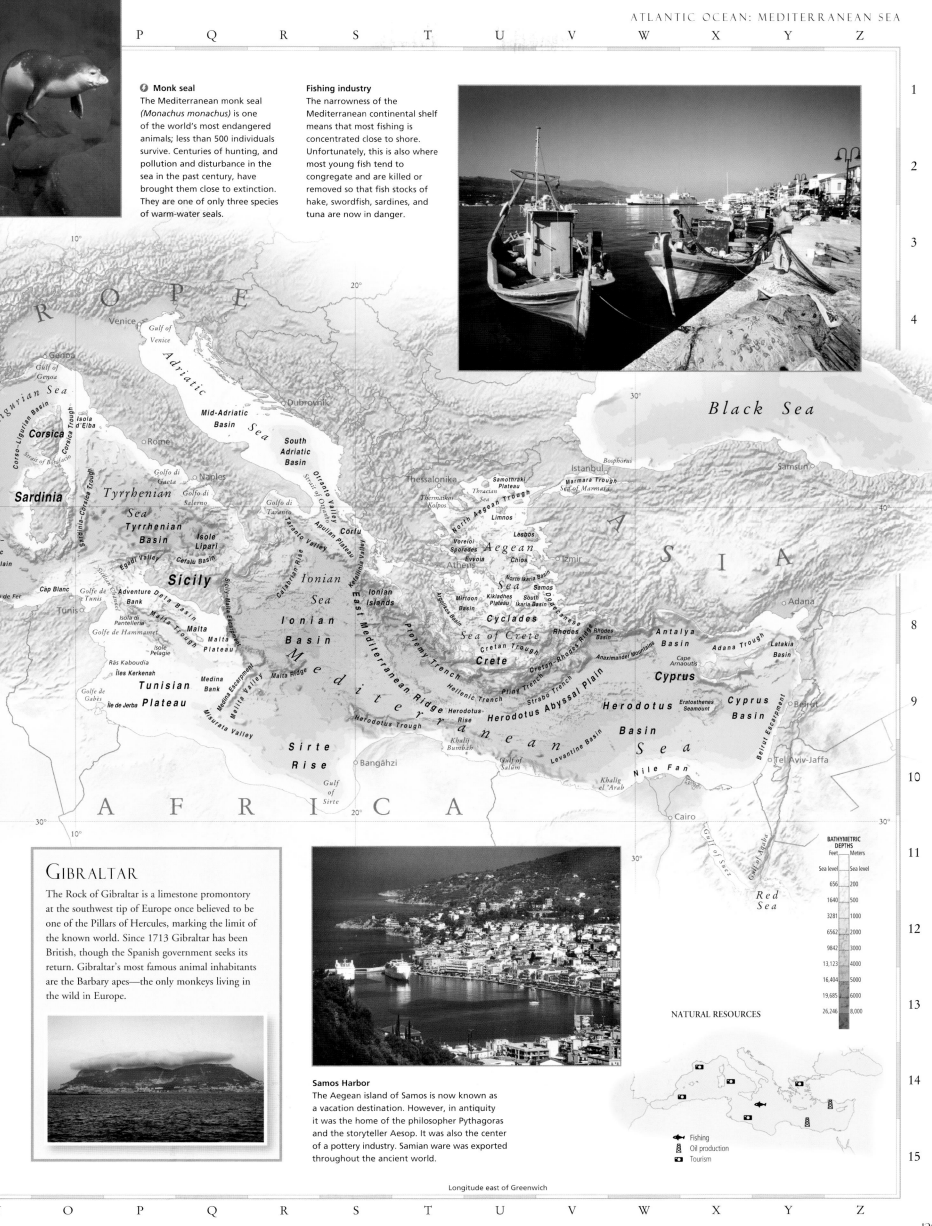

Monk seal
The Mediterranean monk seal (*Monachus monachus*) is one of the world's most endangered animals; less than 500 individuals survive. Centuries of hunting, and pollution and disturbance in the sea in the past century, have brought them close to extinction. They are one of only three species of warm-water seals.

Fishing industry
The narrowness of the Mediterranean continental shelf means that most fishing is concentrated close to shore. Unfortunately, this is also where most young fish tend to congregate and are killed or removed so that fish stocks of hake, swordfish, sardines, and tuna are now in danger.

GIBRALTAR

The Rock of Gibraltar is a limestone promontory at the southwest tip of Europe once believed to be one of the Pillars of Hercules, marking the limit of the known world. Since 1713 Gibraltar has been British, though the Spanish government seeks its return. Gibraltar's most famous animal inhabitants are the Barbary apes—the only monkeys living in the wild in Europe.

Samos Harbor
The Aegean island of Samos is now known as a vacation destination. However, in antiquity it was the home of the philosopher Pythagoras and the storyteller Aesop. It was also the center of a pottery industry. Samian ware was exported throughout the ancient world.

Map labels

EUROPE
Venice
Gulf of Venice
Adriatic Sea
Genoa
Gulf of Genoa
Ligurian Sea
Corsica
Isola d'Elba
Corsica Trough
Corso-Ligurian Basin
Strait of Bonifacio
Sardinia
Sardinia-Corsica Trough
Rome
Mid-Adriatic Basin
South Adriatic Basin
Dubrovnik
Golfo di Gaeta
Naples
Tyrrhenian
Tyrrhenian Sea
Tyrrhenian Basin
Golfo di Salerno
Golfo di Taranto
Otranto Valley
Strait of Otranto
Apulian Plateau
Taranto Valley
Corfu
Ionian Islands
Isole Lipari
Cefalu Basin
Egadi Valley
Sicily
Calabrian Rise
Ionian Sea
Ionian Basin
Thessalonika
Thermaikos Kolpos
Thracian Sea
Samothraki Plateau
North Aegean Trough
Marmara Trough
Sea of Marmara
Istanbul
Bosphorus
Black Sea
Samsun
Limnos
Voreioi Sporades
Evvoia
Aegean Sea
Lesbos
Chios
Izmir
Athens
ASIA
Cap Blanc
Golfe de Tunis
Adventure Bank
Dela Basin
Sicilian-Maltese Escarpment
Sicily-Malta Escarpment
Malta Trough
Malta
Malta Plateau
Malta Ridge
Isola di Pantelleria
Isole Pelagie
Cap de Fer
Tunis
Ràs Kaboudia
Îles Kerkenah
Medina Bank
Tunisian Plateau
Golfe de Hammamet
Golfe de Gabès
Île de Jerba
Medina Escarpment
Melita Valley
Misurata Valley
Malta Valley
Sirte Rise
Gulf of Sirte
AFRICA
Bangāzhi
East Mediterranean Ridge
Mediterranean Ridge
Ptolemy Trench
Hellenic Trench
Herodotus Trough
Herodotus Rise
Mediterranean Sea
North Ikaria Basin
Kikladhes Plateau
Mirtoon Basin
Argolikos Basin
Samos
South Ikaria Basin
Dodecanese
Cyclades
Sea of Crete
Cretan Trough
Crete
Rhodes
Rhodes Basin
Cretan-Rhodes Ridge
Pliny Trench
Strabo Trench
Herodotus Abyssal Plain
Anaximander Mountains
Antalya Basin
Cape Arnaoutis
Cyprus
Adana
Adana Trough
Latakia Basin
Cyprus Basin
Herodotus Basin
Eratosthenes Seamount
Beirut
Beirut Escarpment
Levantine Basin
Khalij Bumbah
Gulf of Salūm
Khalig el 'Arab
Nile Fan
Cairo
Tel Aviv-Jaffa
Gulf of Suez
Gulf of Aqaba
Red Sea

BATHYMETRIC DEPTHS

Feet	Meters
Sea level	Sea level
656	200
1640	500
3281	1000
6562	2000
9842	3000
13,123	4000
16,404	5000
19,685	6000
26,246	8,000

NATURAL RESOURCES

Fishing
Oil production
Tourism

Longitude east of Greenwich

BLACK SEA

The Black Sea is believed by many geologists to have been a freshwater lake until about 8,000 years ago when the post-glacial rise in sea levels allowed seawater from the Aegean Sea to break through what is now the Turkish straits system (the Bosporus, Sea of Marmara and the Dardenelles). Even today the salinity of the Black Sea is only half that of full-strength seawater and the input of major rivers means that there is net positive outflow of water from the Black Sea into the Mediterranean. This fresh water causes much of the Black Sea to become stratified so that the deeper layers do not mix with the surface and become hypoxic and devoid of life. Most marine life is found in the surface waters and the shallow coastal margins, though these areas have been severely affected by decades of industrial and agricultural pollution brought down to the sea by rivers, principally the Danube.

THE FACTS	
Area	196,000 square miles (508,000 km²)
Average depth	4,062 feet (1,240 m)
Maximum depth	7,365 feet (2,245 m)
Maximum width	160 miles (260 km)
Maximum length	730 miles (1,175 km)

First Bosporus bridge
The Bosporus is less than half a mile (700 m) at its narrowest point. The first bridge, completed in 1973, stands beside the Oratokoy mosque. A second bridge was opened in 1988. A third bridge is planned and a railway tunnel is nearing completion.

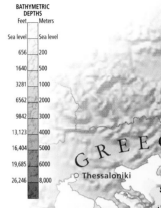

BATHYMETRIC DEPTHS

Feet	Meters
Sea level	Sea level
656	200
1640	500
3281	1000
6562	2000
9842	3000
13,123	4000
16,404	5000
19,685	6000
26,246	8,000

Sea of Azov
The Sea of Azov is a body of brackish water that connects to the Black sea via the Kerch Strait and is the shallowest sea in the world. It has an average depth of 43 feet (13 m) and maximum depth of 50 feet (15.3 m).

GREEC

Thessaloniki

Samo

Anatolian Trough

Limno

Aege

Sea

Moon jellyfish
In the 1970s there was a dramatic rise in the number of moon jellyfish (Aurelia aurita) in the Black Sea and it was suggested that this species, alone, was consuming 62 percent of all zooplankton produced in the surface waters. The zooplankton was food that previously supported important fisheries.

Stingray
The common stingray (Dasyatis pastinaca) lives on sandy or muddy bottoms in the Black Sea, often half-buried in the substrate, and near rocky reefs. It is usually found shallower than 197 feet (60 m). It is also tolerant of low salinity and may be found in estuaries.

Surface currents
There are two types of sea currents in the Black Sea: the surface currents that are driven by the counterclockwise pattern of the winds and the double currents in the Bosporus Strait and Kerch Strait, caused by the exchange of waters with adjacent seas.

→ Tidal exchange
→ Surface circulation

NATURAL RESOURCES

Fishing
Oil production
Gas production
Tourism

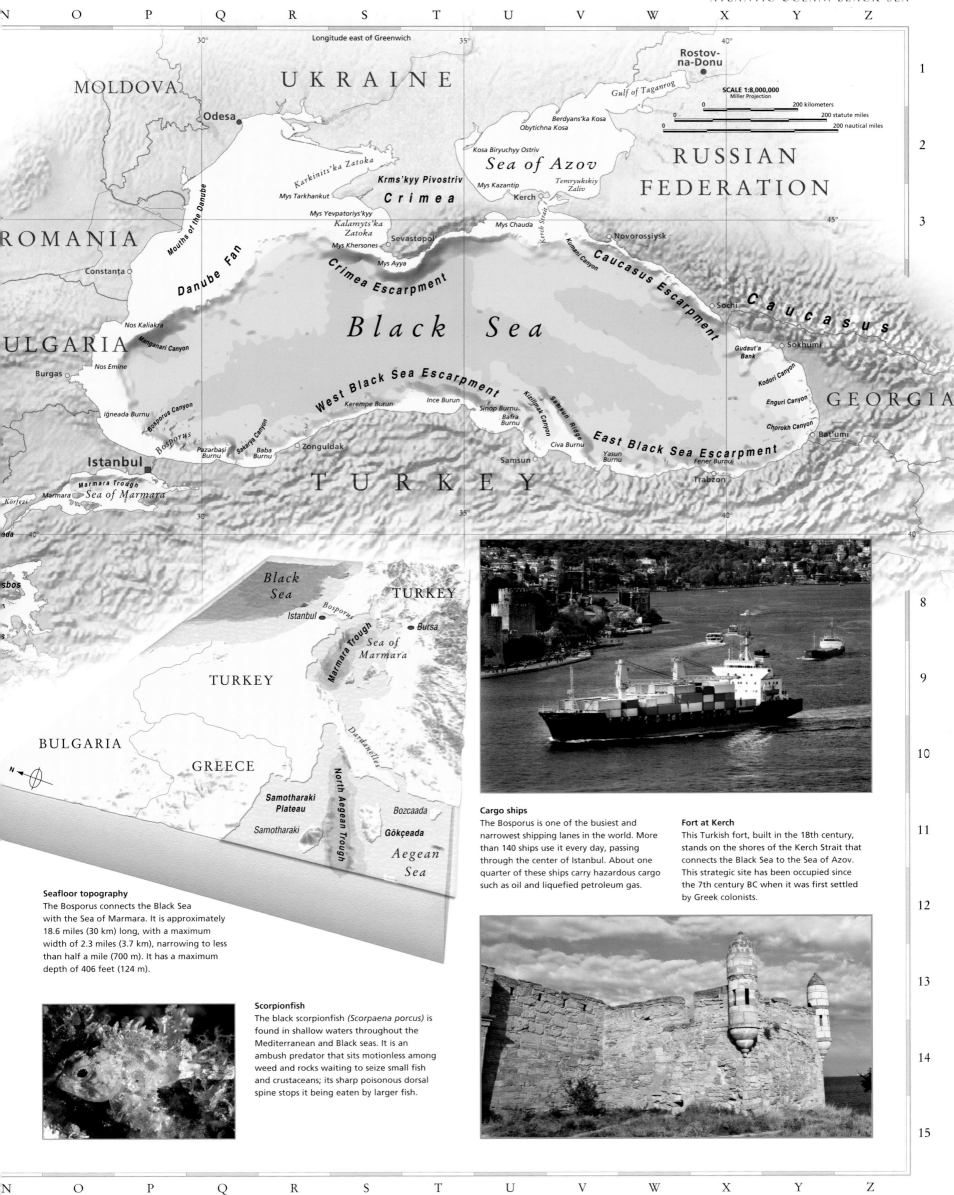

MOLDOVA

UKRAINE

Longitude east of Greenwich

Odesa

ROMANIA

Constanța

Mouths of the Danube

Danube Fan

BULGARIA

Nos Kaliakra

Burgas

Manganari Canyon

Nos Emine

Iğneada Burnu

Bosporus Canyon

Pazarbaşi Burnu

Sakarya Canyon

Baba Burnu

Istanbul

Marmara Trough

Körfezi

Marmara

Sea of Marmara

Karkinits'ka Zatoka

Mys Tarkhankut

Krms'kyy Pivostriv

Crimea

Mys Yevpatoriys'kyy

Kalamyts'ka Zatoka

Mys Khersones

Sevastopol

Mys Ayya

Zonguldak

Kerempe Burun

Ince Burun

Sinop Burnu

Bafra Burnu

West Black Sea Escarpment

Crimea Escarpment

Black Sea

Rostov-na-Donu

Gulf of Taganrog

SCALE 1:8,000,000
Miller Projection

200 kilometers
200 statute miles
200 nautical miles

Berdyans'ka Kosa

Obytichna Kosa

Kosa Biryuchyy Ostriv

Sea of Azov

Mys Kazantip

Temryukskiy Zaliv

Kerch

Mys Chauda

Kerch Strait

Novorossiysk

Kumani Canyon

Caucasus Escarpment

RUSSIAN FEDERATION

Sochi

Caucasus

Gudaut'a Bank

Sokhumi

Kodori Canyon

Enguri Canyon

GEORGIA

Chorokh Canyon

Bat'umi

Kızılırmak Canyon

Samsun Ridge

East Black Sea Escarpment

Civa Burnu

Samsun

Yasun Burnu

Fener Burnu

Trabzon

TURKEY

Seafloor topography

Black Sea

Bosporus

Istanbul

Marmara Trough

Sea of Marmara

TURKEY

Bursa

BULGARIA

GREECE

Dardanelles

N

Samotharaki Plateau

Samotharaki

North Aegean Trough

Bozcaada

Gökçeada

Aegean Sea

Lesbos

The Bosporus connects the Black Sea with the Sea of Marmara. It is approximately 18.6 miles (30 km) long, with a maximum width of 2.3 miles (3.7 km), narrowing to less than half a mile (700 m). It has a maximum depth of 406 feet (124 m).

Scorpionfish

The black scorpionfish (*Scorpaena porcus*) is found in shallow waters throughout the Mediterranean and Black seas. It is an ambush predator that sits motionless among weed and rocks waiting to seize small fish and crustaceans; its sharp poisonous dorsal spine stops it being eaten by larger fish.

Cargo ships

The Bosporus is one of the busiest and narrowest shipping lanes in the world. More than 140 ships use it every day, passing through the center of Istanbul. About one quarter of these ships carry hazardous cargo such as oil and liquefied petroleum gas.

Fort at Kerch

This Turkish fort, built in the 18th century, stands on the shores of the Kerch Strait that connects the Black Sea to the Sea of Azov. This strategic site has been occupied since the 7th century BC when it was first settled by Greek colonists.

131

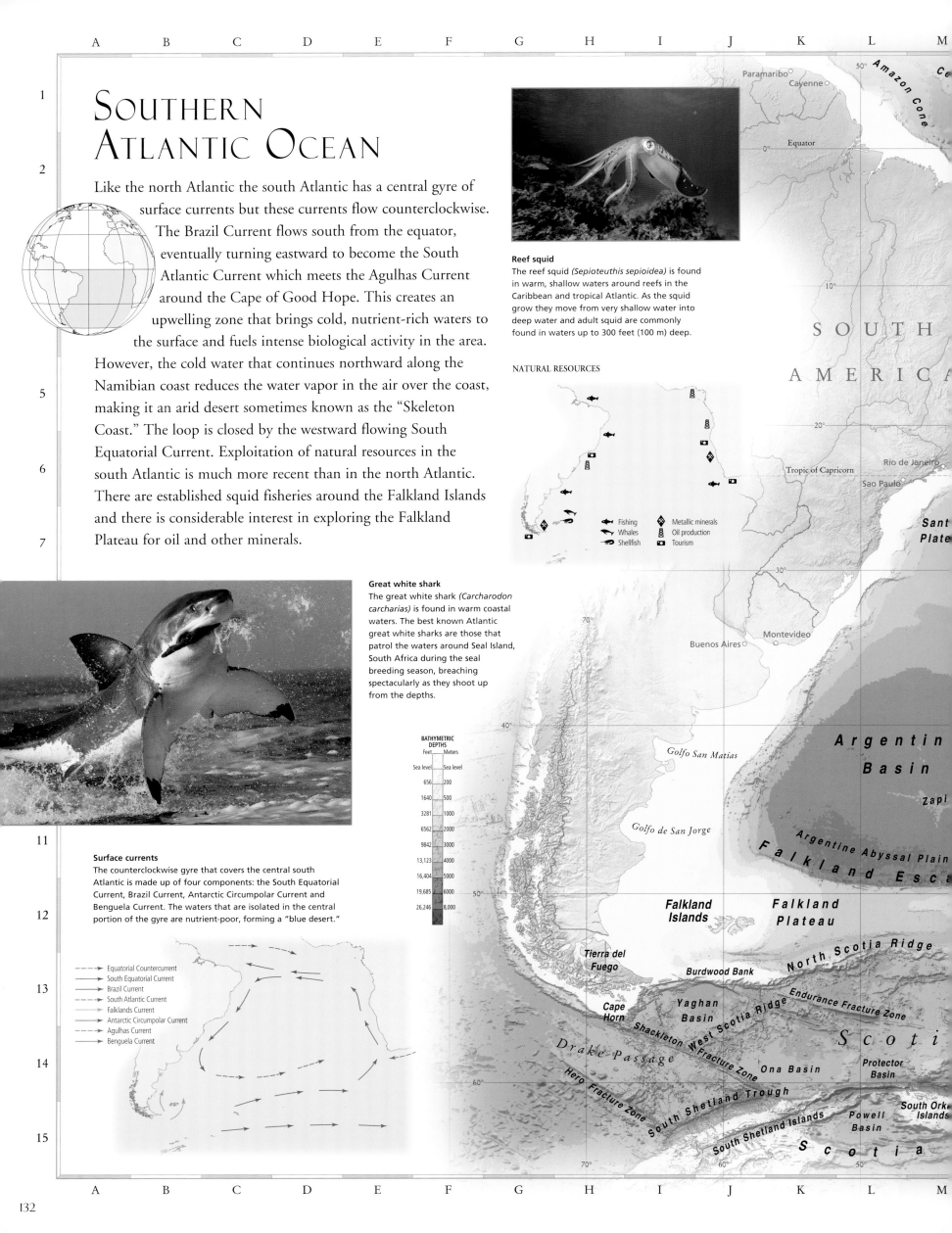

Top grid letters: A B C D E F G H I J K L M

SOUTHERN ATLANTIC OCEAN

Like the north Atlantic the south Atlantic has a central gyre of surface currents but these currents flow counterclockwise. The Brazil Current flows south from the equator, eventually turning eastward to become the South Atlantic Current which meets the Agulhas Current around the Cape of Good Hope. This creates an upwelling zone that brings cold, nutrient-rich waters to the surface and fuels intense biological activity in the area. However, the cold water that continues northward along the Namibian coast reduces the water vapor in the air over the coast, making it an arid desert sometimes known as the "Skeleton Coast." The loop is closed by the westward flowing South Equatorial Current. Exploitation of natural resources in the south Atlantic is much more recent than in the north Atlantic. There are established squid fisheries around the Falkland Islands and there is considerable interest in exploring the Falkland Plateau for oil and other minerals.

Reef squid
The reef squid (*Sepioteuthis sepioidea*) is found in warm, shallow waters around reefs in the Caribbean and tropical Atlantic. As the squid grow they move from very shallow water into deep water and adult squid are commonly found in waters up to 300 feet (100 m) deep.

NATURAL RESOURCES

Fishing
Whales
Shellfish
Metallic minerals
Oil production
Tourism

Great white shark
The great white shark (*Carcharodon carcharias*) is found in warm coastal waters. The best known Atlantic great white sharks are those that patrol the waters around Seal Island, South Africa during the seal breeding season, breaching spectacularly as they shoot up from the depths.

BATHYMETRIC DEPTHS

Feet	Meters
Sea level	Sea level
656	200
1640	500
3281	1000
6562	2000
9842	3000
13,123	4000
16,404	5000
19,685	6000
26,246	8,000

Surface currents
The counterclockwise gyre that covers the central south Atlantic is made up of four components: the South Equatorial Current, Brazil Current, Antarctic Circumpolar Current and Benguela Current. The waters that are isolated in the central portion of the gyre are nutrient-poor, forming a "blue desert."

- - - - Equatorial Countercurrent
——— South Equatorial Current
——— Brazil Current
- - - - South Atlantic Current
——— Falklands Current
——— Antarctic Circumpolar Current
- - - - Agulhas Current
——— Benguela Current

Map labels: Paramaribo, Cayenne, Amazon Cone, Equator, SOUTH AMERICA, Rio de Janeiro, Sao Paulo, Tropic of Capricorn, Sant... Plate..., Montevideo, Buenos Aires, Golfo San Matías, Argentin... Basin, Zapi..., Golfo de San Jorge, Argentine Abyssal Plain, Falkland Esca..., Falkland Islands, Falkland Plateau, Tierra del Fuego, North Scotia Ridge, Burdwood Bank, Endurance Fracture Zone, Cape Horn, Yaghan Basin, Shackleton Fracture Zone, West Scotia Ridge, Scoti..., Drake Passage, Ona Basin, Protector Basin, Hero Fracture Zone, South Shetland Trough, South Shetland Islands, Powell Basin, South Orkney Islands, Scotia

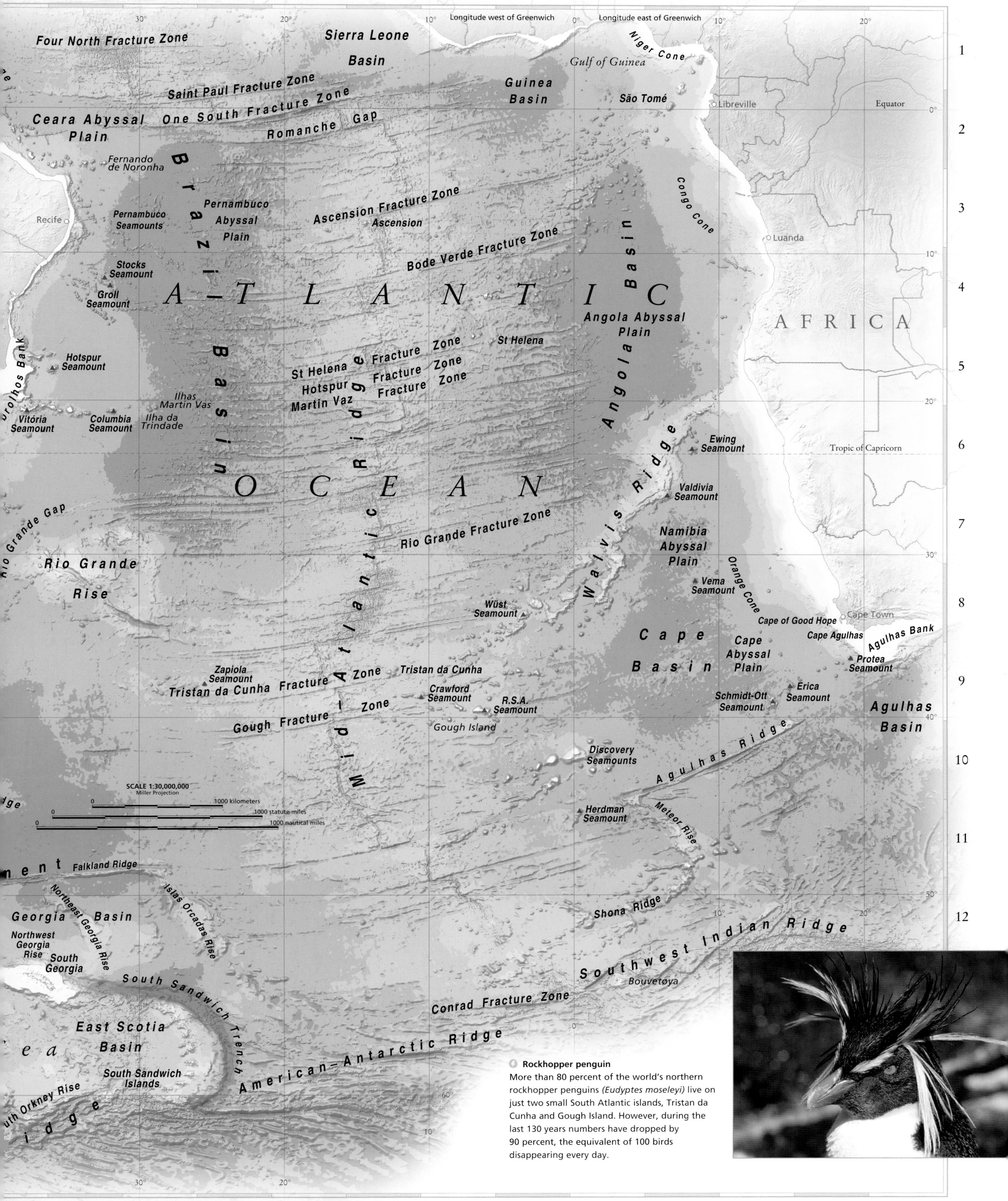

Longitude west of Greenwich
Longitude east of Greenwich

Four North Fracture Zone

Sierra Leone
Basin

Niger Cone

Gulf of Guinea

Saint Paul Fracture Zone

Guinea
Basin

São Tomé

Ceara Abyssal
Plain

One South Fracture Zone

Romanche Gap

Equator

Libreville

Fernando
de Noronha

B
r
a
z
i
l

Pernambuco
Abyssal
Plain

Ascension Fracture Zone

Ascension

Congo Cone

Recife

Pernambuco
Seamounts

A T L A N T I C

Bode Verde Fracture Zone

A
n
g
o
l
a

B
a
s
i
n

Luanda

Stocks
Seamount

Groll
Seamount

B
a
s
i
n

St Helena

Angola Abyssal
Plain

AFRICA

Hotspur
Seamount

St Helena Fracture Zone
Hotspur Fracture Zone
Martin Vaz Fracture Zone

olhos Bank

Ilhas
Martin Vas

Ilha da
Trindade

O C E A N

M
i
d

A
t
l
a
n
t
i
c

R
i
d
g
e

W
a
l
v
i
s

R
i
d
g
e

Ewing
Seamount

Tropic of Capricorn

Vitória
Seamount

Columbia
Seamount

Valdivia
Seamount

Namibia
Abyssal
Plain

Rio Grande Fracture Zone

Orange Cone

Vema
Seamount

Rio Grande Gap

Rio Grande
Rise

Wüst
Seamount

Cape
Basin

Cape
Abyssal
Plain

Cape of Good Hope

Cape Agulhas

Cape Town

Agulhas Bank

Protea
Seamount

Zapiola
Seamount

Tristan da Cunha Fracture Zone

Tristan da Cunha

Schmidt-Ott
Seamount

Erica
Seamount

Agulhas
Basin

Crawford
Seamount

Gough Fracture Zone

R.S.A.
Seamount

Gough Island

Discovery
Seamounts

Agulhas Ridge

SCALE 1:30,000,000
Miller Projection

1000 kilometers
1000 statute miles
1000 nautical miles

Herdman
Seamount

Meteor Rise

Falkland Ridge

Shona Ridge

S
o
u
t
h
w
e
s
t

I
n
d
i
a
n

R
i
d
g
e

ent

Georgia Basin

Northeast Georgia Rise

Islas Orcadas Rise

Bouvetøya

Northwest
Georgia
Rise

South
Georgia

South Sandwich Trench

Conrad Fracture Zone

🐧 **Rockhopper penguin**
More than 80 percent of the world's northern
rockhopper penguins (Eudyptes moseleyi) live on
just two small South Atlantic islands, Tristan da
Cunha and Gough Island. However, during the
last 130 years numbers have dropped by
90 percent, the equivalent of 100 birds
disappearing every day.

East Scotia
Basin

American–Antarctic Ridge

South Sandwich
Islands

h Orkney Rise

idge

GULF OF GUINEA

The coastline of the Gulf of Guinea forms part of the western edge of the African tectonic plate and corresponds remarkably to the continental margin of South America running from Brazil to the Guianas. The coincidence between the geology and the geomorphology of these two coastlines constitutes one of the clearest confirmations of the theory of continental drift. The continental shelf within the gulf is narrower than that of most of the Atlantic margins but contains large and valuable oil and mineral resources, the best known are the oil and gas fields of the Niger Delta. The Benguela Current tends to trap warm water against the coast which is diluted by the inflow of large rivers such as the Niger and Congo. Where the cold Benguela Current water meets the warm waters of the Guinea Current there is upwelling and intense biological activity that sustains a wide variety of marine life. There are also areas of high biological activity, and fisheries, associated with fronts—the boundaries of the major water masses within the gulf.

Coast of Togo
The lagoon at Aneho, on the Togolese coast, is part of a 31-mile (50 km) system of dunes and lagoons. These have been built up from sediments carried westward by strong clockwise coastal currents and longshore drift along this part of the Gulf of Guinea.

ISLANDS OF THE GULF

The flora and fauna of the islands in the Gulf of Guinea have been studied for many decades by biologists seeking to understand the process and patterns of island colonization and biogeography. The gulf islands have each developed a unique community of plants and animals; many species are endemic to one island only.

The islet of Bom Bom to the north of the island of Príncipe has become a major tourist resort and the principal source of income for the local and regional economies.

Leatherback turtle
The leatherback turtle (Dermochelys coriacea) is one of four endangered sea turtle species in the Gulf of Guinea. The main nesting grounds are on Bioko, where it is threatened by the meat and egg trade. However, it nests in small numbers on the other islands.

NATURAL RESOURCES

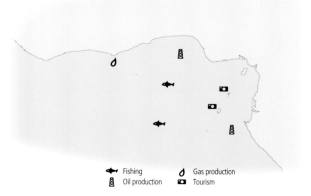

Fishing   Gas production
Oil production   Tourism

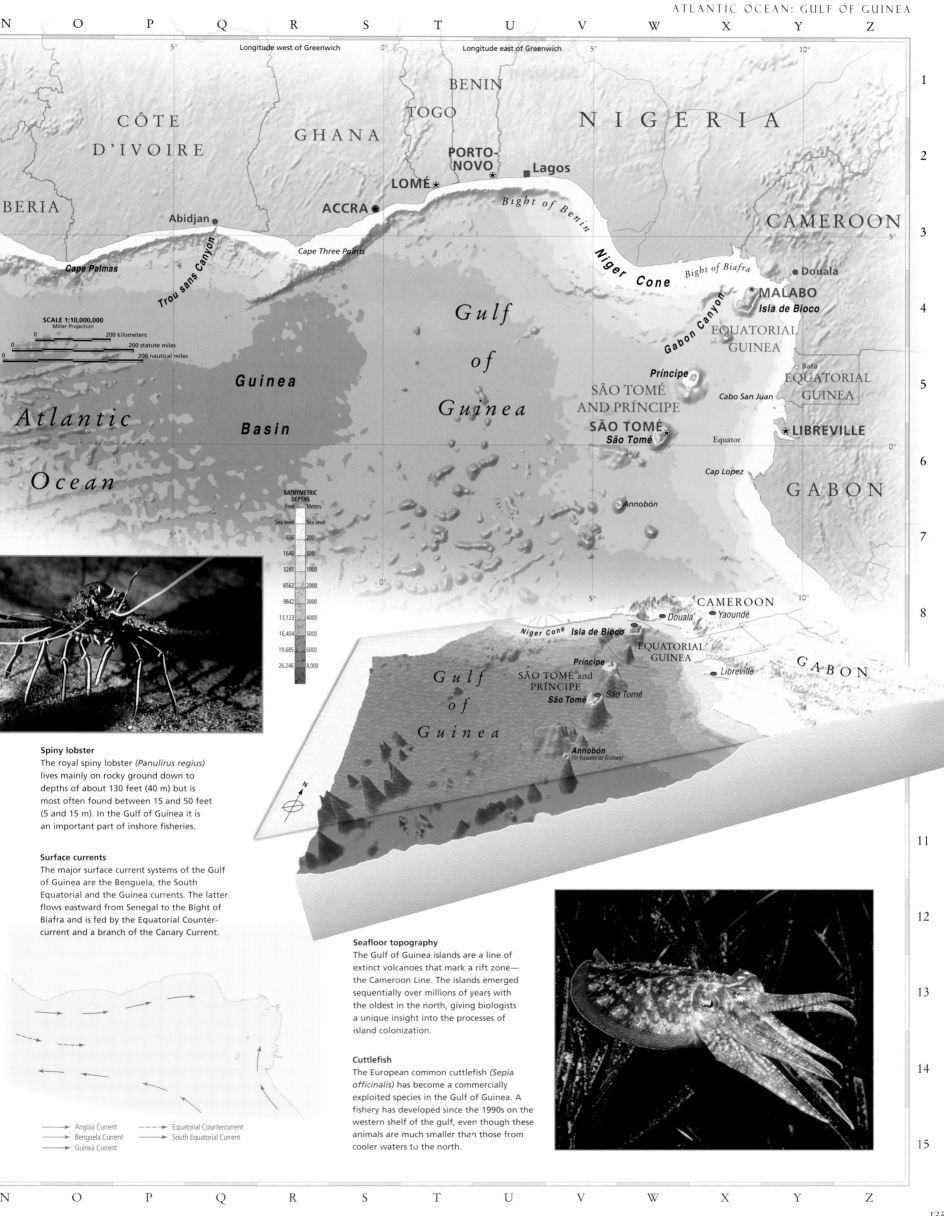

N O P Q R S T U V W X Y Z

Longitude west of Greenwich — 5° — 0° — Longitude east of Greenwich — 5° — 10°

1 2 3 4 5 6 7 8 11 12 13 14 15

Map labels:

CÔTE D'IVOIRE

BENIN

TOGO

GHANA

NIGERIA

LIBERIA

CAMEROON

PORTO-NOVO

LOMÉ

Lagos

ACCRA

Abidjan

Bight of Benin

Cape Three Points

Cape Palmas

Trou sans Canyon

Niger Cone

Bight of Biafra

Douala

MALABO

Isla de Bioco

Gabon Canyon

EQUATORIAL GUINEA

Gulf of Guinea

Príncipe

Bata

EQUATORIAL GUINEA

Guinea Basin

SÃO TOMÉ AND PRÍNCIPE

Cabo San Juan

LIBREVILLE

SÃO TOMÉ

São Tomé

Equator

Atlantic Ocean

Cap Lopez

GABON

Annobón

SCALE 1:10,000,000
Miller Projection

0 — 200 kilometers
0 — 200 statute miles
0 — 200 nautical miles

BATHYMETRIC DEPTHS

Feet	Meters
Sea level	Sea level
656	200
1640	500
3281	1000
6562	2000
9842	3000
13,123	4000
16,404	5000
19,685	6000
26,246	8,000

3D topography labels:

Niger Cone

Isla de Bioco

Douala

Yaoundé

CAMEROON

EQUATORIAL GUINEA

Príncipe

Libreville

GABON

Gulf of Guinea

SÃO TOMÉ and PRÍNCIPE

São Tomé

São Tomé

Annobón
(to Equatorial Guinea)

N

Spiny lobster
The royal spiny lobster (*Panulirus regius*) lives mainly on rocky ground down to depths of about 130 feet (40 m) but is most often found between 15 and 50 feet (5 and 15 m). In the Gulf of Guinea it is an important part of inshore fisheries.

Surface currents
The major surface current systems of the Gulf of Guinea are the Benguela, the South Equatorial and the Guinea currents. The latter flows eastward from Senegal to the Bight of Biafra and is fed by the Equatorial Counter-current and a branch of the Canary Current.

→ Angola Current
→ Benguela Current
→ Guinea Current
--→ Equatorial Countercurrent
→ South Equatorial Current

Seafloor topography
The Gulf of Guinea islands are a line of extinct volcanoes that mark a rift zone—the Cameroon Line. The islands emerged sequentially over millions of years with the oldest in the north, giving biologists a unique insight into the processes of island colonization.

Cuttlefish
The European common cuttlefish (*Sepia officinalis*) has become a commercially exploited species in the Gulf of Guinea. A fishery has developed since the 1990s on the western shelf of the gulf, even though these animals are much smaller than those from cooler waters to the north.

WEST AFRICAN COAST

The surface waters of the southwest African coast are some of the most productive in the world, the abundant plankton sustains both fin fish and crustacean shellfish fisheries. This intense biological activity depends on cold, nutrient-rich water brought northward by the Benguela Current and brought to the surface by the upwelling produced by the prevailing south and south-easterly winds blowing over the sea surface. The cooling of the winds causes coastal fogs and the air that blows inland carries very little moisture, so that the adjacent land is some of the most arid in the world. Fishing is mainly centered around the seamounts in the region, which are also believed to have diamond deposits. However, suction dredging of these deposits causes major damage to the seabed wiping out local seabed communities and producing plumes of fine waste material that adversely affect a much wider area by smothering them. A decline in some commercial species such the rock lobster has been attributed to offshore mining activity.

Skeleton Coast
This part of the Namibian coast originally got its name from the bleached bones that once covered the shore, left by whaling and seal hunting. There are also more than a thousand rusting hulks from the numerous shipwrecks caused by the dense fogs and offshore rocks.

Black oystercatcher
The African black oystercatcher (*Haematopus moquini*) lives and breeds on the rocky coasts and islands of southern Africa. It uses its strong beak to open bivalves or to probe for worms. The species is now endangered and there are less than 5,000 adults left.

Ocean fog
On the west African coast the upwelling of the cold Benguela Current cools the air above it to the point where the water vapor in it starts to condense. This gives rise to dense ocean fogs, known locally as "cassimbo," that occur for most of the year.

Langstrand
In recent years tourists looking for isolation and privacy have sought places such as Langstrand on the Namibian coast. The town mainly consists of holiday homes and beach villas built close to water to catch sea breezes and escape the intense heat of the Namibian hinterland.

NATURAL RESOURCES

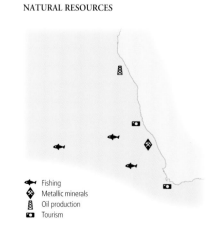

- Fishing
- Metallic minerals
- Oil production
- Tourism

N O P Q R S T U V W X Y Z

5° Longitude east of Greenwich 10° 15°

Ponta do Enfião

ANGOLA

Baia dos Tigres

Angola

Basin

Angola

Abyssal

Plain

Cape Fria

Rocky Point

20°

Palgrave Point

NAMIBIA

Atlantic

W a l v i s   R i d g e

Ocean

N a m i b   D e s e r t

Ewing Seamount

Namibia

Abyssal

Plain

Walvis Bay • Langstrand

○ Walvis Bay

Sandwich Bay

Tropic of Capricorn

25°

Dolphin Head

W a l v i s   R i d g e

Lüderitz Bay

Díaz Point ○ Lüderitz

Cape Dernberg

20°

Cape

Basin

5°

Wreck Point

Alexander
Bay ○

Orange Canyon

REPUBLIC

Vema Seamount

Cone

OF

SOUTH AFRICA

30°

Lamberts Bay ○

10°

Saint Helena Bay

Cape

Cape Columbine ○

Abyssal

Plain

CAPE TOWN

Mossel Bay ○

15°

Cape of Good Hope

False Bay

Port Beaufort ○

Cape Agulhas

35°

20°

Surface currents

The principal surface current along the west African coast is the Benguela Current that forms part of the South Atlantic Gyre. Earth's west to east rotation brings up deep, cold water into the current and offshore winds increase the upwelling effect along the west African coast.

→ Benguela Current

Cape gannet colony

Bird Island at Lamberts Bay on the west coast of South Africa is famed for its colony of Cape gannets (*Morus capensis*). Apart from some small cormorant colonies on rock stacks, there are no large seabird breeding colonies north of Lamberts Bay until the Namibian islands.

BATHYMETRIC DEPTHS

Feet	Meters
Sea level	Sea level
656	200
1640	500
3281	1000
6562	2000
9842	3000
13,123	4000
16,404	5000
19,685	6000
26,246	8,000

SCALE 1:10,000,000
Miller Projection

0 200 kilometers

0 200 statute miles

0 200 nautical miles

N O P Q R S T U V W X Y Z

CAPE HORN

It is a testament to the ferocity of the weather conditions in the area that for nearly a hundred years, until 1624, European sailors did not realize that Cape Horn was an island and not part of the mainland of Tierra del Fuego. Until the opening of the Panama Canal in 1914 the only route for ships traveling between the Pacific and Atlantic oceans was around Cape Horn, which meant sailors had to face the mountainous seas and year-round storms found there. At latitudes below 40°S, prevailing winds blow from west to east around the world, almost uninterrupted by land, giving rise to the "roaring forties" and the "furious fifties." The turbulence and speed of these winds intensify around Cape Horn as the funneling effect of the Andes and the Antarctic peninsula channel the winds into the relatively narrow Drake Passage. Wave heights here can reach enormous sizes. An area of shallow water around Cape Horn further increases wave heights and "rogue waves" can reach 100 feet (30 m).

Rounding Cape Horn
The Drake Passage is a body of water 600 miles (1,000 km) wide between Cape Horn and Antarctica that links the Pacific and Atlantic oceans. Its rough weather, ice, and mountainous seas make the passage a severe test of endurance for ships and their crews.

Whale migration
The southern right whale (Eubalaena australis) migrates northward to breed during the austral winter and is seen as far north as Brazil and Namibia. The population is estimated to be 12,000 animals and, since the hunting ban, stocks are estimated to have grown by seven percent a year.

Tierra del Fuego
Tierra del Fuego is an archipelago whose southern tip is Cape Horn. The islands have a cold, inhospitable subpolar climate. The archipelago gets its name from the smoke and fires lit by the indigenous people for warmth that were seen by the explorer Magellan in 1520.

Magellanic penguins
Magellanic penguins (Spheniscus magellanicus) have their main breeding grounds around Cape Horn, Tierra del Fuego and the Falkland Islands. During the austral winter the penguins from the Atlantic coast of South America and the Falkland Islands all migrate northward to the coast of Brazil.

Surface currents
The Antarctic Circumpolar Current is a wind-driven current that is able to circle the globe unimpeded by landmasses. However, the Drake Passage is a choke point so that some water is diverted northward into the Peru Current, the rest eventually linking with the South Atlantic gyre.

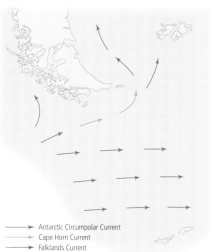

→ Antarctic Circumpolar Current
→ Cape Horn Current
→ Falklands Current

NATURAL RESOURCES

⬩ Whales
◆ Metallic minerals
⬧ Oil production
⬛ Tourism

N O P Q R S T U V W X Y Z

1

Bahía Grande

ARGENTINA

Cabo Buen Tiempo

FALKLAND
ISLANDS
(to U.K.)

King George Bay
Queen Charlotte Bay

West
Falkland

East
Falkland

Pebble
Island

Cape Dolphin

Macbride Head

STANLEY

CHILE

Longitude west of Greenwich

70°

65°

60°

A t l a n t i c

Weddell Island

Port Stephens

Cape Meredith

Choiseul Sound

Beauchene Island

Península
Muñoz
Gamero

Cabo Vírgenes

2

Isla Riesco

Seno Skyring

Seno Otway

Punta de Arenas

Bahía de San Sebastián

O c e a n

Punta
Arenas

Península de
Brunswick

3

Isla
Santa Inés

Isla Grande
de
Tierra del Fuego

Burdwood Bank

Isla
Clarence

Isla
Dawson

Bahía Inútil

Isla
Aracena

Isla Noir

Peninsula Brecknock

Cabo
San Diego

Isla de
los Estados

4

Canal Ballenero

Ushuaia

Península Mitre

55°

Isla Stewart

Isla
Gordon

Isla Londonderry

Isla Navarino

Isla Picton

Isla Hoste

Bahía
Nassau

Isla Nueva

Isla Lennox

Yaghan

5

Bahía de Cook

False Cape Horn

Islas Wollaston

Basin

Cape Horn

Islas
Diego Ramírez

6

S c o t i a

West Scotia Ridge

7

D r a k e   P a s s a g e

70°

Shackleton Fracture Zone

Ona

8

S e a

Basin

Striated caracara

The striated caracara (*Phalcoboenus
australis*) is a bird of prey, though on the
Falkland Islands it is known as "Johnny
Rook." It breeds on several islands in
Tierra del Fuego, but is more abundant in
the Falklands where the population is
estimated at 500 breeding pairs.

Sars
Seamount

Hero Fracture Zone

60°

60°

9

10

South Shetland Trough

South Shetland
Islands

11

King George Island

Nelson Island

Robert Island

Greenwich Island

South Orkney
Islands

Livingston Island

Rugged Island

Snow Island

60°

Powell
Basin

Ona
Basin

Elephant Island

N

12

Shackleton Fracture Zone

South
Shetland
Islands

South Shetland Trough

Weddell Sea

65°

BATHYMETRIC
DEPTHS

Feet   Meters

13

Scotia

Sea

Larsen Ice
Shelf

SCALE 1:8,000,000
Miller Projection

0   200 kilometers

Sea level   Sea level

656   200

1640   500

Antarctic Peninsula

0   200 statute miles

0   200 nautical miles

3281   1000

6562   2000

9842   3000

14

Seafloor topography

The South Shetland Islands are a 336-mile
(540-km) chain of four island groups,
consisting of eleven major islands at the
southern boundary of the Scotia Sea. To
the islands' north the sea floor drops down
into the deep South Shetland Trough.

13,123   4000

16,404   5000

19,685   6000

26,246   8,000

15

N O P Q R S T U V W X Y Z

The Andaman Islands, set in the tropical waters of the Indian Ocean's Andaman Sea, are fringed by coral reefs. The submarine scenery is spectacular and divers who make the trip to this site are richly rewarded. One of the group, Havelock Island, is home to some domesticated Indian elephants *(Elephas maximus)* that also relish a swim in the warm sea.

INDIAN OCEAN

INDIAN OCEAN

The Indian Ocean is the smallest of the world's four major oceans and has some unique characteristics. Unlike the Atlantic and Pacific oceans it is completely closed to the north, by the Asian landmass, and it hosts a major current, the Somali Current, that reverses its direction on a seasonal basis. All other subtropical basins such as the South Atlantic and the North Pacific have a strong western boundary current flowing poleward and a weak, wide drift as an eastern boundary current. By contrast the South Indian Ocean has a strong poleward current as well, the Leeuwin, along the west coast of Australia. The Indian Ocean has a mid-ocean ridge, as do the Pacific and the Atlantic, but the Indian Ocean's ridge is complicated by the landmass of Madagascar and a number of other ridges running mostly in a north–south direction.

THE FACTS	
Area	26.5 million square miles (68.6 million km²)
Average depth	12,644 feet (3,854 m)
Maximum depth	23,376 feet (7,125 m)
Maximum width	6,300 miles (10,200 km)
Maximum length	5,800 miles (9,400 km)

Ocean Share

Indian Ocean
26.5 million sq miles
(68.6 million km²)
21%

All other oceans

Seychelles Islands
Tropical islands, such as the Seychelles, are a key part of the Indian Ocean environment. Their coral reefs and abundant ecosystems play a major role in maintaining biodiversity. Ecotourism on such islands may well help to preserve many marine species.

Endangered species
Hawksbill turtles (*Eretmochelys imbricata*) and pristine coral reefs are both endangered entities in the Indian Ocean. The former are being caught for the high quality of their tortoiseshell and meat; the latter are at risk because of overexploitation, pollution, and ocean acidification.

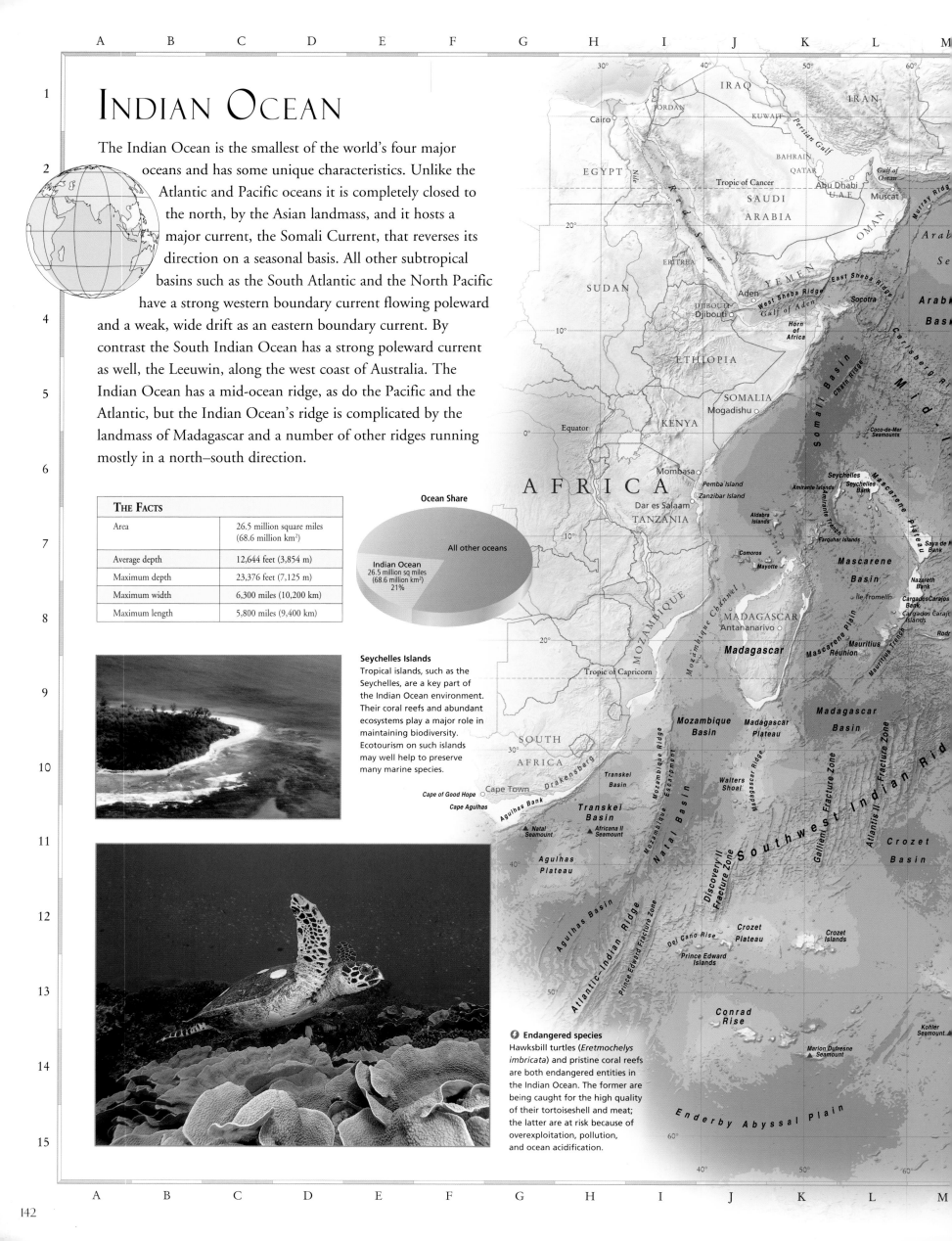

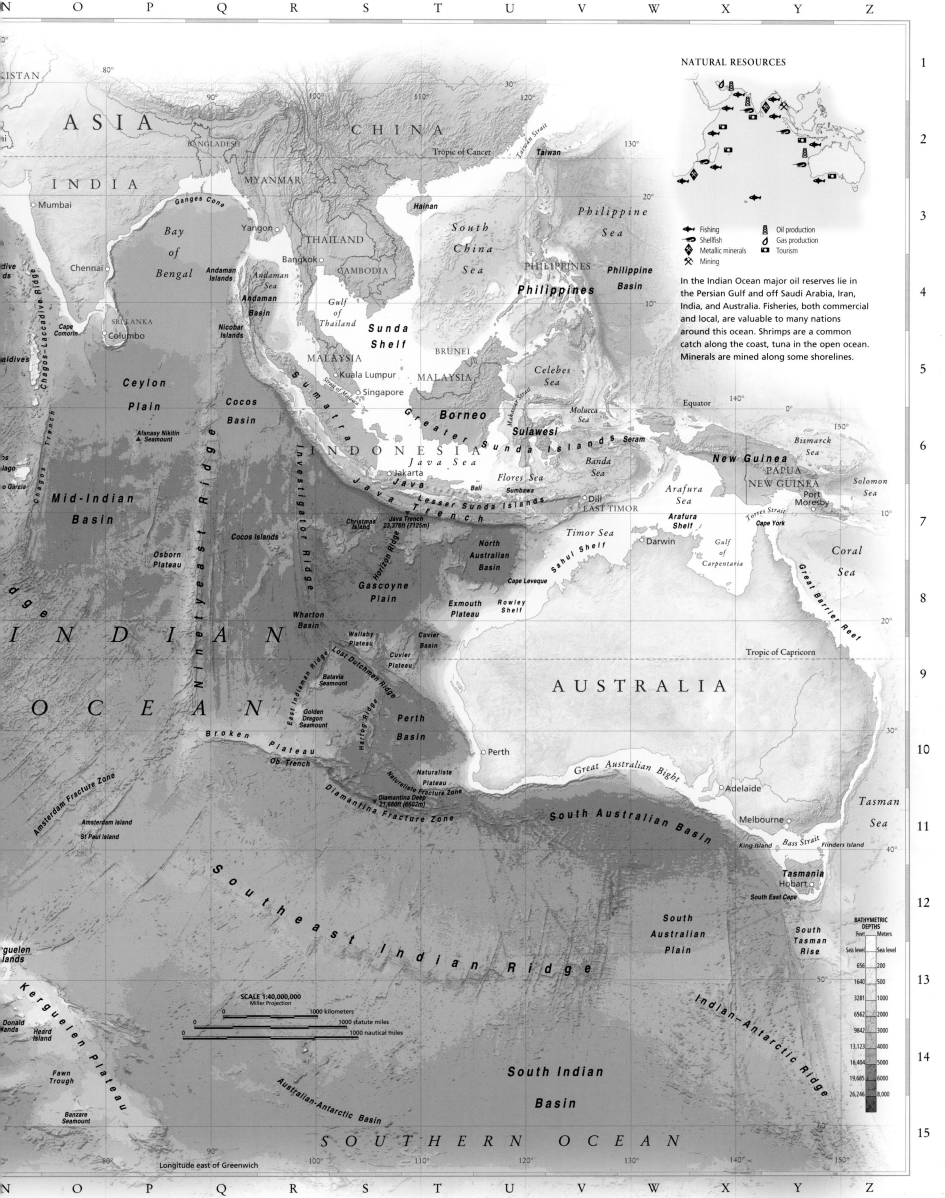

NATURAL RESOURCES

Fishing
Shellfish
Metallic minerals
Mining
Oil production
Gas production
Tourism

In the Indian Ocean major oil reserves lie in the Persian Gulf and off Saudi Arabia, Iran, India, and Australia. Fisheries, both commercial and local, are valuable to many nations around this ocean. Shrimps are a common catch along the coast, tuna in the open ocean. Minerals are mined along some shorelines.

ASIA

CHINA

BANGLADESH

Taiwan

Tropic of Cancer

INDIA

MYANMAR

Hainan

Philippine Sea

Mumbai

Ganges Cone

Yangon

Bay of Bengal

Chennai

THAILAND

Bangkok

CAMBODIA

South China Sea

PHILIPPINES

Philippine Basin

Philippines

Columbo

SRI LANKA

Andaman Islands

Andaman Sea

Andaman Basin

Gulf of Thailand

MALAYSIA

Kuala Lumpur

Strait of Malacca

Singapore

Philippine

Celebes Sea

BRUNEI

MALAYSIA

Chagos-Laccadive Ridge

Maldives

Cape Comorin

Diego Garcia

Chagos Trench

Ceylon Plain

Nicobar Islands

Cocos Basin

Sumatra

Sunda Shelf

Borneo

Greater Sunda Islands

Sulawesi

Molucca Sea

Seram

Banda Sea

Bismarck Sea

New Guinea

PAPUA NEW GUINEA

Solomon Sea

Afanasy Nikitin Seamount

Mid-Indian Basin

Ninetyeast Ridge

Investigator Ridge

INDONESIA

Java Sea

Java

Jakarta

Bali

Flores Sea

Sumbawa

Lesser Sunda Islands

Dili

EAST TIMOR

Arafura Sea

Port Moresby

Torres Strait

Cape York

Coral Sea

Osborn Plateau

Cocos Islands

Christmas Island

Java Trench 23,376ft (7125m)

Horizon Ridge

Gascoyne Plain

North Australian Basin

Timor Sea

Darwin

Arafura Shelf

Gulf of Carpentaria

Great Barrier Reef

Wharton Basin

Wallaby Plateau

Cuvier Plateau

Cuvier Basin

Exmouth Plateau

Rowley Shelf

Cape Leveque

Sahul Shelf

INDIAN OCEAN

East Indiaman Ridge

Lost Dutchmen Ridge

Batavia Seamount

Golden Dragon Seamount

Hartog Ridge

Perth Basin

AUSTRALIA

Tropic of Capricorn

Broken Plateau

Ob Trench

Naturaliste Plateau

Naturaliste Fracture Zone

Perth

Amsterdam Fracture Zone

Amsterdam Island

St Paul Island

Diamantina Deep 21,660ft (6602m)

Diamantina Fracture Zone

Great Australian Bight

Adelaide

South Australian Basin

Melbourne

Tasman Sea

King Island

Bass Strait

Flinders Island

Southeast Indian Ridge

Tasmania

Hobart

South East Cape

Kerguelen Islands

South Australian Plain

South Tasman Rise

Indian-Antarctic Ridge

Donald Islands

Heard Island

Kerguelen Plateau

SCALE 1:40,000,000
Miller Projection

1000 kilometers
1000 statute miles
1000 nautical miles

Australian-Antarctic Basin

South Indian Basin

Fawn Trough

Banzare Seamount

Longitude east of Greenwich

SOUTHERN OCEAN

BATHYMETRIC DEPTHS

Feet	Meters
Sea level	Sea level
656	200
1640	500
3281	1000
6562	2000
9842	3000
13,123	4000
16,404	5000
19,685	6000
26,246	8,000

NORTHERN INDIAN OCEAN

The northern Indian Ocean, north of the equator, represents less than one-third of the total Indian Ocean. The waters here are generally warm, supporting coral reefs and extensive areas of mangroves. Sea turtles nest on the Indian coastline and many shark species thrive here. At the center of this expanse of ocean are the Indian subcontinent and its extension, the Chagos-Laccadive Ridge. Together these geographical features split this ocean into two roughly equal parts—the Arabian Sea and the Bay of Bengal. Adjacent seas, the Red Sea and the Persian Gulf, contribute their highly saline waters to those of the northern Indian Ocean. Currents here have a decided seasonality that is largely, but not entirely, driven by the monsoonal winds. During the northeast monsoon a westward North Equatorial Current is found at the equator and the circulation in both the Arabian Sea and the Bay of Bengal is clockwise. During the southwest monsoon the flow along the equator is eastward as the Southwest Monsoon Current; the flow in the Bay of Bengal is partially counterclockwise.

Seaside monument
The town of Kanniyakumari is situated at the southernmost tip of the Indian peninsula, where the Arabian Sea and the Bay of Bengal meet. Here, on a rocky islet, a monument has been erected to Swami Vivekananda, a Bengali religious leader, philosopher, and social reformer.

NATURAL RESOURCES

- 🐟 Fishing
- 〜 Shellfish
- ◆ Metallic minerals
- ⚒ Mining
- 🛢 Oil production
- ⛱ Tourism

Oman coastline
An abandoned fishing boat lies on the beach near Musandam, Oman. Subsistence and artisanal fisheries still play a major role in the economies of coastal communities around the northern Indian Ocean. They supply a significant part of the protein requirements of many people living near the coastline.

Surface currents
Northern Indian Ocean currents are influenced by monsoonal winds. The southwest monsoon blows from June to October, the northeast monsoon from December to April. The latter causes the reversal of the Somali Current and the formation of the Equatorial Countercurrent.

- --→ Equatorial Countercurrent
- —→ North Equatorial Current
- —→ Northeast monsoon

Lionfish
Lionfish (*Pterois miles*) are a venomous marine species; they have long poisonous dorsal spines. An Indo-Pacific fish, seen here in the Andaman Sea among soft gorgonian corals, they have been displaced to the Atlantic where they are now an invasive species.

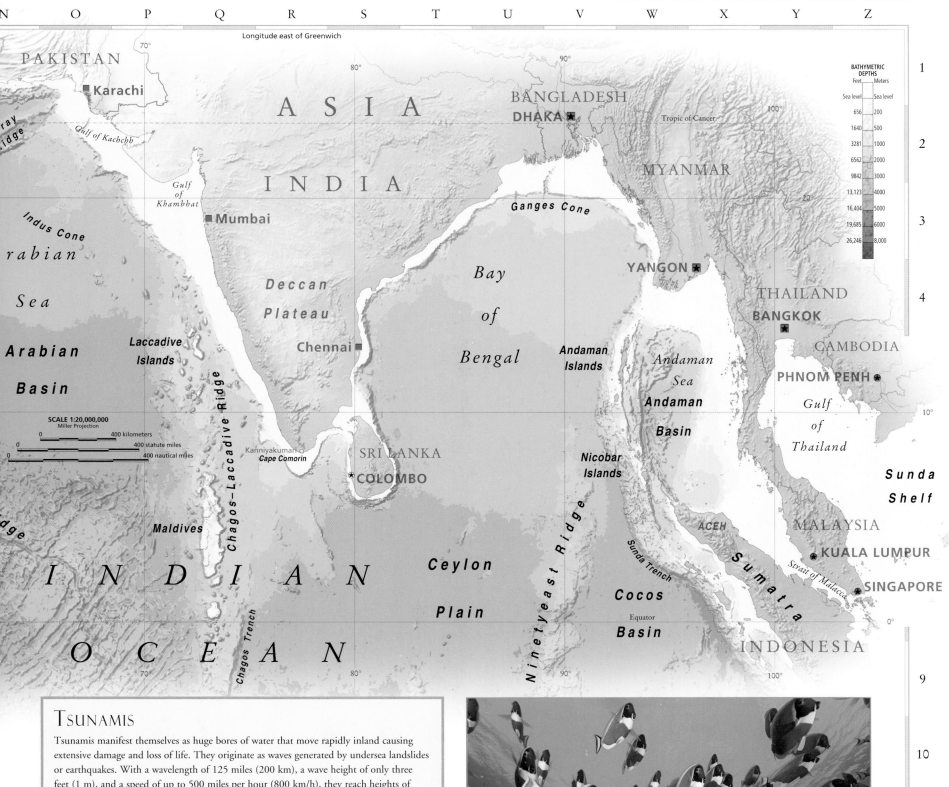

Longitude east of Greenwich

PAKISTAN

● **Karachi**

Gulf of Kachchh

Murray Ridge

Indus Cone

A S I A

I N D I A

Gulf of Khambhat

● **Mumbai**

Deccan

Plateau

Chennai ■

rabian

Sea

Arabian

Basin

Laccadive
Islands

Chagos–Laccadive Ridge

Kanniyakumari ○
Cape Comorin

SRI LANKA

* **COLOMBO**

Maldives

Ceylon

Plain

I N D I A N

O C E A N

Chagos Trench

BANGLADESH

DHAKA ✴

Ganges Cone

Bay

of

Bengal

Andaman
Islands

Andaman

Sea

Andaman

Basin

Nicobar
Islands

Ninetyeast Ridge

Sunda Trench

Cocos

Equator

Basin

MYANMAR

Tropic of Cancer

YANGON ✴

THAILAND

BANGKOK ✴

CAMBODIA

PHNOM PENH ✴

Gulf

of

Thailand

Sunda

Shelf

ACEH

MALAYSIA

✴ **KUALA LUMPUR**

Strait of Malacca

✴ **SINGAPORE**

Sumatra

INDONESIA

BATHYMETRIC
DEPTHS

Feet	Meters
Sea level	Sea level
656	200
1640	500
3281	1000
6562	2000
9842	3000
13,123	4000
16,404	5000
19,685	6000
26,246	8,000

SCALE 1:20,000,000
Miller Projection

0 ——— 400 kilometers
0 ——— 400 statute miles
0 ——— 400 nautical miles

Tsunamis

Tsunamis manifest themselves as huge bores of water that move rapidly inland causing extensive damage and loss of life. They originate as waves generated by undersea landslides or earthquakes. With a wavelength of 125 miles (200 km), a wave height of only three feet (1 m), and a speed of up to 500 miles per hour (800 km/h), they reach heights of up to 100 feet (30 m) as they shoal near the coast.

Devastation wrought by the 2004 tsunami on Aceh, the northern part of Indonesia. This was one of the most destructive tsumanis in modern history and cost the lives of thousands of people.

Surgeonfish
There are many species of surgeonfish, here the powder blue (*Acanthurus leucosternon*). Surgeonfish are invariably brightly colored, grow to 6–16 inches (15–40 cm), and are found among coral reefs in the tropics where they graze on algae. They have sharp spines at either side of the tail.

BAY OF BENGAL

This ocean region is not a bay in the usual coastal sense of the word, but constitutes the sea between India and Southeast Asia. The major currents here undergo seasonal reversal. From January to July the flow along the coast of India, the East Indian Current, is north-eastward; from September to December it is south-eastward, both contrary to the dominant wind directions. The main winds are the monsoon winds; the southwest or summer monsoon from about June to September and the northeast or winter monsoon from March to April. In winter the East Indian Current flows strongly with speeds exceeding 3.3 feet (1 m) per second and its fresher water is then fed into the adjacent Arabian Sea. A substantial part of the Bay of Bengal is less than 9,840 feet (3,000 m) deep, including all of the Andaman Sea along its eastern side. Much of the seafloor is flat, the result of sediment from the main rivers of the Indian subcontinent accumulating here over millenia.

Chlorophyll
In this satellite image of the Bay of Bengal the green coloration gives a good indication of the density of chlorophyll in the water, which in turn can be related to the presence of phytoplankton, marine algae. Regions colored red show where phytoplankton is abundant.

Subsistence fisheries
Fishermen in Orissa, India, remove a meager catch from their nets while others wait to take the fish to market. Subsistence or artisanal fisheries are found along the whole coastline of the Bay of Bengal, but in many places overfishing has caused fish stocks to collapse.

THE FACTS	
Area	838,613 square miles (2,172,000 km²)
Average depth	8,500 feet (2,600 m)
Maximum depth	15,400 feet (4,694 m)
Maximum width	1,000 miles (1,610 km)
Maximum length	1,300 miles (2,090 km)

NATURAL RESOURCES

Fishing
Metallic minerals

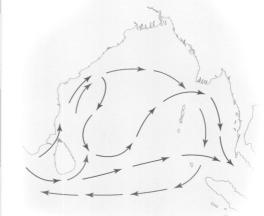

Surface currents
The surface currents here are affected by monsoonal winds. The currents off the northeastern coast of the Indian subcontinent reverse direction seasonally. However, the duration and intensity of monsoonal winds are not identical every year, so the currents also vary from year to year.

Summer
Winter

Colubrine sea krait
Banded sea snakes, such as this colubrine sea krait (Laticauda colubrina), are reptiles found in the ocean waters of the Indo-Pacific tropics. Females of this species may grow to 4.5 feet (1.4 m), nearly double the length of males. Sea kraits are venomous, but are not aggressive toward divers.

N O P Q R S T U V W X Y Z

THE GANGES DELTA

The Ganges has the world's largest river delta, stretching 220 miles (350 km) from east to west and extending across the border of two countries, India and Bangladesh. A very productive region, it is home to about 140 million people. It is formed by the confluence of a number of rivers and is slowly extending farther seaward as sediments brought down by the rivers accumulate in the sea.

As seen from space, the Ganges river delta forms an intricate web of ever-changing rivers and rivulets. Yellow sediment from the delta fans out into the sea.

BATHYMETRIC DEPTHS

Feet	Meters
Sea level	Sea level
656	200
1640	500
3281	1000
6562	2000
9842	3000
13,123	4000
16,404	5000
19,685	6000
26,246	8,000

Mangrove forests
Mangrove forests are coastal ecosystems consisting of a large number of species all adapted to tidal inundation and brackish water with low levels of oxygen. They impede water flow, protecting otherwise vulnerable coasts against storm surges and tsunamis.

NEPAL

BHUTAN

Brahmaputra

Ganges

BANGLADESH

**DACCA
(DHAKA)** ★

Tropic of Cancer

Kolkata ■

● Chittagong

Mouths of the Ganges

Palmyras Point

False Point

Combermere Bay

Cheduba Island

MYANMAR

**RANGOON
(YANGON)** ★

*Gulf
of
Martaban*

Mouths of the Irrawaddy

Vishakhapatnam ●

Cape Godavari

Point Narasapatnam

Cape Chirala

Ganges

Cone

Bay

of

Bengal

Preparis North Channel

Preparis Island

Preparis South Channel

Great Coco Island
Little Coco Island

Landfall Island

Coco Channel

Narcondam Island

North Reef Island
Interview Island

**North
Andaman**

Andaman Islands
(to India)

Barren Island

**Middle
Andaman**

Ritchie's Archipelago

Havelock Island

INDIA

Coromandel Coast

Chennai ●

**South
Andaman**

Neill Island

North Sentinel
Island

Rutland Island

Sisters

Duncan Passage

Brothers

**Little
Andaman**

Andaman

Basin

Andaman

*Mergui
Archipelago*

Palk Strait

Point Pedro

Ten Degree Channel

Mannar Island

Sea

Car Nicobar

**Gulf
of
Mannar**

Cape Comorin

**SRI
LANKA**

COLOMBO ●

Batti Malv

Tillanchong
Island

Teressa Island

Katchall

Camorta
Nancowry

Nicobar Islands
(to India)

Little Nicobar

Great Nicobar

Dondra Head

SCALE 1:10,000,000
Miller Projection

0   200 kilometers
0   200 statute miles
0   200 nautical miles

Great Channel

Sumatra

Ninetyeast Ridge

Nicobar

Basin

INDONESIA

Central Indian Basin

INDIAN OCEAN

Sunda Trench

Longitude east of Greenwich

RED SEA

The Red Sea is part of a rift valley that formed when the African continent separated from Arabia. Lying between two desert regions, the Red Sea receives little runoff from land but experiences high levels of evaporation; some of the most saline waters in the world's seas are to be found here. The Red Sea is more than 6,560 feet (2,000 m) deep at its center but its access to the open sea is over a shallow sill at the Bab al Mandab strait that is only 360 feet (110 m) deep. As a result of this structure in the seafloor topography, fresher water moves in at the sea surface and dense, highly saline water with a low oxygen content escapes below the inflow. The extreme characteristics of Red Sea water allow it to be traced through most of the western Indian Ocean. It is even to be found in the Agulhas Current and the Agulhas Rings south of Africa.

THE FACTS	
Area	169,100 square miles (438,000 km²)
Average depth	1,608 feet (490 m)
Maximum depth	9,974 feet (3,040 m)
Maximum width	220 miles (355 km)
Maximum length	1,398 miles (2,250 km)

Hawksbill turtle
A hawksbill sea turtle (Eretmochelys imbricata) feeds on sea sponges over a coral reef, its preferred habitat. The hawksbill has a wide distribution but it is critically endangered; in some countries it is harvested for its meat. One of its major nesting sites is in the Red Sea.

Twobar anemonefish
At home among the tentacles of the sea anemone, the brilliantly colored twobar anemonefish (Amphiprion bicinctus) is safe from predators. Anemonefish are found in warm seas worldwide but particularly on coral or rocky reefs in the Indo-Pacific region.

Bottlenose dolphin
The most common of ocean dolphins, bottlenose dolphins (Tursiops truncatus), inhabit warm seas worldwide. They live in pods of 15 or more and hunt small fish. They use echolocation to locate prey, and sound for communication. Many are killed as bycatch of tuna fisheries.

Surface currents
Surface currents in the Red Sea are largely driven by the dominant winds. In winter the flow is northward. In summer the winds blow from the opposite direction, but in general only weaken the northward flow. Surface waters sink and eventually leave the Red Sea at depth.

→ Summer
→ Winter

SUEZ CANAL

Connecting the Mediterranean Sea with the Red Sea, the Suez Canal was opened to shipping in 1869. It is 120 miles (193 km) long and can handle ships of 150,000 tons displacement and 53 feet (16 m) draft. Up to 160 ships pass through it each day. There is a negligible difference in height between the waters of the oceans at each end, so no locks are needed in the canal.

A seagoing freighter sails through the Suez Canal on its way to the Red Sea. Ships pass through the canal at low speeds to avoid creating a bow wash that could erode the shoreline.

N O P Q R S T U V W X Y Z

SYRIA

Mediterranean Sea

ISRAEL
West Bank
★ JERUSALEM
Tel Aviv-Jaffa
Gaza Strip
Port Said
Alexandria

Nile Delta

Suez Canal

JORDAN

Bitter Lakes

Suez

CAIRO
(EL QÂHIRA)

Sinai

Gulf of Suez

Eastern Desert

Strait of Tiran

Strait of Gubal

Shaŕm
el Sheikh

Râs Muhammad

Nile

SAUDI ARABIA

Râs Abu Sôma

Sha'b
Quway'

Shaban
Deep'

Luxor

Umm Urûmah
Mashâbih
Shaybârâ

Elphinstone
Reef

Red

Sha'b
Ghadira

Râs Abu Madd

Aswân

Kebrit
Deep   Râs Baridi

Râs Banâs
Foul Bay

Shi'b
as Sab'ah

Tropic of Cancer

*Lake
Nasser*

Râs Mastûrah
Siyal Islands   Shi'b
Kharrâr

Halaib
Triangle
(Administered by Sudan)

Râs Hardârba   Râs Hâtibah

(Administered by Egypt)

Atlantis II
Deep

Mecca

NATURAL RESOURCES

Nubian

Discovery Deep
Râs Abu Shagara
Mukawwar'

Jeddah

Abû Shawk
Reefs

Desert

Sea

Shi'b Rûmi

Red Sea's deepest point
9,974ft (3,040m)

Suakin Archipelago

Râs Kasar

■ Oil production
▣ Tourism

Râs at Tarfâ'

Saunders
Reef

Harmil

Jazâ'ir
Farasân

YEMEN

YEMEN

Nora

Dahlak
Archipelago
Dahlak Kebr

Jazirat
Antufash

ASMARA ⊛

ERITREA

Aden

West Sheba Ridge

Gulf of Aden

Berbera

Red   Sea

ERITREA

SOMALIA

Massawa

Djibouti
DJIBOUTI

ETHIOPIA

Jazâ'ir az Zubayr

Râs Manrec

Kamarân

Râs al Katib

Jazirat
Jabal Zuqar

Jazirat al Hanish
al Kabîr

Afar
Depression

Barim (Perim)
Bab al Mandab   Ra's Barim al Mandab

Aden

West Sheba Ridge

ETHIOPIA   DJIBOUTI

Gulf   of   Aden

Râs Caluula

DJIBOUTI

Golfe de Tadjoura

Râs Surûd

Râs Caseyr

Râs Khansiir

Ahmar Mountains

ADDIS
ABABA

SOMALIA

N O P Q R S T U V W X Y Z

Coral reefs

Coral reefs, which are built by living organisms in ocean water with low levels of nutrients, support a great variety of animal and plant life. They do not flourish at depths greater than 160 feet (50 m) and need an optimal temperature of 80°F (27°C). They are currently threatened by ocean acidification.

SCALE 1:10,000,000
Miller Projection

0 — 200 kilometers
0 — 200 statute miles
0 — 200 nautical miles

West Sheba Ridge
Gulf of Aden

Seafloor topography

The deepest part of the Red Sea is 9,974 feet (3,040 m) deep, the sill at its mouth at Bab al Mandab is only 360 feet (110 m) deep. One result of this is that a reservoir of very salty, deep water builds up before escaping across the sill. Fresher seawater flows in to replace it.

N

ARABIAN SEA

Maritime trade routes have crossed the Arabian Sea since ancient times and the modern-day vessels that use the Suez Canal continue to pass through here. Lying to the west of the Indian subcontinent and the Chagos-Laccadive Ridge, the Arabian Sea has two mediterranean seas that feed water into it, the Persian Gulf and the Red Sea. The flow in the Arabian Sea itself is seasonal with clockwise flow in summer, fed by the Somali Current, and a weak counterclockwise flow in winter. The winter flow along the west coast of India is about 250 miles (400 km) wide and 650 feet (200 m) deep before it is fed fresher water by a jet current from the Bay of Bengal. A notable feature of the region is strong, wind-driven upwelling on the east coast of Arabia. However, the strong East Arabian Current on the western boundary inhibits the build-up of a productive ecosystem by rapidly removing most of the phytoplankton that is produced. Upwelling is also found on the western Indian continental shelf during the southwest monsoon.

THE FACTS

Area	1.5 million square miles (3.9 million km²)
Average depth	9,022 feet (2,750 m)
Maximum depth	15,262 feet (4,652 m)
Maximum width	1,490 miles (2,400 km)

NATURAL RESOURCES

- Fishing
- Shellfish
- Oil production
- Tourism

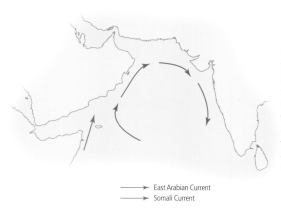

Surface currents
The Arabian Sea has surface currents largely influenced by the monsoonal winds and, as these winds may differ in duration from year to year, so do the currents. At depth the waters are influenced by the dense, salty water that emerges from the two adjacent seas, the Red Sea and the Persian Gulf.

→ East Arabian Current
→ Somali Current

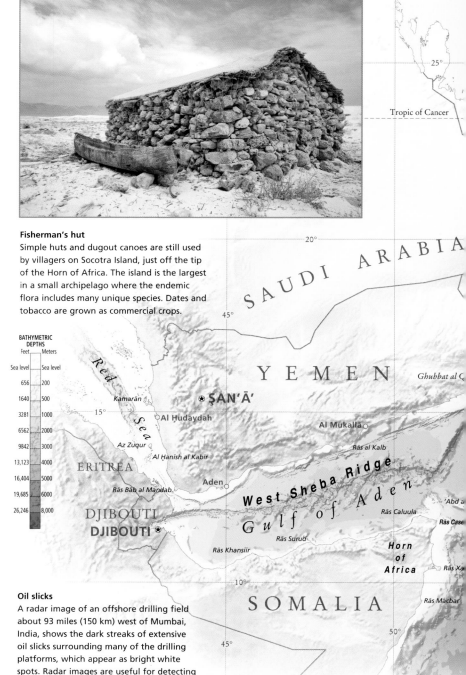

Fisherman's hut
Simple huts and dugout canoes are still used by villagers on Socotra Island, just off the tip of the Horn of Africa. The island is the largest in a small archipelago where the endemic flora includes many unique species. Dates and tobacco are grown as commercial crops.

BATHYMETRIC DEPTHS

Feet	Meters
Sea level	Sea level
656	200
1640	500
3281	1000
6562	2000
9842	3000
13,123	4000
16,404	5000
19,685	6000
26,246	8,000

Oil slicks
A radar image of an offshore drilling field about 93 miles (150 km) west of Mumbai, India, shows the dark streaks of extensive oil slicks surrounding many of the drilling platforms, which appear as bright white spots. Radar images are useful for detecting oil pollution on the ocean's surface.

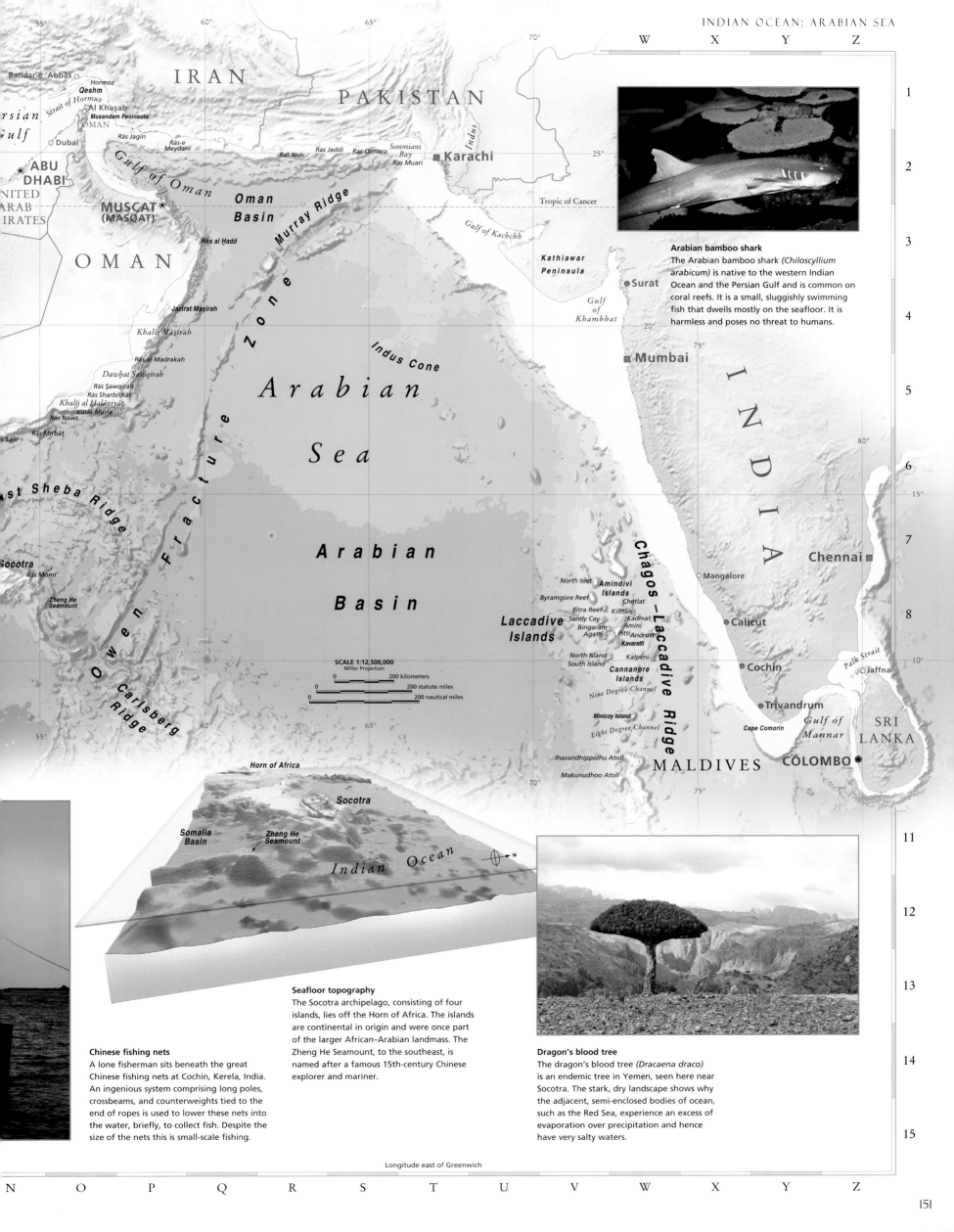

IRAN

PAKISTAN

Bandar-e ʿAbbās
Hormoz
Qeshm
Strait of Hormuz
Al Khaṣab
OMAN
Musandam Peninsula
Persian Gulf
Dubai
Rās Jagin
Rās-e Meydani
ABU DHABI
UNITED ARAB EMIRATES
MUSCAT (MASQAT)
Rās al Ḥadd
OMAN
Jazirat Maşirah
Khalīj Maşirah
Rās al Madrakah
Dawhat Sawqirah
Rās Sawqirah
Rās Sharbithāt
Khalij al Halāniyāt
Kuria Muria
Rās Naws
Rās Mirbāṭ
s Sajir

Ras Nuh
Ras Jaddi
Ras Ormara
Sonmiani Bay
Ras Muari
Karachi

Tropic of Cancer

Gulf of Oman
Oman Basin
Murray Ridge
Indus

Gulf of Kachchh
Kathiawar Peninsula
Surat
Gulf of Khambhat
Mumbai

Arabian Sea

Arabian Basin

Indus Cone

Fracture Zone

East Sheba Ridge

Socotra
Rās Momi

Zheng He Seamount

Owen Fracture Zone

Carlsberg Ridge

I N D I A

Mangalore
North Islet
Byramgore Reef
Amindivi Islands
Chetlat
Bitra Reef
Kiltan
Sandy Cay
Kadmat
Bingaram
Amini
Agatti
Pitti
Andrott
Kavaratti
Laccadive Islands
North Island
South Island
Kalpeni
Cannanore Islands
Nine Degree Channel
Minicoy Island
Eight Degree Channel
Ihavandhippolhu Atoll
Makunudhoo Atoll
MALDIVES

Chagos – Laccadive Ridge

Calicut
Cochin
Palk Strait
Jaffna
Trivandrum
Cape Comorin
Gulf of Mannar
SRI LANKA
COLOMBO

Chennai

SCALE 1:12,500,000
Miller Projection
0   200 kilometers
0   200 statute miles
0   200 nautical miles

Arabian bamboo shark
The Arabian bamboo shark (*Chiloscyllium arabicum*) is native to the western Indian Ocean and the Persian Gulf and is common on coral reefs. It is a small, sluggishly swimming fish that dwells mostly on the seafloor. It is harmless and poses no threat to humans.

Horn of Africa
Socotra
Somalia Basin
Zheng He Seamount
Indian Ocean
N

Chinese fishing nets
A lone fisherman sits beneath the great Chinese fishing nets at Cochin, Kerela, India. An ingenious system comprising long poles, crossbeams, and counterweights tied to the end of ropes is used to lower these nets into the water, briefly, to collect fish. Despite the size of the nets this is small-scale fishing.

Seafloor topography
The Socotra archipelago, consisting of four islands, lies off the Horn of Africa. The islands are continental in origin and were once part of the larger African–Arabian landmass. The Zheng He Seamount, to the southeast, is named after a famous 15th-century Chinese explorer and mariner.

Dragon's blood tree
The dragon's blood tree (*Dracaena draco*) is an endemic tree in Yemen, seen here near Socotra. The stark, dry landscape shows why the adjacent, semi-enclosed bodies of ocean, such as the Red Sea, experience an excess of evaporation over precipitation and hence have very salty waters.

Longitude east of Greenwich

PERSIAN GULF

The Persian Gulf region is the site of vast crude oil and gas reserves and the drilling operations that extract these valuable commodities put pressure on the natural environment. In both its geography and the salinity of its water the Persian Gulf is in many respects very similar to the Red Sea. It is long and narrow, with a narrow strait at its southern end, and is bordered by land that is predominantly arid. However, in contrast to the Red Sea it is very shallow. Its waters are also strongly saline because there is an excess of evaporation over rainfall. This salinity is formed despite the runoff into the Persian Gulf from the Tigris and the Euphrates rivers. The water that flows out of the gulf at the Strait of Hormuz is very salty, but with a much higher oxygen content than the outflow from the Red Sea. In some parts of the Indian Ocean this difference in dissolved oxygen values makes it possible to differentiate between waters coming from these two mediterranean seas.

THE FACTS	
Area	96,911 square miles (251,000 km²)
Average depth	164 feet (50 m)
Maximum depth	344 feet (119 m)
Maximum width	35 miles (56 km)
Maximum length	615 miles (989 km)

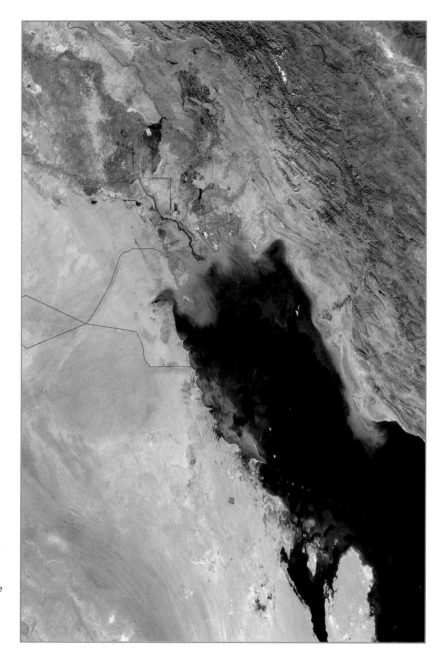

Sediment flow
A satellite image shows the true color of the sea at the head of the Persian Gulf. Here the combined waters of the Tigris and Euphrates rivers, laden with sediment, enter the sea. They appear light brown where they enter, and then dissipate into turquoise swirls as they drift southward.

Dugong
Dugongs (*Dugong dugon*) are large, placid marine mammals found in the Indo-Pacific. They eat seagrasses and are found largely in bays and mangrove channels, where they may be vulnerable to predators. Although capable of living for 70 years they are now extinct in many parts of their former range.

Oil rig
Oil platforms are enormous structures housing machinery for drilling wells into the seafloor in search of oil and gas, processing plants, and accommodation for workers. Platforms may be afloat or attached to the seafloor, depending on the depth of the water.

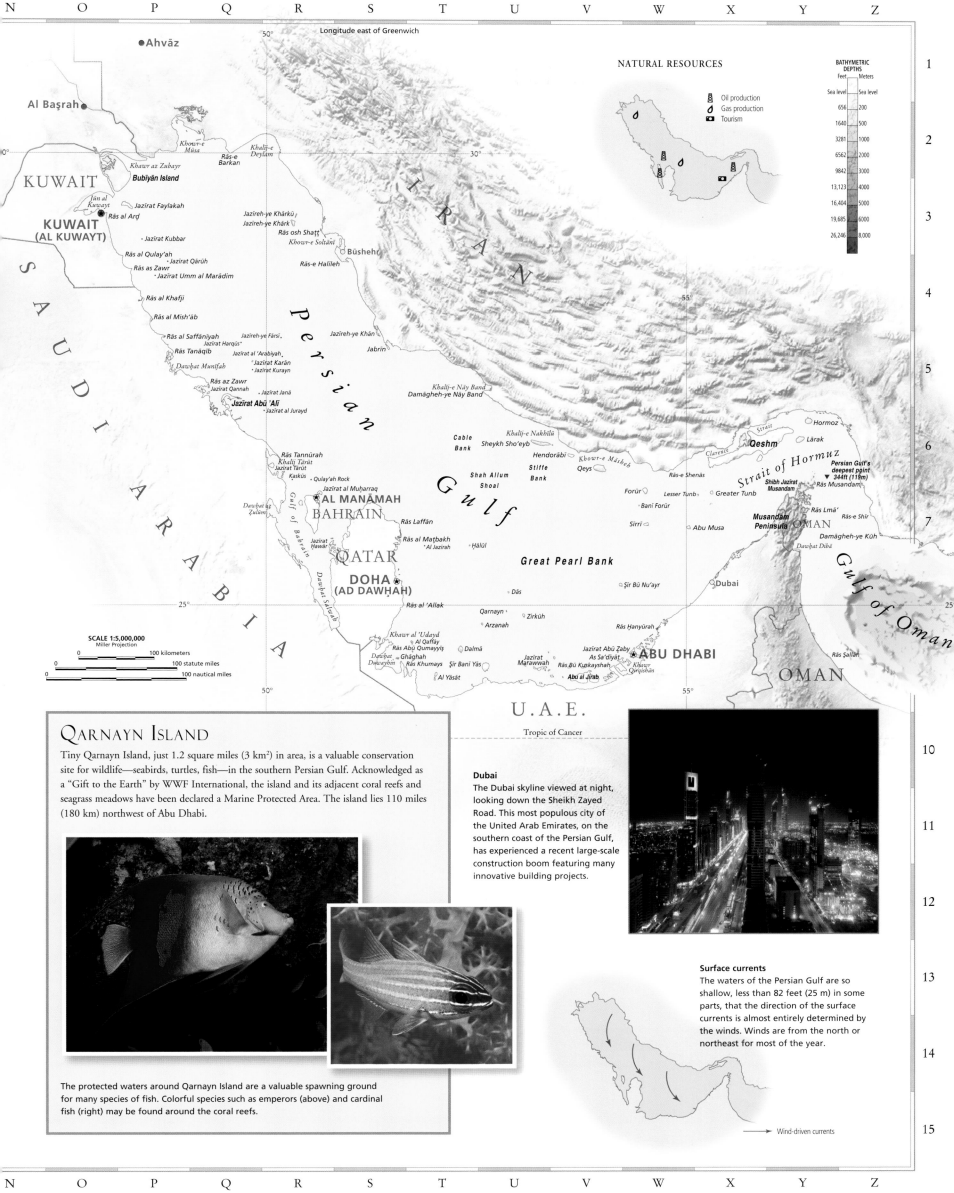

N O P Q R S T U V W X Y Z

Longitude east of Greenwich

●Ahvāz

50°

NATURAL RESOURCES

BATHYMETRIC
DEPTHS

Feet	Meters
Sea level	Sea level
656	200
1640	500
3281	1000
6562	2000
9842	3000
13,123	4000
16,404	5000
19,685	6000
26,246	8,000

⛏ Oil production
◓ Gas production
▭ Tourism

Al Başrah ●

Khowr-e Mūsā

Khalīj-e Deylam

Rās-e Barkan

0°

KUWAIT

Bubīyān Island

Jūn al Kuwayt

Jazīrat Faylakah

Rās al Arḍ

KUWAIT (AL KUWAYT)

Jazīreh-ye Khārkū
Jazīreh-ye Khārk

Jazīrat Kubbar

Rās osh Shaṭṭ

Khowr-e Solṭānī

● Būshehr

Rās al Qulay'ah

Jazīrat Qārūh

Rās as Zawr

Jazīrat Umm al Marādim

Rās-e Halīleh

I R A N

30°

55°

Rās al Khafji

S

Rās al Mish'āb

Rās al Saffānīyah

Jazīreh-ye Fārsī

Jazīreh-ye Khān

Jazīrat Harqūs

Rās Tanāqib

Jazīrat al 'Arabīyah

Jabrīn

A

Jazīrat Karān

Dawḥat Munīfah

Jazīrat Kurayn

Rās az Zawr

Jazīrat Janā

Jazīrat Qannah

U

P

Jazīrat Abū 'Alī

Jazīrat al Jurayd

Khalīj-e Nāy Band

Damāgheh-ye Nāy Band

e

D

r

Cable Bank

Khalīj-e Nakhīlū

Sheykh Sho'eyb

Hormoz

Lārak

Strait

s

Qeshm

Rās Tannūrah

Khalīj Tārūt
Jazīrat Tārūt

Shah Allum Shoal

Stiffe Bank

Hendorābī

Khowr-e Māsheh

Qeys

Clarence

i

I

Strait of Hormuz

Persian Gulf's deepest point
▼ 344ft (119m)

Kaskūs

Qulay'ah Rock

Rās-e Shenās

Shibh Jazīrat Musandam

Rās Musandam

a

A

Jazīrat al Muḥarraq

Forūr

Lesser Tunb
Greater Tunb

n

R

AL MANĀMAH ★

Ras Laffān

Bani Forūr

Rās Lma'

Rās-e Shīr

B

BAHRAIN

Jazīrat Hawār

Rās al Maṭbakh

'Al Jazīrah

Ḥālūl

Sīrrī

Abu Musa

Musandam Peninsula

OMAN

Damāgheh-ye Kūh

A

QATAR

G

Dawḥat aş Şulaym

Great Pearl Bank

Dawḥat Dibā

DOHA (AD DAWḤAH) ★

u

Dās

Dubai ●

25°

Dawḥat Salwah

Rās al 'Allak

Qarnayn

l

Şīr Bū Nu'ayr

Arzanah

Zirkūh

Rās Ḩanyūrah

f

25°

SCALE 1:5,000,000
Miller Projection

Khawr al 'Udayd
Al Qaffāy

Dalmā

Rās Abū Qumayyiş

Jazīrat Abū Ẕaby

As Sa'dīyāt

★ **ABU DHABI**

Rās Şailan

0   100 kilometers
0   100 statute miles
0   100 nautical miles

Dawḥat Duwayhin

Ghāghah

Şīr Banī Yās

Rās Bū Kuskayshah

OMAN

Rās Qirţishan

Al Yāsāt

Jazīrat Marawwah

Abu al Jirab

50°

55°

U.A.E.

Tropic of Cancer

Qarnayn Island

Tiny Qarnayn Island, just 1.2 square miles (3 km²) in area, is a valuable conservation site for wildlife—seabirds, turtles, fish—in the southern Persian Gulf. Acknowledged as a "Gift to the Earth" by WWF International, the island and its adjacent coral reefs and seagrass meadows have been declared a Marine Protected Area. The island lies 110 miles (180 km) northwest of Abu Dhabi.

The protected waters around Qarnayn Island are a valuable spawning ground for many species of fish. Colorful species such as emperors (above) and cardinal fish (right) may be found around the coral reefs.

Dubai
The Dubai skyline viewed at night, looking down the Sheikh Zayed Road. This most populous city of the United Arab Emirates, on the southern coast of the Persian Gulf, has experienced a recent large-scale construction boom featuring many innovative building projects.

Surface currents
The waters of the Persian Gulf are so shallow, less than 82 feet (25 m) in some parts, that the direction of the surface currents is almost entirely determined by the winds. Winds are from the north or northeast for most of the year.

→ Wind-driven currents

N O P Q R S T U V W X Y Z

WESTERN INDIAN OCEAN

From the head of the Arabian Sea to beyond the southern tip of the African continent, the western Indian Ocean covers a vast region. A number of complex currents are found here. Along the Horn of Africa the Somali Current flows northward during the southwest monsoon and southward during the northeast monsoon. Currents in the equatorial belt and in the Arabian Basin are also influenced by these changing monsoon winds. The powerful Agulhas Current carries water southward along southern Africa and part of the water from this current leaks into the South Atlantic as Agulhas Rings. Highly saline water from the Red Sea can be traced to the southern tip of Africa. Fresher water at intermediate depths comes from the Southern Ocean and moves northward. A number of north–south ridges such as the Mascarene Plateau and the Chagos-Laccadive Ridge influence the movement of deep and bottom waters. Localised coastal upwelling is found in the Somali, East Madagascar, and Agulhas systems, stimulating higher biological productivity.

Granite shores
Large boulders are common on the shoreline of granitic islands in the Seychelles, where endemic plants and large colonies of seabirds thrive. Human settlement displaced the giant tortoise (Dipsochelys hololissa) but it is found on many of the archipelago's coral islands.

Agulhas Current
The Agulhas Current is one of the world's major ocean currents. It extends to a depth of 9,845 feet (3,000 m) and flows swiftly. In this satellite image clouds are gray, warm Agulhas waters red, and colder water green.

NATURAL RESOURCES

Fishing   Oil production
Shellfish   Tourism
Mining

Surface currents
The surface flow along the east coast of Africa is dominated by three currents: the southward Agulhas Current, the northward East African Coastal Current, fed by the South Equatorial Current, and the seasonally reversing Somali Current. The Arabian Sea has clockwise flow in summer, counterclockwise flow in winter.

Agulhas Current
Agulhas Return Current
Antarctic Circumpolar Current
East Madagascar Current
South Equatorial Current

Seafloor topography
The islands of Réunion and Mauritius, which lie east of Madagascar, are both volcanic. The volcano on Réunion is quite active. North of Mauritius the shallow Mascarene Plateau forms a formidable barrier to east–west currents such as the South Equatorial Current.

Cargados Carajos Islands
Cargados Carajos Bank
Rodrigues Island
Mauritius
Réunion
Mascarene Islands
Mascarene Plain
Mauritius Trench
Indian Ocean

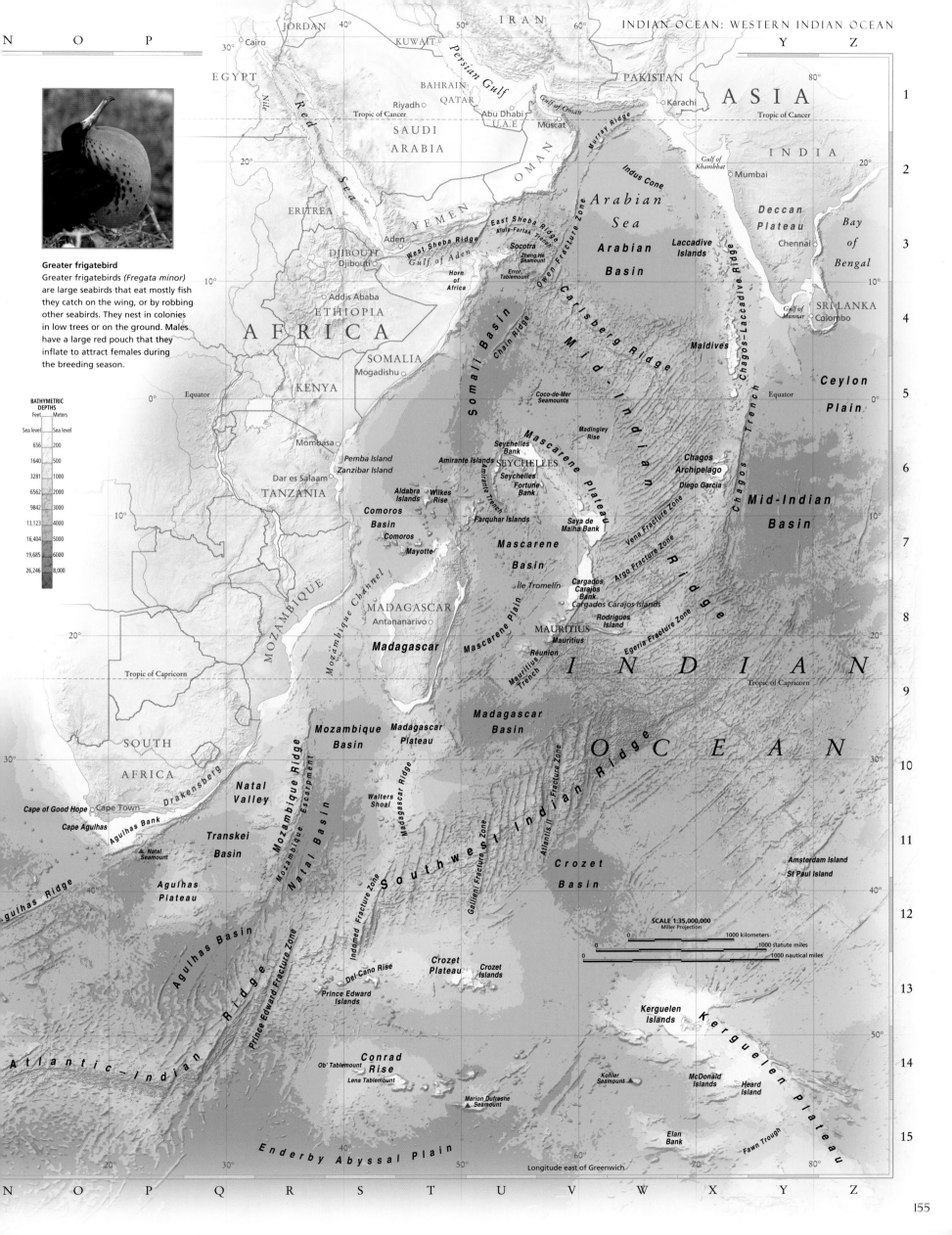

Greater frigatebird

Greater frigatebirds *(Fregata minor)* are large seabirds that eat mostly fish they catch on the wing, or by robbing other seabirds. They nest in colonies in low trees or on the ground. Males have a large red pouch that they inflate to attract females during the breeding season.

BATHYMETRIC DEPTHS

Feet	Meters
Sea level	Sea level
656	200
1640	500
3281	1000
6562	2000
9842	3000
13,123	4000
16,404	5000
19,685	6000
26,246	8,000

JORDAN
40°
50°
IRAN
60°
Y Z
KUWAIT
30°
Cairo
80°
EGYPT
BAHRAIN
QATAR
Riyadh
Abu Dhabi
U.A.E
Muscat
PAKISTAN
Karachi
ASIA
Tropic of Cancer
INDIA
Tropic of Cancer
1

SAUDI
ARABIA
20°
YEMEN
OMAN
Gulf of Oman
Murray Ridge
Gulf of Khambhat
Mumbai
20°
2

Persian Gulf
Red Sea
Indus Cone
Arabian Sea
Deccan Plateau
Bay of Bengal

ERITREA
Aden
Gulf of Aden
East Sheba Ridge
Alula-Fartak Trench
Socotra
Zheng He Seamount
Owen Fracture Zone
Arabian Basin
Laccadive Islands
Chennai
3

West Sheba Ridge
Error Tablemount
Carlsberg Ridge
Chagos–Laccadive Ridge
SRI LANKA

DJIBOUTI
Djibouti
Horn of Africa
Gulf of Mannar
Colombo

Addis Ababa
ETHIOPIA
AFRICA
Somali Basin
Chain Ridge
Mid-Indian
Maldives
Ceylon Plain
4

SOMALIA
Mogadishu
Mascarene Plateau
Madingley Rise
Chagos Archipelago
Mid-Indian Basin

KENYA
Equator
Coco-de-Mer Seamounts
Equator
5

Mombasa
Seychelles Bank
Amirante Islands
SEYCHELLES
Seychelles
Diego Garcia

Pemba Island
Zanzibar Island
Amirante Trench
Fortune Bank
Chagos Trench
6

Dar es Salaam
TANZANIA
Aldabra Islands
Wilkes Rise
Farquhar Islands
Saya de Malha Bank
Vena Fracture Zone

Comoros Basin
Mascarene Basin
Cargados Carajos Bank
Argo Fracture Zone
7

Comoros
Mayotte
Île Tromelin
Cargados Carajos Islands
Rodrigues Island

MOZAMBIQUE
Mozambique Channel
MADAGASCAR
Antananarivo
Mascarene plain
MAURITIUS
Mauritius
Réunion
Egeria Fracture Zone
8

Madagascar
Mauritius Trench
INDIAN
Tropic of Capricorn
9

Madagascar Basin
OCEAN
Mozambique Ridge
Mozambique Basin
Madagascar Plateau
SOUTH AFRICA
Drakensberg
Natal Valley
Mozambique Escarpment
Natal Basin
Walters Shoal
Madagascar Ridge
Southwest Indian Ridge
Amsterdam Island
St Paul Island
10

Cape of Good Hope
Cape Town
Cape Agulhas
Agulhas Bank
Transkei Basin
Atlantis II Fracture Zone
Crozet Basin
11

Agulhas Ridge
Natal Seamount
Gallieni Fracture Zone

Agulhas Plateau
Agulhas Basin
Indomed Fracture Zone
SCALE 1:35,000,000
Miller Projection
1000 kilometers
40°
12

1000 statute miles
1000 nautical miles

Prince Edward Fracture Zone
Del Cano Rise
Crozet Plateau
Crozet Islands
Kerguelen Islands
13

Prince Edward Islands
Kerguelen Plateau
50°

Atlantic–Indian Ridge
Conrad Rise
Ob' Tablemount
Lena Tablemount
Marion Dufresne Seamount
Kohler Seamount
McDonald Islands
Heard Island
14

Enderby Abyssal Plain
20°
30°
40°
50°
60°
70°
80°
Elan Bank
Fawn Trough
15

Longitude east of Greenwich

N O P Q R S T U V W X Y Z

MOZAMBIQUE CHANNEL

Lying between the landmass of Africa and the island of Madagascar, the waters of the Mozambique Channel are influenced by both. The circulation in the channel and the local winds systems are both influenced by the adjacent land. Contrary to other parts of the east African coastline, the flow in the Mozambique Channel does not consist of an intense, continuous current. Instead it is characterized by a train of large eddies slowly drifting southward. These eddies are formed at the narrows of the channel and have an influence on the deep-sea ecosystems. Marine birds prefer to feed at their edges. The shallowest part of the channel is only about 6,560 feet (2,000 m) deep, thus preventing deeper water masses from flowing straight through it. Coral reefs are an important ecological component on the eastern side of the channel. On the western side major rivers, such as the Zambezi, influence the shelf waters, especially when they intermittently come down in flood, laden with silt.

Estuary flow
On the northwest coast of Madagascar, seawater penetrates inland to join the freshwater outflow of the Betsiboka River. Numerous islands and sandbars have formed from the sediment in this estuary and have been shaped by the push and pull of tides.

Ghost crab
The ghost crab (*Ocypode cordimana*), which has one claw larger than the other, is common along Indo-Pacific shores. It is able to move rapidly and can disappear from sight with amazing speed. Ghost crabs may hibernate for up to six months through winter.

Coastal fishing
Villagers in Mozambique who rely on fishing have many challenges to contend with. Declining fish stocks, extreme weather events such as tropical cyclones, and regular flooding of low-lying villages by rivers bursting their banks make their trade a hazardous one.

Seafloor topography
The seafloor structure of the Mozambique Channel and its surroundings is complex. The channel narrows toward the north and also becomes shallower, so water deeper than 6,560 feet (2,000 m) cannot pass through. The shallow Mozambique and Madagascar ridges extend southward at either side of the mouth of the channel.

Surface currents
The flow in the Mozambique Channel is not a continuous north to south current. It consists of a series of eddies, whirlpools of water that drift southward on the western side of the channel. They may draw coastal waters into the deep sea.

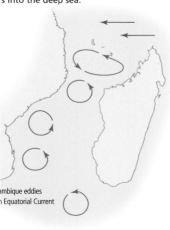

→ Mozambique eddies
→ South Equatorial Current

NATURAL RESOURCES

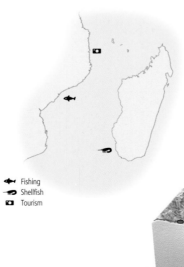

🐟 Fishing
🦐 Shellfish
🏛 Tourism

Grande Comore · Mohéli · Anjouan
MALAWI · Juan de Nova · Grand Terre
ZIMBABWE · Beira · Bassas da India
Antananarivo · MADAGASCAR
MOZAMBIQUE · Île Europa · Indian Ocean
Maputo · Mozambique Channel
SWAZILAND
SOUTH AFRICA
Durban
N

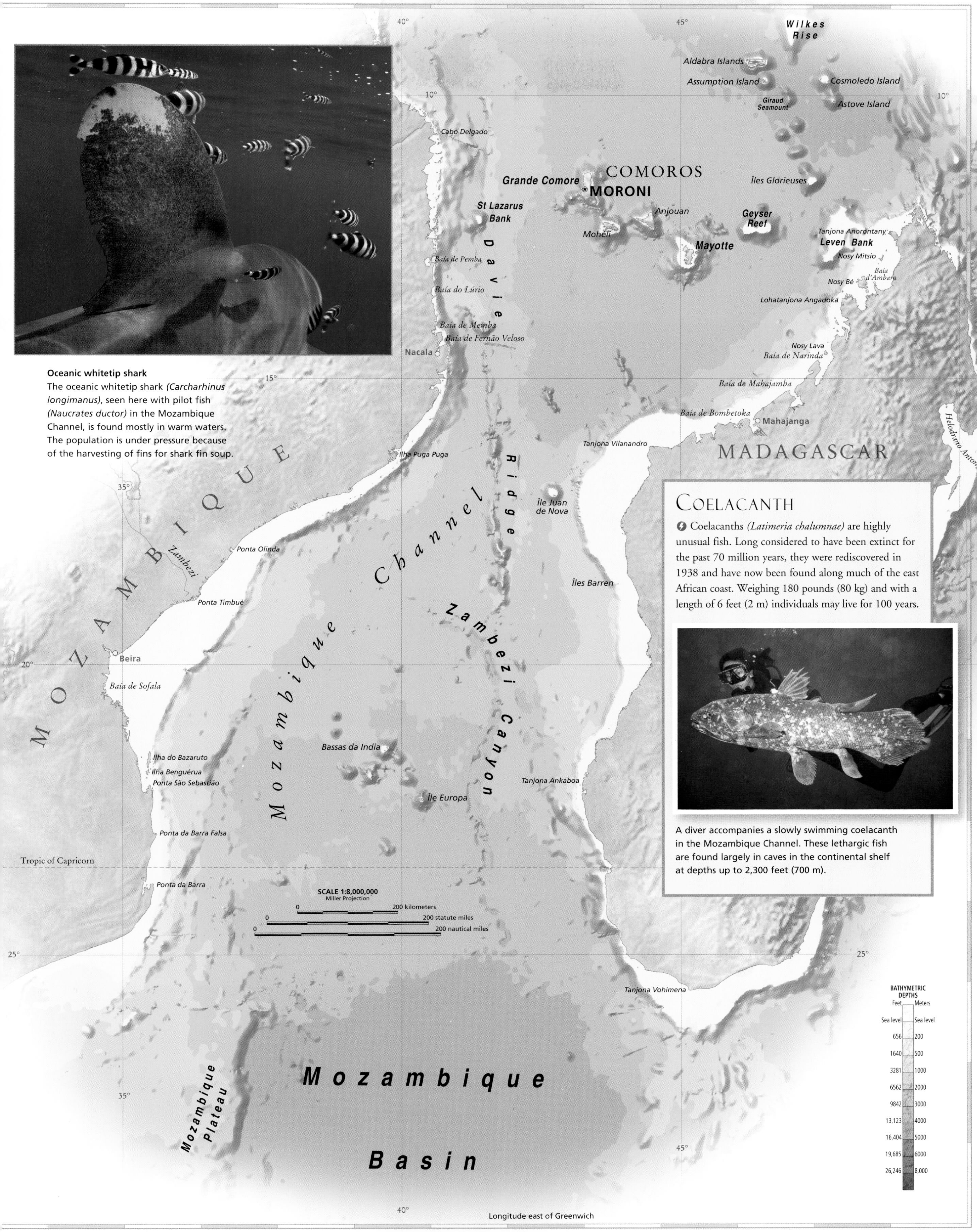

Oceanic whitetip shark
The oceanic whitetip shark (*Carcharhinus longimanus*), seen here with pilot fish (*Naucrates ductor*) in the Mozambique Channel, is found mostly in warm waters. The population is under pressure because of the harvesting of fins for shark fin soup.

COELACANTH

Coelacanths (*Latimeria chalumnae*) are highly unusual fish. Long considered to have been extinct for the past 70 million years, they were rediscovered in 1938 and have now been found along much of the east African coast. Weighing 180 pounds (80 kg) and with a length of 6 feet (2 m) individuals may live for 100 years.

A diver accompanies a slowly swimming coelacanth in the Mozambique Channel. These lethargic fish are found largely in caves in the continental shelf at depths up to 2,300 feet (700 m).

SCALE 1:8,000,000
Miller Projection
200 kilometers
200 statute miles
200 nautical miles

Wilkes Rise
Aldabra Islands
Assumption Island
Cosmoledo Island
Giraud Seamount
Astove Island
Cabo Delgado
COMOROS
Grande Comore
MORONI
Îles Glorieuses
St Lazarus Bank
Anjouan
Geyser Reef
Tanjona Anorontany
Leven Bank
Mohéli
Mayotte
Nosy Mitsio
Baía de Pemba
Nosy Bé
Baía d'Ambaro
Baía do Lúrio
Lohatanjona Angadoka
Davie
Baía de Memba
Baía de Fernão Veloso
Nosy Lava
Baía de Narinda
Nacala
Baía de Mahajamba
Baía de Bombetoka
Mahajanga
Ilha Puga Puga
Tanjona Vilanandro
MADAGASCAR
Ridge
Île Juan de Nova
Ponta Olinda
Zambezi
Îles Barren
Ponta Timbué
Zambezi Canyon
Beira
Mozambique Channel
Baía de Sofala
Mozambique
Ilha do Bazaruto
Bassas da India
Ilha Benguérua
Ponta São Sebastião
Île Europa
Tanjona Ankaboa
Ponta da Barra Falsa
Tropic of Capricorn
Ponta da Barra
Tanjona Vohimena
MOZAMBIQUE
Zambezi
Helodrano Antongila
Mozambique Plateau
Mozambique
Basin
Longitude east of Greenwich

BATHYMETRIC DEPTHS
Feet	Meters
Sea level	Sea level
656	200
1640	500
3281	1000
6562	2000
9842	3000
13,123	4000
16,404	5000
19,685	6000
26,246	8,000

EASTERN INDIAN OCEAN

A large part of this ocean region is bisected north–south by the Ninetyeast Ridge, with the Mid-Indian Ocean Basin to its west and the Wharton Basin to the east. South of the equator the flow is dominated by the wide South Equatorial Current during the southwest monsoon. The flow of the Southwest Monsoon Current is eastward at the equator. During the northeast monsoon the westward currents, the North Equatorial current and the South Equatorial Current, are bisected by an eastward Equatorial Countercurrent. Throughout the year water flows into the Indian Ocean from the Pacific—the Indonesian Throughflow. In February, during the northeast monsoon, flow to the Indian Ocean is minimal but by August, during the southwest monsoon, currents flow strongly. The southward Leeuwin Current flows along the Australian coastline. The ocean's eastern boundary currents disrupt upwelling and biological productivity, which is therefore underdeveloped.

NINGALOO REEF

Ningaloo Reef, the longest fringing coral reef in the world, stretches for 125 miles (200 km) along the west coast of Australia, 745 miles (1,200 km) north of Perth. The reef is on the migratory route of dolphins, dugongs and humpback whales. It is now a declared marine park and its beaches are important breeding grounds for loggerhead, green and hawksbill turtles.

The whale shark (Rhincodon typus), a filter feeder, swims with its mouth open to capture plankton. Found at the Ningaloo Reef from March to June, these are the largest living fish species, growing to 40 feet (12 m) in length.

Ningaloo Reef's close proximity to the shore, less than 1,600 feet (500 m) in some places, adds to its attractions for those wanting to swim among the abundant marine life.

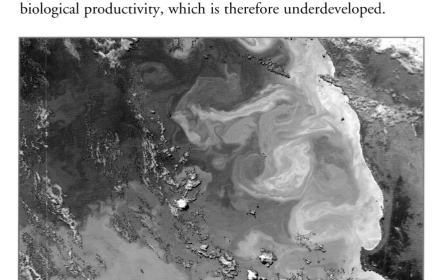

Leeuwin Current chlorophyll
A satellite image of chlorophyll shows a huge eddy or vortex in the Leeuwin Current off the west coast of Australia. The high concentrations of chlorophyll are yellow against an aquamarine background of lower concentrations, and come from coastal plankton, or marine algae, in the water.

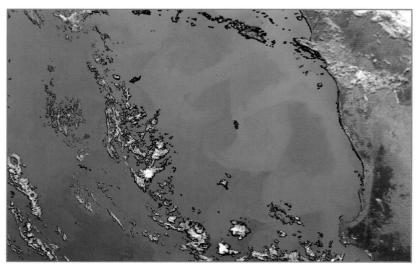

Leeuwin Current temperatures
A satellite image in thermal infrared shows sea-surface temperatures at the west coast of Australia. The huge eddies formed by the Leeuwin Current are visible. These eddies are about 125 miles (200 km) wide, 3,300 feet (1,000 m) deep, and spin at three miles per hour (5 km/h).

Surface currents
The eastern Indian Ocean is characterized by currents parallel to the equator, the Leeuwin Current flowing poleward along the west coast of Australia, and leakage of Pacific water through the Indonesian archipelago. Some water from the Great Australian Bight also enters the Indian Ocean.

→ Antarctic Circumpolar Current	⋯→ South Equatorial Current
⇢ Equatorial Countercurrent	→ Leeuwin Current
→ North Equatorial Current	→ Throughflow

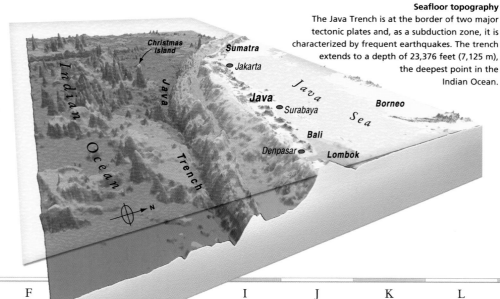

Seafloor topography
The Java Trench is at the border of two major tectonic plates and, as a subduction zone, it is characterized by frequent earthquakes. The trench extends to a depth of 23,376 feet (7,125 m), the deepest point in the Indian Ocean.

N O P Q R S T U V W X Y Z

NATURAL RESOURCES

BATHYMETRIC DEPTHS

Feet	Meters
Sea level	Sea level
656	200
1640	500
3281	1000
6562	2000
9842	3000
13,123	4000
16,404	5000
19,685	6000
26,246	8,000

Fishing
Shellfish
Metallic minerals
Mining
Oil production
Tourism

Leafy seadragon

Leafy seadragons (*Phycodurus eques*) are marine fish related to the seahorse. Found along the coast of western and southern Australia, their leafy body structures serve as camouflage. Moving slowly through the water they appear to be pieces of floating seaweed.

BANGLADESH
Dhaka
Tropic of Cancer
INDIA
80°
20°
MYANMAR
Yangen
THAILAND
Bangkok
100°
20°
Chennai
Bay of Bengal
Andaman Islands
Andaman Sea
Gulf of Thailand
SRI LANKA
Colombo
Gulf of Mannar
Nicobar Islands
Andaman Basin
MALAYSIA
Kuala Lumpur
Strait of Malacca
Singapore
Ceylon Plain
Equator
Cocos Basin
Sunda Trench
Sumatra
INDONESIA
Borneo
Java Sea
Jakarta
Java
Bali
Lesser Sunda Islands
Sunda Sea
Arafura Sea
Dili
EAST TIMOR
New Guinea
PAPUA NEW GUINEA
Port Moresby
130°
Equator
0°
140°
Afanasy Nikitin Seamount
Investigator Ridge
Sunda Trough
Java Trench
Christmas Island
Java Trench 23,376ft (7125m)
Horizon Ridge
North Australian Basin
Arafura Shelf
Timor Sea
Sahul Shelf
Darwin
Gulf of Carpentaria
Torres Strait
Cape York
10°
Coral Sea
Mid-Indian Ocean Basin
Cocos Islands
Gascoyne Plain
Cape Leveque
Rowley Shelf
Osborn Plateau
Ninetyeast Ridge
Wharton Basin
Exmouth Plateau
Ningaloo Reef
Cuvier Basin
20°
INDIAN
Tropic of Capricorn
Wallaby Plateau
Lost Dutchmen Ridge
Cuvier Plateau
Tropic of Capricorn
East Indiaman Ridge
Batavia Seamount
AUSTRALIA
OCEAN
Golden Dragon Seamount
Harlog Ridge
Perth Basin
30°
Broken Plateau
Ob Trench
Naturaliste Plateau
Perth
Great Australian Bight
Naturaliste Fracture Zone
Diamantina Deep 21,860ft (6602m)
Adelaide
Amsterdam Island
St Paul Island
Diamantina Fracture Zone
South Australian Basin
Melbourne
King Island
Bass Strait
40°
SCALE 1:35,000,000
Miller Projection
0 1000 kilometers
0 1000 statute miles
0 1000 nautical miles
Tasmania
Hobart
South East Cape
Southeast Indian Ridge
South Australian Plain
South Tasman Rise
50°
Kerguelen Plateau
Fawn Trough
Australian-Antarctic Basin
Indian-Antarctic Ridge
Banzare Seamounts
South Indian Basin
Longitude east of Greenwich
80° 90° 100° 110° 120° 130° 140°
60°

N O P Q R S T U V W X Y Z

1 2 3 4 5 6 7 8 9 10 11 12 13 14 15

GREAT AUSTRALIAN BIGHT

The ocean area south of the Australian landmass is the
easternmost extension of the Indian Ocean. In its
extreme east it adds a cold-water connection to the
Pacific Ocean. Warm water from the Leeuwin
Current, which flows southward along the west coast
of Australia, may round Cape Leeuwin on the
southwest corner of the continent and penetrate into
the bight. Bottom water formed at the coast of Antarctica
moves north but, where its flow is obstructed by the Australian
continental shelf, it moves in an easterly direction into the
Indian Ocean. The flow at intermediate depths, around 3,280
feet (1,000 m), is also from the Great Australian Bight into the
Indian Ocean, so the bight is inferred to have a greater influence
on the Indian Ocean than on the Pacific. The dry atmosphere
over parts of the bight causes excessive evaporation that forms
highly saline, dense water, which descends to greater depths.

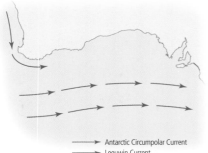

Surface currents
South of Australia, at the northern
boundary of the Southern Ocean, the
powerful Antarctic Circumpolar Current
carries water west to east. On Australia's
west coast, warm waters from the
southward flowing Leeuwin Current
occasionally flow east into the Great
Australian Bight and penetrate the cold
Antarctic waters.

→ Antarctic Circumpolar Current
→ Leeuwin Current

Great white shark
The great white shark (*Carcharodon
carcharias*), the largest predatory fish in the
world, can grow to 20 feet (6 m) and may
weigh as much as 5,000 pounds (2,300 kg). It
can dive to depths of 4,200 feet (1,300 m) and
individuals have been tracked migrating from
South African to Australian waters.

NULLARBOR COAST

The Nullarbor Plain is an extensive, flat, almost treeless region at the southern edge of the
Australian continent, adjacent to the Great Australian Bight. This arid, semi-desert region
receives only about seven inches (200 mm) of rainfall per year and is sparsely populated.
Thought to have once been part of an ancient seabed, it is the largest limestone area on
earth. Its daytime temperatures may reach 120°F (49°C).

The spectacular 213-foot- (65 m) high Bunda Cliffs of the Nullarbor coast form part
of the northern border of the Great Australian Bight. The cliffs are an excellent
vantage point for whale-watching.

NATURAL RESOURCES

🐟 Fishing
📷 Tourism

Kangaroo Island
Seal Bay Conservation Park, on the coast
of Kangaroo Island, offers protected
beaches where marine mammals,
including the Australian sea lion
(*Neophoca cinerea*), raise their young.

Australian sea lion
The Australian sea lion (*Neophoca cinerea*)
is found only along the southern coast of
Australia. It hunts for fish and squid at sea
and comes ashore on rocky islands to
breed. Members of the eared seal family,
sea lions have small, furled ears. Males can
weigh up to 660 pounds (300 kg) at
maturity, females 176 pounds (80 kg).

N O P Q R S T U V W X Y Z

Longitude east of Greenwich

WESTERN

AUSTRALIA

AUSTRALIA

SOUTH

AUSTRALIA

Nullarbor *Plain*

Eucla
Bunda
Cliffs
Head of
Bight
Point Adieu
Fowlers
Bay
Ceduna

Red Rocks Point

Point Dover

Point Culver

Great *Australian* *Bight*

Streaky Bay

Port Augusta

Anxious Bay

Eyre
Peninsula

Esperance

Israelite Bay

Cape Le Grand
Cape Arid
Cape Pasley

Archipelago of the Recherche

Point Hood
Cape Knob

Flinders Island
Investigator Group
Pearson Isles

Spencer Gulf

Bald Island

Coffin Bay

Yorke
Peninsula

Adelaide

Bald Head

Coffin Bay Peninsula

Port Lincoln
Cape Catastrophe

Cape Spencer

Gulf St. Vincent

Kangaroo Island

Seal Bay

Encounter
Bay

Cape Jaffa

South *Australian* *Basin*

I N D I A N *O C E A N*

SCALE 1:10,000,000
Miller Projection

0 ____ 200 kilometers
0 ____ 200 statute miles
0 ____ 200 nautical miles

South *Australian* *Plain*

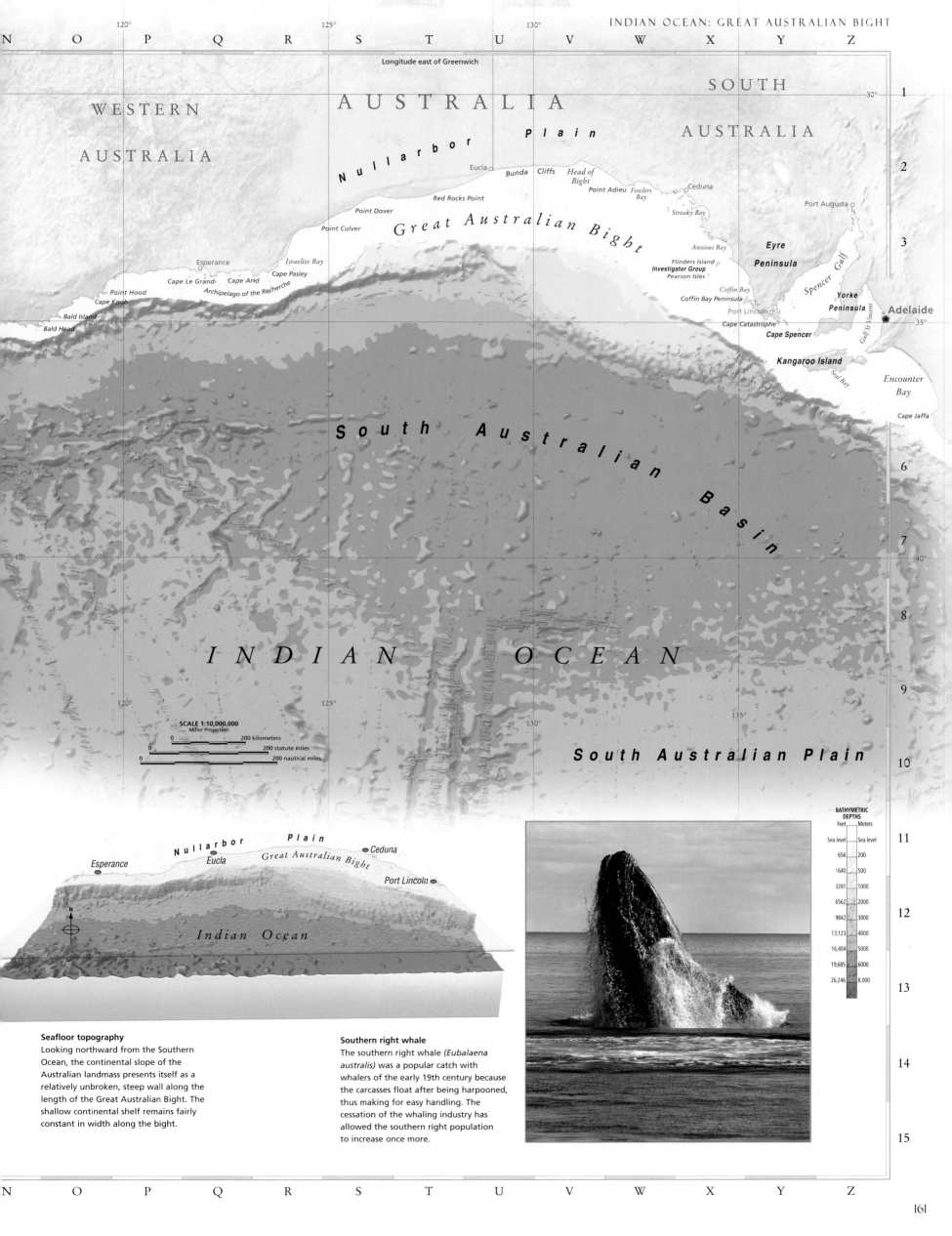

Seafloor topography
Looking northward from the Southern
Ocean, the continental slope of the
Australian landmass presents itself as a
relatively unbroken, steep wall along the
length of the Great Australian Bight. The
shallow continental shelf remains fairly
constant in width along the bight.

Esperance

Nullarbor *Plain*

Eucla

Ceduna

Great Australian Bight

Port Lincoln

Indian Ocean

Southern right whale
The southern right whale *(Eubalaena
australis)* was a popular catch with
whalers of the early 19th century because
the carcasses float after being harpooned,
thus making for easy handling. The
cessation of the whaling industry has
allowed the southern right population
to increase once more.

BATHYMETRIC
DEPTHS

Feet	Meters
Sea level	Sea level
656	200
1640	500
3281	1000
6562	2000
9842	3000
13,123	4000
16,404	5000
19,685	6000
26,246	8,000

SOUTHERN INDIAN OCEAN

The southern Indian Ocean extends from the African mainland to the west and south coasts of Australia, with the landmass of Madagascar as the only interruption. The general, wind-driven circulation is counterclockwise, except close to the equator, and it intensifies to the west where the strong Agulhas Current flows along the African coast, and the East Madagascar Current along the east coast of that island. The southern border of this ocean is the Subtropical Convergence, an oceanic front that separates South Indian Ocean waters from the colder, more nutrient-rich waters of the Southern Ocean farther to the south. The current that flows along this front is known as the Agulhas Return Current on the western side of the basin and as the South Indian Ocean Current to the east. On the west coast of Australia the warm Leeuwin Current flows southward; in the subtropics the South Indian Countercurrent carries water eastward against the general flow.

African penguins
African penguins (*Spheniscus demersus*), formerly known as jackass penguins for their braying cry, live in colonies on islands off the southwest coast of Africa. The colony shown here is one of few on land. This 28-inch- (70 cm) tall penguin has black feet and a distinctive black stripe on the chest.

Phytoplankton
The southern tip of Africa as seen by satellite. The ocean color has been enhanced and shows the location of high levels of phytoplankton (green), particularly along the west coast where coastal upwelling brings nutrients to the sea surface.

NATURAL RESOURCES

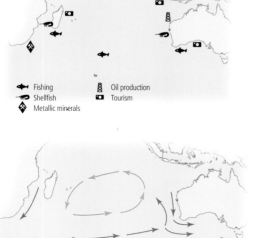

- Fishing
- Shellfish
- Metallic minerals
- Oil production
- Tourism

Surface currents
Surface flow is generally counter-clockwise in the gyres of all southern hemisphere basins. In the southern Indian Ocean it is highly concentrated in the western part and the strong Agulhas Current is the final recipient of much of this recirculating water.

→ Agulhas Current
→ Antarctic Circumpolar Current
→ Leeuwin Current
→ Subtropical Gyre

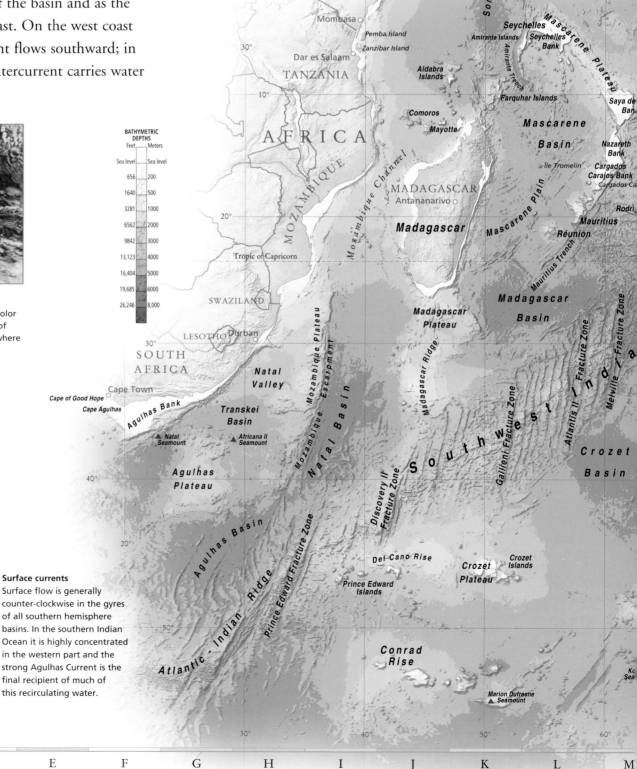

BATHYMETRIC DEPTHS

Feet	Meters
Sea level	Sea level
656	200
1640	500
3281	1000
6562	2000
9842	3000
13,123	4000
16,404	5000
19,685	6000
26,246	8,000

SOMALIA
Equator
KENYA
Mombasa
Pemba Island
Dar es Salaam
Zanzibar Island
TANZANIA
Aldabra Islands
Comoros
Mayotte
AFRICA
MOZAMBIQUE
Mozambique Channel
MADAGASCAR
Antananarivo
Tropic of Capricorn
SWAZILAND
LESOTHO
Durban
SOUTH AFRICA
Cape Town
Cape of Good Hope
Cape Agulhas
Agulhas Bank
Natal Valley
Transkei Basin
Africana II Seamount
Natal Seamount
Agulhas Plateau
Agulhas Basin
Atlantic-Indian Ridge
Prince Edward Fracture Zone
Prince Edward Islands
Del Cano Rise
Mozambique Plateau
Mozambique Escarpment
Natal Basin
Madagascar Ridge
Madagascar Plateau
Madagascar Basin
Mascarene Plain
Mascarene Basin
Seychelles
Seychelles Bank
Amirante Islands
Amirante Trench
Farquhar Islands
Saya de Ban
Somali Basin
Mascarene Plateau
Nazareth Bank
Cargados Carajos Bank
Cargados Ca
Ile Tromelin
Mauritius
Réunion
Mauritius Trench
Rodri
Southwest Indi
Galtieni Fracture Zone
Atlantis II Fracture Zone
Melville Fracture Zone
Crozet Basin
Discovery II Fracture Zone
Crozet Plateau
Crozet Islands
Conrad Rise
Marion Dufresne Seamount
Ko Sea

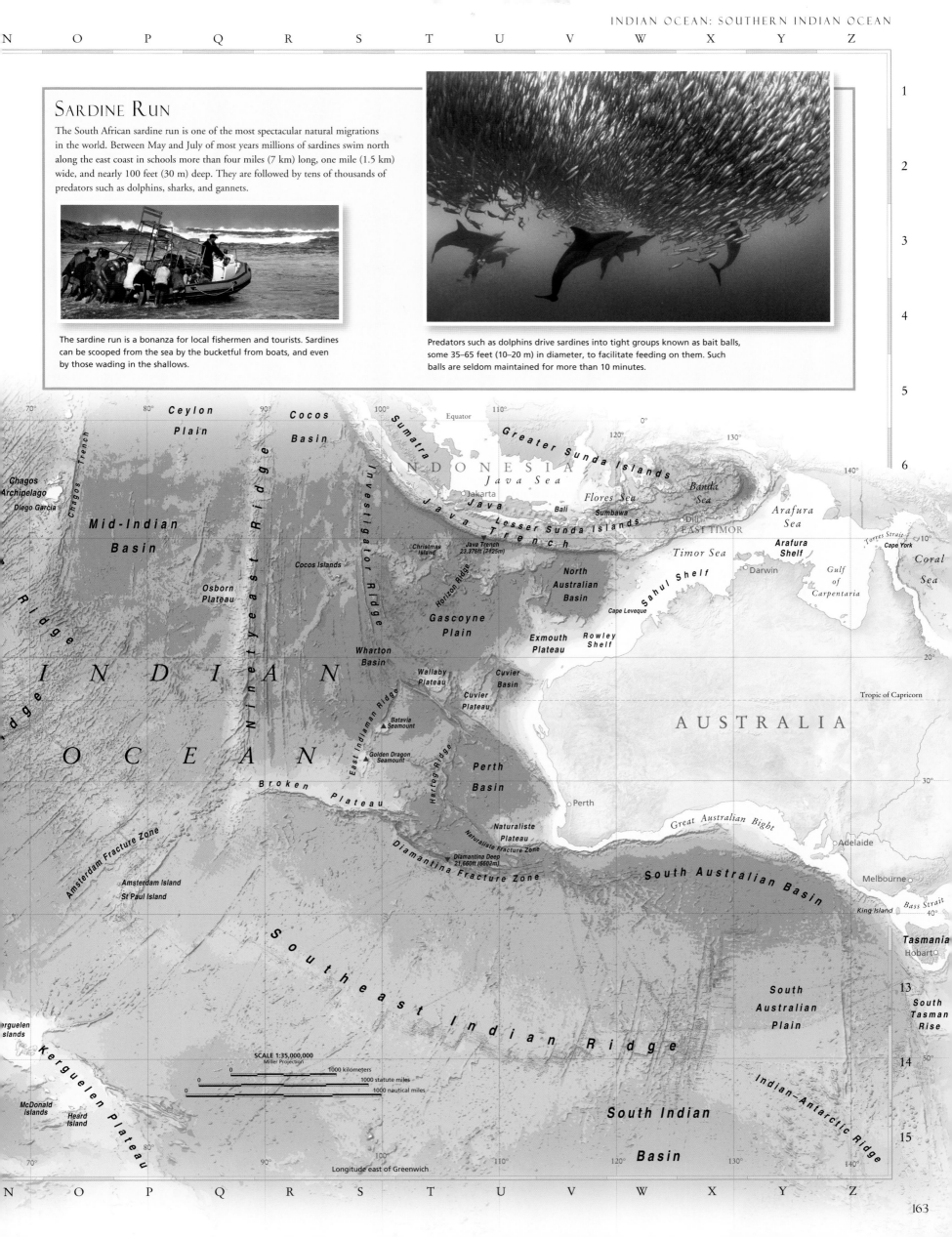

SARDINE RUN

The South African sardine run is one of the most spectacular natural migrations in the world. Between May and July of most years millions of sardines swim north along the east coast in schools more than four miles (7 km) long, one mile (1.5 km) wide, and nearly 100 feet (30 m) deep. They are followed by tens of thousands of predators such as dolphins, sharks, and gannets.

The sardine run is a bonanza for local fishermen and tourists. Sardines can be scooped from the sea by the bucketful from boats, and even by those wading in the shallows.

Predators such as dolphins drive sardines into tight groups known as bait balls, some 35–65 feet (10–20 m) in diameter, to facilitate feeding on them. Such balls are seldom maintained for more than 10 minutes.

A humpback whale *(Megaptera novaeangliae)* and her calf cruise the
vast expanse of the Pacific Ocean, while the father, now a lone traveler
far away, fills the ocean with his song for hours. Whale songs change
over time, but at any one time all North Pacific humpbacks sing the
same version. South Pacific humpbacks sing a different song.

PACIFIC OCEAN

PACIFIC OCEAN

The Pacific Ocean is the largest of all oceans. The East Pacific Rise divides it rather unequally into the narrow Peru and Chile basins in the east and a vast featureless plain in the center. A "Ring of Fire" marked by earthquakes and volcanic eruptions surrounds it and generates powerful tsunamis. Tectonic movement of the crustal plates forms some of the world's deepest trenches along its rim. Thousands of seamounts, remnants of submarine volcanoes and homes to isolated, highly productive ecosystems, rise from the ocean floor, often to within 1,000 feet (300 m) or less of the surface. The Portuguese explorer Magellan, who sailed across the Pacific in 1521 under its pleasant trade winds, named it the "pacific" (peaceful) ocean; but swell from storms of the Roaring Forties always reaches the tropics. Micronesian, Melanesian, and Polynesian sailors navigated between the many thousands of islands in the southern hemisphere and the northwestern Pacific for centuries.

THE FACTS	
Area	60.1 million square miles (155.6 million km²)
Average depth	13,127 feet (4,001 m)
Maximum depth	35,826 feet (10,920 m)
Maximum width	11,200 miles (18,000 km)
Maximum length	8,600 miles (13,900 km)

Ocean Share

Pacific Ocean
60.1 million sq miles
(155.6 million km²)
46%

All other oceans

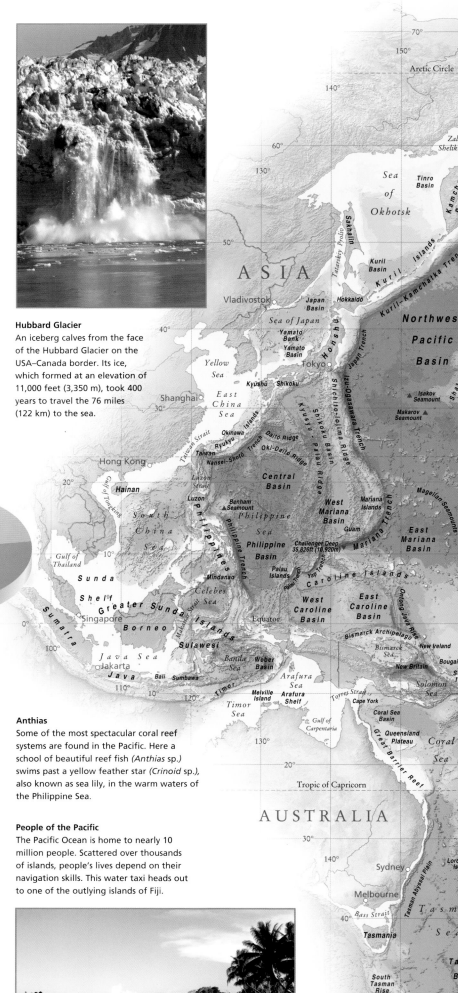

Hubbard Glacier
An iceberg calves from the face of the Hubbard Glacier on the USA–Canada border. Its ice, which formed at an elevation of 11,000 feet (3,350 m), took 400 years to travel the 76 miles (122 km) to the sea.

Anthias
Some of the most spectacular coral reef systems are found in the Pacific. Here a school of beautiful reef fish (Anthias sp.) swims past a yellow feather star (Crinoid sp.), also known as sea lily, in the warm waters of the Philippine Sea.

People of the Pacific
The Pacific Ocean is home to nearly 10 million people. Scattered over thousands of islands, people's lives depend on their navigation skills. This water taxi heads out to one of the outlying islands of Fiji.

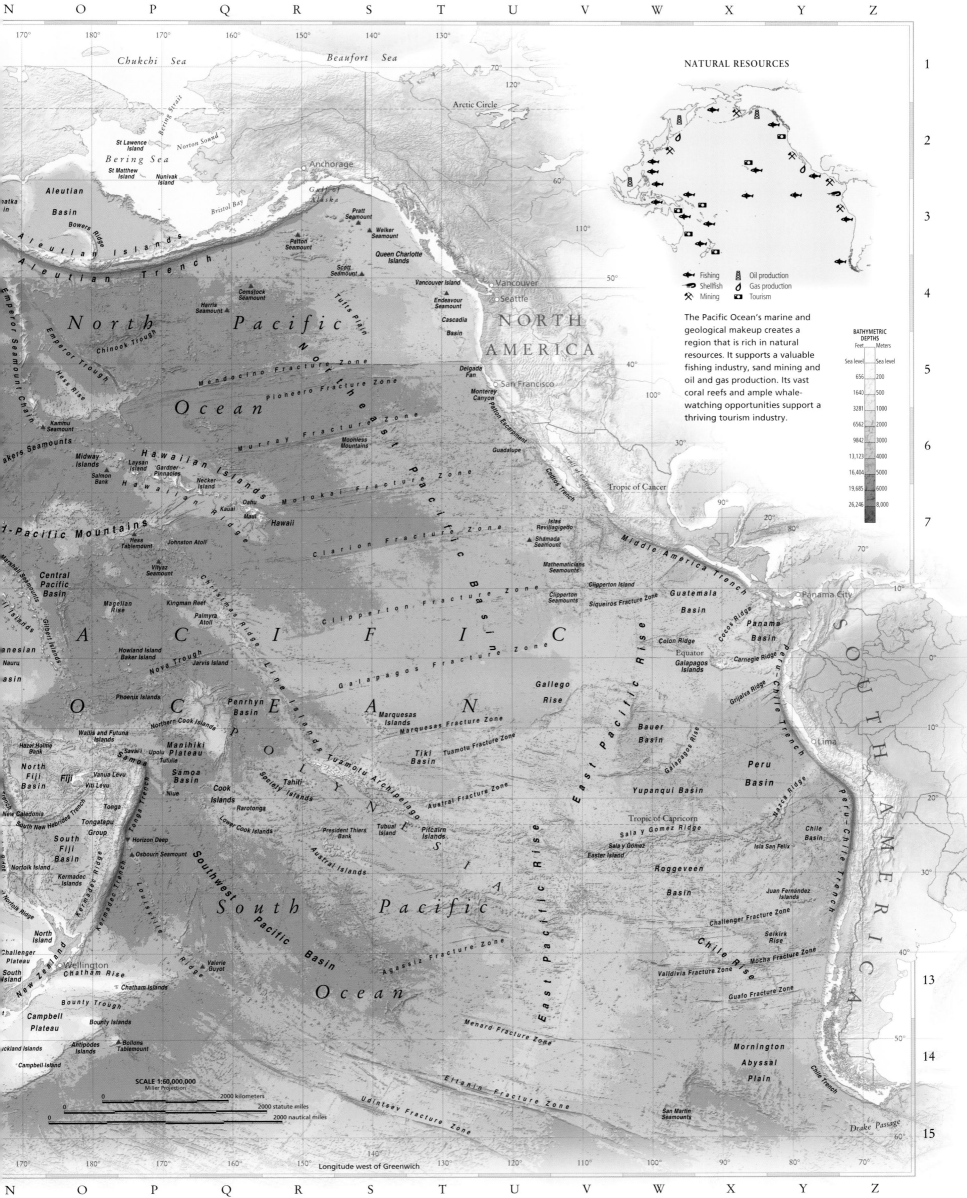

NATURAL RESOURCES

The Pacific Ocean's marine and geological makeup creates a region that is rich in natural resources. It supports a valuable fishing industry, sand mining and oil and gas production. Its vast coral reefs and ample whale-watching opportunities support a thriving tourism industry.

NORTHERN NORTH PACIFIC OCEAN

The northern sector of the North Pacific has the most uniform bathymetry of all ocean basins. Two big circulation systems dominate the region. The North Equatorial, Philippines, Kuroshio, North Pacific, and California currents form the clockwise circulation of the Subtropical Gyre. Water movement at its center is downward, depriving the upper ocean of nutrients, so its waters display the deep blue of the ocean's deserts. Plastic and other land-based or ship-derived garbage accumulates in the gyre, particularly between North America and the Hawaiian Islands. The Alaska Current, Alaskan Stream, Oyashio, and North Pacific currents form the counterclockwise circulation of the Subpolar Gyre, in which upward water movement brings nutrients to the surface, making it a region of high productivity and preferred fishing grounds. The Oyashio and Kuroshio currents meet along 35°N in the Kuroshio Extension, which forms a convoluted fast-flowing current across the Shatsky Rise and Emperor Seamounts, dominated by meanders and eddies.

Sea lion
The Steller sea lion (*Eumetopias jubatus*), the largest of all sea lion species, is found from the Kuril Islands and the Sea of Okhotsk to the Gulf of Alaska and central California. Its numbers have been declining and it is on the endangered species list.

BATHYMETRIC DEPTHS

Feet	Meters
Sea level	Sea level
656	200
1640	500
3281	1000
6562	2000
9842	3000
13,123	4000
16,404	5000
19,685	6000
26,246	8,000

NATURAL RESOURCES

- 🐟 Fishing
- ▣ Tourism
- ⚒ Mining
- ⛏ Oil production

Surface currents

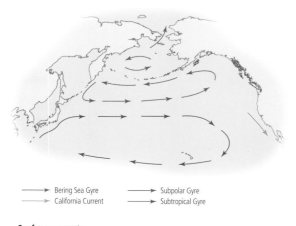

- → Bering Sea Gyre
- → California Current
- → Subpolar Gyre
- → Subtropical Gyre

Two basin-wide gyres dominate the North Pacific. South of 40°N the American coastal waters experience upwelling from the California Current. Currents in the deep basin of the Bering Sea move counterclockwise while, over the shelf, northward movement feeds into the Arctic Ocean.

Aleutian Islands

Open sky between clouds in the south and in the north allows a clear view of the snow-covered peaks of the Alaskan Peninsula and the Aleutian Islands. More than 300 volcanic islands, in an arc 1,200 miles (1,900 km) long, form the southern boundary of the Bering Sea.

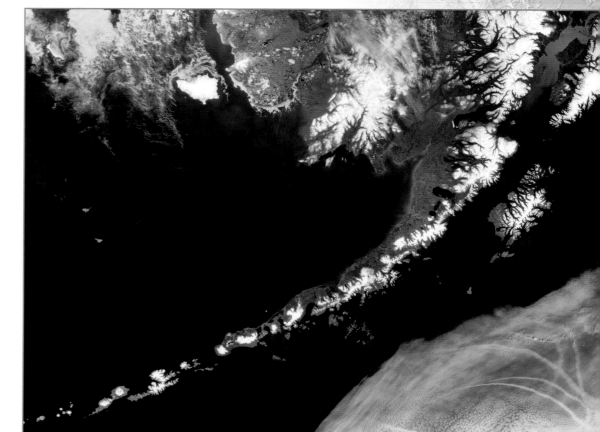

Map labels: RUSSIA, Zac Shelik, Sea of Okhotsk, Tinro Basin, Deryugina Basin, Instituta Okeanologii Rise, Akademii Nauk Rise, Kuril Basin, Kuril Islands, Kuril–Kamchatka Trench, Zenkevich Rise, CHINA, Sakhalin, Tatarskiy Proliv, Vladivostok, Japan Basin, Hokkaidō, Northwest Pacific Basin, NORTH KOREA, Sea of Japan, P'yongyang, Yamato Bank, JAPAN, Seoul, Yamato Basin, SOUTH KOREA, Yellow Sea, Honshū, Tokyo, Japan Trench, Shichito-Iōjima Ridge, Isakov Seamount, Shah Ris, Kyūshū, Shikoku, East China Sea, Nankai Trough, Shikoku Basin, Izu-Ogasawara Trench, Makarov Seamount, Daitō Ridge, Oki-Daitō Ridge, Kyushu-palau Ridge, Mid-Pacif

Albatross population
Before the 1930s millions of short-tailed albatrosses *(Phoebastria albatrus)* roamed the North Pacific. Hunted for its feathers, the bird was considered extinct by 1950. But some 50 juveniles survived at sea and began breeding again on Torishima Island in Japan. Today's population is estimated at 1,200.

SCALE 1:40,000,000
Miller Projection

1000 kilometers
1000 statute miles
1000 nautical miles

Siwash Rock
The moon sets over the approaches to the Port of Vancouver, Canada. Siwash Rock stands guard near the city's Stanley Park. A striking landmark during both calm and stormy days, the rock features in native American legends.

Mount Augustine
Augustine volcano on Augustine Island in Cook Inlet, Alaska, 174 miles (280 km) southwest of Anchorage, is one of several active volcanoes of the Ring of Fire. Steam plumes rich in sulfur dioxide disrupted air traffic in 1986, 1994, and 2006, and deposited ash on the city of Anchorage.

Bering Sea

The Bering Sea is the world's third largest marginal sea (after the Arctic Ocean and the Mediterranean Sea). In the northeast it forms part of the highly productive Siberian–Alaskan shelf. In the south it consists of a deep basin that is subdivided by the Shirshov and Bowers ridges. The Aleutian Islands form part of the Ring of Fire and carry several active volcanoes. Bering Strait, its connection with the Arctic Ocean, is only 53 miles (85 km) wide and less than 160 feet (50 m) deep but is important for the global water budget by returning to the Atlantic the fresh water that came as rain across the Isthmus of Panama. Sea ice builds up in November and covers the shelf from January. Ice break-up begins in April; by July the entire region is ice-free. To protect spectacular cold-water "coral gardens," 60 percent of the Aleutian shallow water habitat is closed to bottom trawling.

Adak Island
Adak Island, in the Andreanof group of the Aleutian Islands, was abandoned by the native Aleut in the 1800s. During World War II its population grew to 6,000; today it has a population of about 300. In 1957 an earthquake in this region caused a tsunami that reached a height of 52 feet (16 m) in Hawaii.

The Facts

Area	884,900 square miles (2,291,880 km²)
Average depth	5,075 feet (1547 m)
Maximum depth	15,659 feet (4,773 m)
Maximum width	1,490 miles (2,398 km)
Maximum length	990 miles (1,593 km)

NATURAL RESOURCES

- Fishing
- Shellfish

Surface currents
Two systems make up the currents of the Bering Sea. Counterclockwise circulation in the deep basin supplies some water to the Oyashio through the Kamchatka Current, while water from the Alaskan Stream crosses the shallow eastern region to join the Anadyr Current toward Bering Strait.

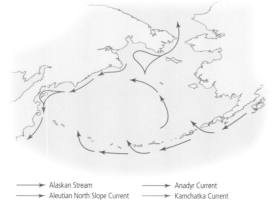

- Alaskan Stream
- Aleutian North Slope Current
- Anadyr Current
- Kamchatka Current

Humpback whale
Humpback whales (*Megaptera novaeangliae*) live in distinct populations in all polar waters during summer and migrate to give birth in subtropical or tropical waters in winter. Males communicate through songs that change from year to year.

Beluga
The beluga or white whale (*Delphinapterus leucas*), a whale species of the Arctic and subarctic oceans, grows to 15 feet (5 m) in length. It spends the summers in bays, estuaries, and shallow inlets and follows the progressing ice edge into open water in winter.

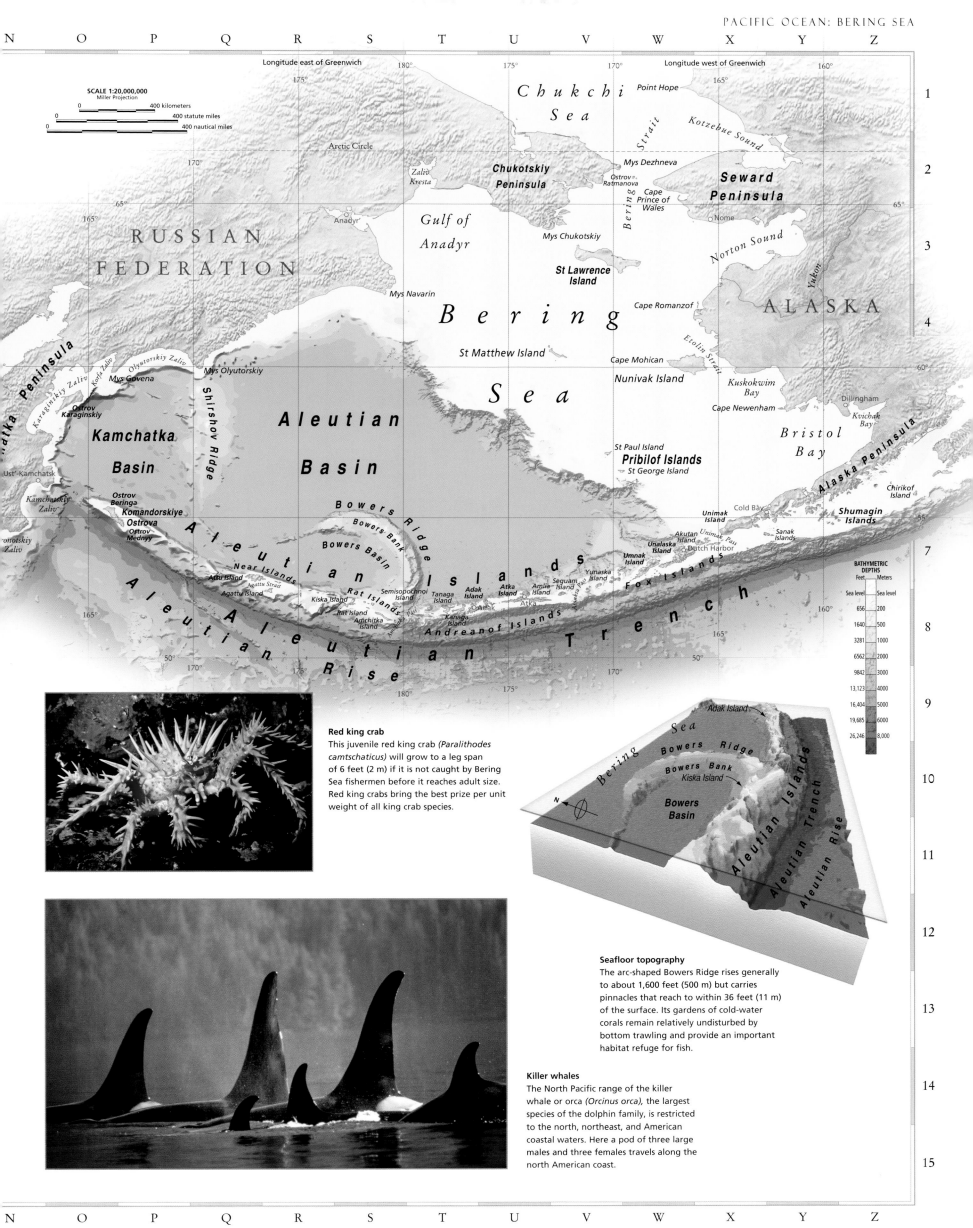

N O P Q R S T U V W X Y Z

Longitude east of Greenwich   Longitude west of Greenwich

SCALE 1:20,000,000
Miller Projection

0   400 kilometers
0   400 statute miles
0   400 nautical miles

Chukchi Sea

Point Hope

Arctic Circle

Kotzebue Sound

Mys Dezhneva
Ostrov Ratmanova

Chukotskiy Peninsula

Cape Prince of Wales

Seward Peninsula

Zaliv Kresta

Nome

Anadyr'

Gulf of Anadyr

Mys Chukotskiy

Norton Sound

RUSSIAN FEDERATION

St Lawrence Island

Cape Romanzof

ALASKA

Mys Navarin

Bering

St Matthew Island

Cape Mohican

Sea

Nunivak Island

Kuskokwim Bay

Dillingham

Kvichak Bay

Kamchatka Peninsula

Olyutorskiy Zaliv
Mys Govena
Mys Olyutorskiy

Shirshov Ridge

Aleutian Basin

Cape Newenham

Bristol Bay

St Paul Island

Pribilof Islands
St George Island

Ust'-Kamchatsk

Kamchatka Basin

Ostrov Karaginskiy
Karaginskiy Zaliv
Kronotskiy Zaliv
Kamchatskiy Zaliv

Ostrov Beringa
Komandorskiye Ostrova
Ostrov Mednyy

Bowers Ridge
Bowers Bank
Bowers Basin

Unimak Island

Cold Bay

Alaska Peninsula

Chirikof Island

Aleutian Rise

Near Islands

Attu Island
Agattu Island
Agattu Strait
Kiska Island

Aleutian

Rat Islands
Rat Island
Amchitka Island

Semisopochnoi Island
Tanaga Island
Kanaga Island
Adak

Islands

Adak Island
Atka Island
Atka

Amlia Island

Seguam Island

Yunaska Island

Fox Islands

Umnak Island

Unalaska Island
Akutan Island
Dutch Harbor

Unimak Pass

Sanak Islands

Shumagin Islands

Aleutian Trench

BATHYMETRIC DEPTHS

Feet	Meters
Sea level	Sea level
656	200
1640	500
3281	1000
6562	2000
9842	3000
13,123	4000
16,404	5000
19,685	6000
26,246	8,000

Red king crab
This juvenile red king crab *(Paralithodes camtschaticus)* will grow to a leg span of 6 feet (2 m) if it is not caught by Bering Sea fishermen before it reaches adult size. Red king crabs bring the best prize per unit weight of all king crab species.

Adak Island

Bering Sea

Bowers Ridge
Bowers Bank
Kiska Island
Bowers Basin

N

Aleutian Islands

Aleutian Trench

Aleutian Rise

Seafloor topography
The arc-shaped Bowers Ridge rises generally to about 1,600 feet (500 m) but carries pinnacles that reach to within 36 feet (11 m) of the surface. Its gardens of cold-water corals remain relatively undisturbed by bottom trawling and provide an important habitat refuge for fish.

Killer whales
The North Pacific range of the killer whale or orca *(Orcinus orca),* the largest species of the dolphin family, is restricted to the north, northeast, and American coastal waters. Here a pod of three large males and three females travels along the north American coast.

N O P Q R S T U V W X Y Z

Gulf of Alaska

The circulation system in the Gulf of Alaska is determined by the eastern part of the Subpolar Gyre. Fed by the North Pacific Current, the Alaska Current and the Alaskan Stream follow the coast from the Alexander Archipelago to Unimak Island. Eddies measuring 120 miles (200 km) across are regularly found near Sitka and Queen Charlotte Islands. Fresh water from calving glaciers in Glacier Bay National Park and Preserve and other fjords lowers the salinity in the Alaska Current. The Inside Passage between the Alexander Archipelago and the mainland allows ships to avoid storms in the open gulf. The gulf is also exposed to tsunamis generated by earthquakes in the Queen Charlotte–Fairweather Fault System; the largest tsunami ever observed was triggered by a rockfall in Lituya Bay. A hot spot near Queen Charlotte Islands created the now-extinct volcanoes of the Kodiak-Bowie Seamount Chain. Cold-water corals are found near Kodiak and Queen Charlotte islands.

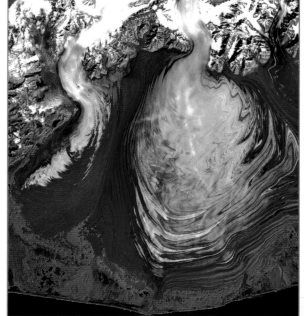
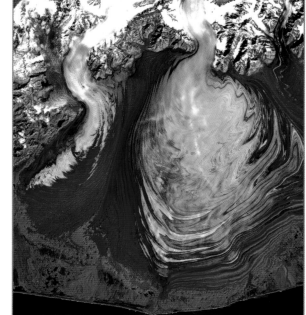

Malaspina Glacier
Where several valley glaciers spill onto the Alaskan coastal plain they form the Malaspina Glacier, seen here in a false-color satellite image. As a typical "piedmont glacier" the Malaspina Glacier does not reach the gulf but supplies its meltwater through streams from two lakes.

The Facts

Area	592,000 square miles (1,533,273 km²)
Average depth	7,976 feet (2,431 m)
Maximum depth	16,500 feet (5,029 m)
Maximum width	240 miles (400 km)
Maximum length	1,200 miles (2,000 km)

NATURAL RESOURCES

➤ Fishing
▣ Tourism

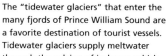

Surface currents
Water transport in the Alaska Current, also known as the Alaska Coastal Current, increases along its way due to freshwater input from meltwater and rivers. Its temperature, however, remains high, above 39°F (4°C), due to the supply of warm water from the North Pacific Current.

→ Alaska Current
→ Alaskan Stream
→ North Pacific Current

Prince William Sound
The "tidewater glaciers" that enter the many fjords of Prince William Sound are a favorite destination of tourist vessels. Tidewater glaciers supply meltwater through the calving of icebergs, which can create a huge wave. Cruise ships are well advised to keep their distance.

Breadcrumb sponge
A breadcrumb sponge (Halichondria panicea) is exposed at low tide on Kodiak Island. Breadcrumb sponges are common in the intertidal zone of all oceans. They occur in a wide range of forms and colors and have been described under more than 50 different names.

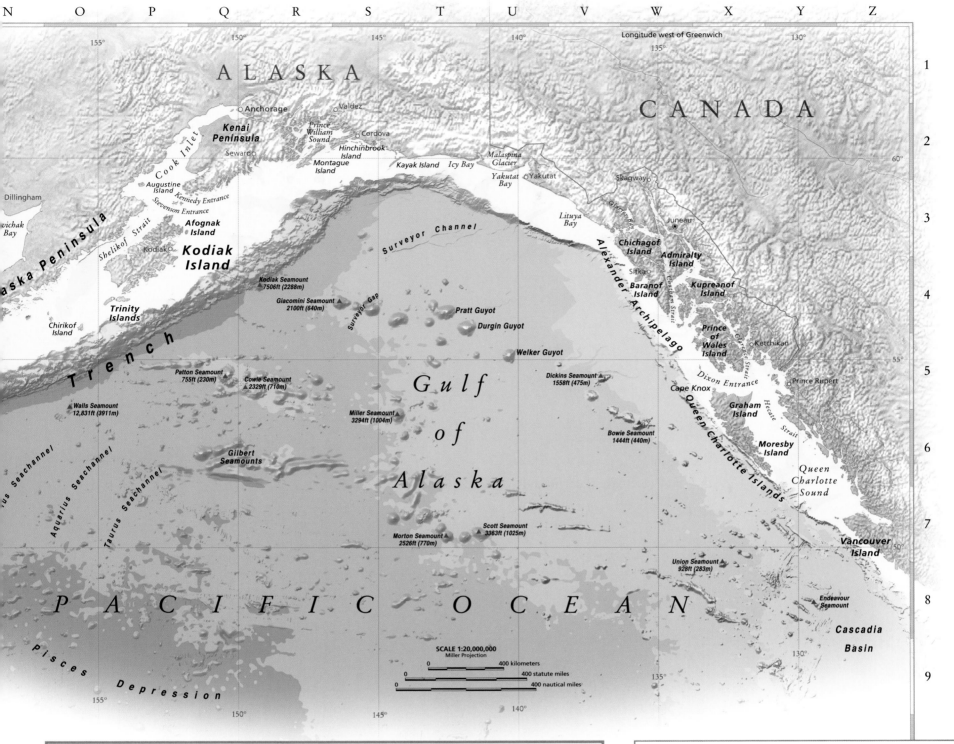

N O P Q R S T U V W X Y Z

Longitude west of Greenwich

150°   145°   140°   135°   130°

1

ALASKA

Anchorage

CANADA

Valdez

Kenai Peninsula

Prince William Sound

Cordova

Seward

Hinchinbrook Island

Montague Island

Kayak Island   Icy Bay

Malaspina Glacier

Yakutat Bay   Yakutat

2

60°

Dillingham

Augustine Island

Kennedy Entrance

Stevenson Entrance

Alaska Peninsula

vichak Bay

Shelikof Strait

Afognak Island

Kodiak

Kodiak Island

Lituya Bay

Skagway

Juneau

Chichagof Island

Admiralty Island

Sitka

Baranof Island

Alexander Archipelago

Kupreanof Island

3

Chirikof Island

Trinity Islands

Kodiak Seamount 7506ft (2288m)

Giacomini Seamount 2100ft (640m)

Surveyor Gap

Surveyor Channel

Pratt Guyot

Durgin Guyot

Welker Guyot

Prince of Wales Island

Ketchikan

Cape Knox

Dixon Entrance

Prince Rupert

4

55°

Trench

Patton Seamount 755ft (230m)

Cowie Seamount 2329ft (710m)

Gulf of Alaska

Miller Seamount 3294ft (1004m)

Dickins Seamount 1558ft (475m)

Bowie Seamount 1444ft (440m)

Graham Island

Hecate Strait

Moresby Island

Queen Charlotte Islands

5

Walls Seamount 12,831ft (3911m)

us Seachannel

Aquarius Seachannel

Taurus Seachannel

Gilbert Seamounts

Morton Seamount 2526ft (770m)

Scott Seamount 3363ft (1025m)

Union Seamount 928ft (283m)

Queen Charlotte Sound

6

Vancouver Island

50°

7

P A C I F I C   O C E A N

Endeavour Seamount

8

Pisces Depression

SCALE 1:20,000,000
Miller Projection

0   400 kilometers

0   400 statute miles

0   400 nautical miles

Cascadia Basin

130°

135°

9

155°   150°   145°   140°

N O P Q R S T U V W X Y Z

13

14

15

173

SOCKEYE SALMON

Sockeye salmon *(Oncorhynchus nerka)* are found in cold waters from northern Japan in the west to Canada in the east. They spawn in streams and lakes, where the young fish spend up to four years before they migrate to the ocean. After another one to four years they change from bluish–green to red, and return to the rivers to spawn.

Marine Highway
A ferry of the Alaska Marine Highway System, a ferry service that forms part of the National Highway System of the USA, makes its way through the Inside Passage. The ferries serve 32 destinations, some without road access, over a distance of 3,500 miles (5,600 km).

HAWAIIAN ISLANDS

Formed over a hot spot to their southeast, the Hawaiian Islands are a chain of 137 islands and atolls, numerous smaller islands, and seamounts that stretch northwestward to Midway and Kure atolls. Mauna Loa and Kilauea on Hawaii, the largest of the nine major islands and the closest to the hot spot, are the only active island volcanoes today. Loihi, a submerged volcano closer to the hot spot, is still 3,200 feet (975 m) below the surface but is growing and active. The smaller islands and atolls form a marine protected area, the Papahanaumokuakea Marine National Monument. Tsunamis from distant shores have reached the Hawaiian Islands on several occasions. The islands form an obstacle to the North Equatorial Current and the trade winds, and create a wake effect some 1,900 miles (3,000 km) long in the atmosphere. This produces an eastward-flowing counter-current on their western side.

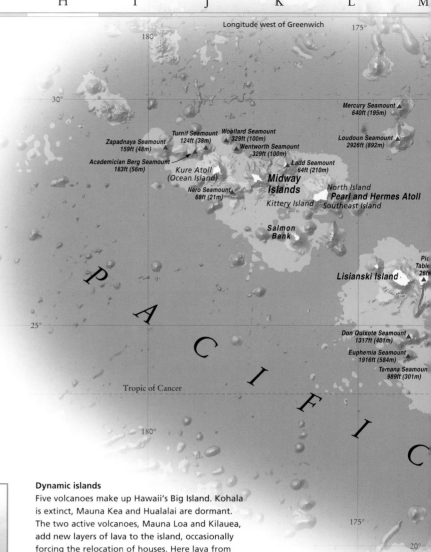

Dynamic islands
Five volcanoes make up Hawaii's Big Island. Kohala is extinct, Mauna Kea and Hualalai are dormant. The two active volcanoes, Mauna Loa and Kilauea, add new layers of lava to the island, occasionally forcing the relocation of houses. Here lava from Kilauea reaches the ocean.

VOLCANOES

Hawaii's volcanoes are "shield volcanoes," built by the supply of low-viscosity lava that can flow over great distances. This false-color composite image of the Big Island (processed to simulate true color) shows the spreading range of Mauna Loa to the south, with Mauna Kea's crater to the north. Kilauea is in the east, Kohala in the northwest.

SCALE 1:10,000,000
Miller Projection

0   200 kilometers
0   200 statute miles
0   200 nautical miles

Surface currents
The Hawaiian Islands are located in the center of the Subtropical Gyre, so currents in their vicinity are relatively weak and undefined. The prevailing flow follows the North Equatorial Current but is interrupted by several countercurrents produced in the wake of the major islands.

→ North Equatorial Current
→ North Pacific Current
→ Subtropical Countercurrents

BATHYMETRIC DEPTHS
Feet	Meters
Sea level	Sea level
656	200
1640	500
3281	1000
6562	2000
9842	3000
13,123	4000
16,404	5000
19,685	6000
26,246	8,000

Mauna Kea crater
The snow-capped crater of Mauna Kea, which rises to 13,803 feet (4,207 m) above the sea and 33,476 feet (10,203 m) above its base on the ocean floor.

NATURAL RESOURCES

✦ Fishing
▣ Tourism

Green turtle
The green turtle (Chelonia mydas) lives in tropical and subtropical waters of all oceans. Its Hawaiian subpopulation nests on French Frigate Shoals 500 miles (800 km) northwest of the islands. A tagging and research program, begun in 1973, brought the population back from near-extinction.

Lionfish
Lionfishes are found in the Indian and Pacific oceans. Easily recognized by their long, separated spines, they are among the most venomous fish in the ocean. This Hawaiian lionfish (Pterois sphex), a species endemic to Hawaii, rests in a slate pencil sea urchin (Heterocentrotus mammillatus).

SEA OF OKHOTSK

The Sea of Okhotsk is set between the Siberian coast in the west and north, the Kamchatka Peninsula in the east, and the volcanically active Kuril Islands in the south. It falls off gradually from a wide shelf in the north to a deep basin in the south. Numerous deep passages between the Kuril Islands connect it with the main Pacific basins; straits east and west of Sakhalin Island provide connections to the Sea of Japan. During the winter monsoon (October–April) the sea is covered with drift ice, but storm winds from Siberia can still cause waves to rise up to 30 feet (10 m). Summer winds are light and calm conditions are encountered for 30 percent of the time. Currents circulate counterclockwise with moderate speed; in the south the Soya Warm Current, an extension of the Tsushima Current, passes rapidly from the Sea of Japan through the southern Kuril Islands.

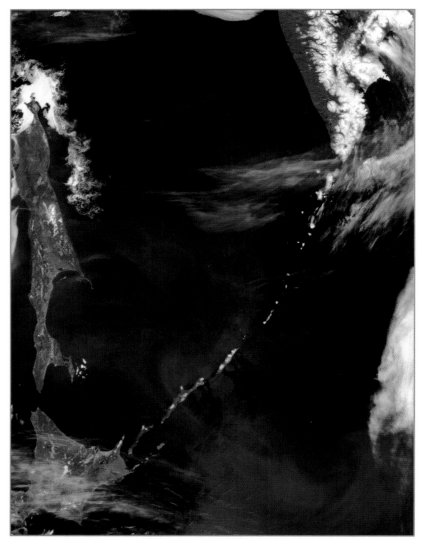

THE FACTS	
Area	611,000 square miles (1,582,483 km²)
Average depth	2,818 feet (859 m)
Maximum depth	11,063 feet (3,742 m)
Maximum width	932 miles (1,500 km)
Maximum length	1,530 miles (2,463 km)

Kuril Islands
Snow covers the peaks of the 56 Kuril Islands that stretch for 700 miles (1,300 km) from Hokkaido, Japan, to Kamchatka, Russia. Different water coloration, visible under thin cloud cover, indicates patches of high productivity where the Soya Warm Current and the Kamchatka Current meet.

NATURAL RESOURCES

↤ Fishing
⛽ Oil production

ICE FLOES

Salt lowers the freezing point of water, so the first ice to form is from fresh water in rivers. When the temperature drops to 28.8°F (-1.8°C) ice begins to form on the sea. Wind and waves break it up into pancake ice. Compacted pancake ice builds up to ice floes that drift with the current and can be piled up into pack ice.

Oil rig
The shelf regions of the Sea of Okhotsk contain large oil and gas reserves that are difficult to access because of the extreme weather conditions in winter. This tanker-loading unit on the Sakhalin shelf is used to transfer oil from a pipeline to tankers.

A low winter sun shines on a thin sheet of new ice that forms in a river mouth. In the background the current carries parcels of older ice toward the sea.

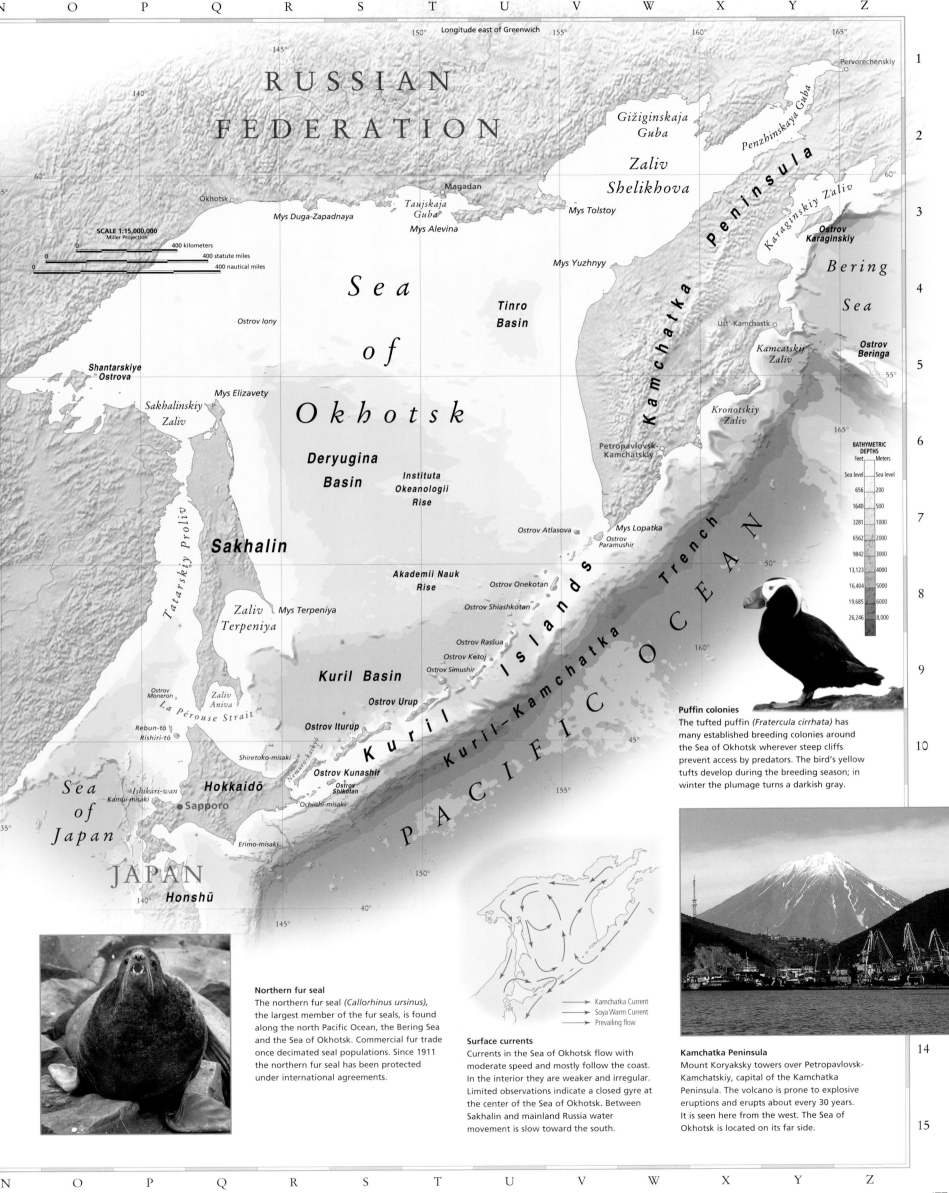

N O P Q R S T U V W X Y Z

1

Longitude east of Greenwich

RUSSIAN

FEDERATION

Gižiginskaja
Guba

Penzhinskaya Guba

2

Zaliv
Shelikhova

Kamchatka Peninsula

60°

Okhotsk

Magadan

Mys Tolstoy

Karaginskiy Z'aliv

Ostrov
Karaginskiy

3

Mys Duga-Zapadnaya

Taujskaja
Guba

Mys Alevina

SCALE 1:15,000,000
Miller Projection

400 kilometers

400 statute miles

400 nautical miles

Mys Yuzhnyy

Bering

Sea

Sea

of

Okhotsk

Ostrov Iony

Tinro
Basin

Ust'-Kamchastk

Ostrov
Beringa

Kamcatskij
Zaliv

4

55°

5

Shantarskiye
Ostrova

Mys Elizavety

Sakhalinskiy
Zaliv

Kronotskiy
Zaliv

165°

6

Deryugina

Basin

Instituta
Okeanologii
Rise

Petropavlovsk-
Kamchatskiy

BATHYMETRIC
DEPTHS
Feet   Meters

Sea level   Sea level

656   200

1640   500

3281   1000

6562   2000

9842   3000

13,123   4000

16,404   5000

19,685   6000

26,246   8,000

7

Sakhalin

Tatarskiy Proliv

Ostrov Atlasova

Mys Lopatka

Ostrov
Paramushir

8

Akademii Nauk
Rise

Ostrov Onekotan

Zaliv
Terpeniya

Mys Terpeniya

Ostrov Shiashkotan

50°

160°

Puffin colonies

9

Kuril Basin

Ostrov Rassua

Ostrov Ketoj

Ostrov Simushir

Ostrov Urup

Kuril Islands

Kuril–Kamchatka Trench

PACIFIC OCEAN

The tufted puffin (*Fratercula cirrhata*) has
many established breeding colonies around
the Sea of Okhotsk wherever steep cliffs
prevent access by predators. The bird's yellow
tufts develop during the breeding season; in
winter the plumage turns a darkish gray.

Ostrov
Moneron

Zaliv
Aniva

La Pérouse Strait

Rebun-tō
Rishiri-tō

Ostrov Iturup

Shiretoko-misaki

Nemuro-kaikyō

45°

10

Sea
of
Japan

Ishikari-wan
Kamui-misaki

Sapporo

Hokkaidō

Ostrov Kunashir

Ostrov
Shikotan

Ochiishi-misaki

155°

135°

JAPAN

140°

Honshū

Erimo-misaki

40°

150°

14

Northern fur seal

The northern fur seal (*Callorhinus ursinus*),
the largest member of the fur seals, is found
along the north Pacific Ocean, the Bering Sea
and the Sea of Okhotsk. Commercial fur trade
once decimated seal populations. Since 1911
the northern fur seal has been protected
under international agreements.

Kamchatka Current

Soya Warm Current

Prevailing flow

Surface currents

Currents in the Sea of Okhotsk flow with
moderate speed and mostly follow the coast.
In the interior they are weaker and irregular.
Limited observations indicate a closed gyre at
the center of the Sea of Okhotsk. Between
Sakhalin and mainland Russia water
movement is slow toward the south.

Kamchatka Peninsula

Mount Koryaksky towers over Petropavlovsk-
Kamchatskiy, capital of the Kamchatka
Peninsula. The volcano is prone to explosive
eruptions and erupts about every 30 years.
It is seen here from the west. The Sea of
Okhotsk is located on its far side.

15

N O P Q R S T U V W X Y Z

SEA OF JAPAN (EAST SEA)

The Sea of Japan, or East Sea, consists of isolated deep basins separated by a shallow ridge on which the Yamato Bank comes up to a depth of 177 feet (285 m). It connects with the Yellow Sea through Korea Strait, with the Sea of Okhotsk through La Perouse Strait and Tartar Strait, and with the main Pacific basins through Tsugaru Strait in the north and the narrow Kanmon Straits in the south. All of these straits are less than 120 feet (200 m) deep, so water in the basins is renewed through the sinking of cold surface water during winter. The North Korea Cold Current carries water from the Sea of Okhotsk to the subtropics. The warm Tsushima Current, a branch of the Kuroshio, flows swiftly northward. An unstable front between the two currents sheds eddies some 120 miles (200 km) wide every year. These eddies dominate most of the southern region.

THE FACTS	
Area	377,600 square miles (977,979 km^2)
Average depth	5,748 feet (1,751 m)
Maximum depth	12,276 feet (3,742 m)

Moray eel
The tiger moray eel *(Enchelycore pardalis)*, one of some 200 moray eel species, lives in coral reefs in shallow water of the tropical and subtropical Indo-Pacific. Morays are shy and reclusive. They rest in crevices during the day and are nocturnal predators.

Shark fins
Kesennuma in northeast Honshu is the center of a shark-fin industry. Shark-fin soup is a delicacy in China, where growing prosperity has led to increased demand. Many countries have banned the practice of cutting fins from living sharks and leaving the animals to die.

SPIDER CRAB

The Japanese spider crab *(Macrocheira kaempferi)* is the largest crab of the world's oceans. With a body of around 15 inches (40 cm) its legs reach a span of more than 10 feet (3 m). It lives around the islands of Japan at depths below 100 feet (300 m), where it feeds on dead animals and shellfish. At maturity it may weigh about 44 pounds (20 kg) and is believed to be very long-lived.

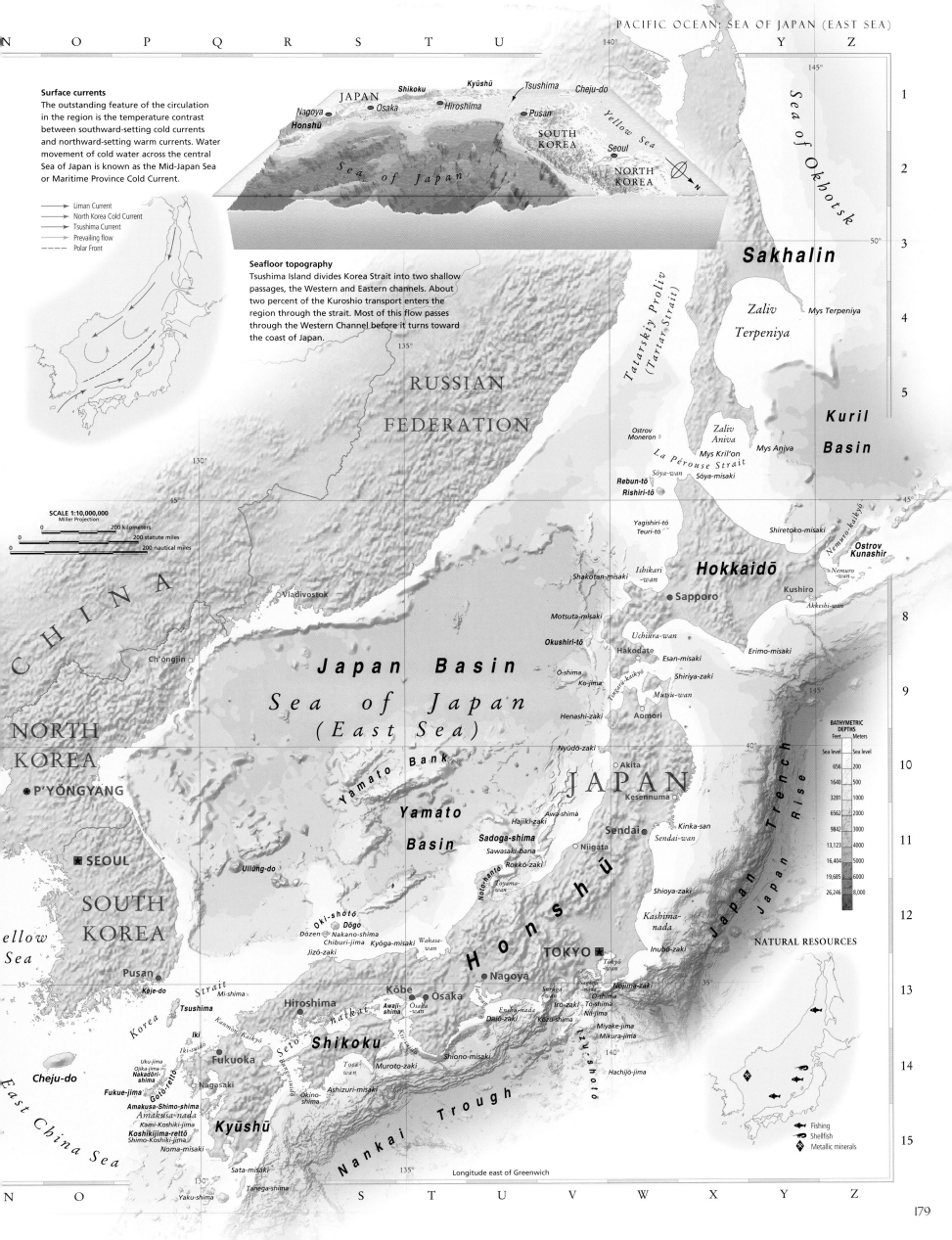

Surface currents

The outstanding feature of the circulation in the region is the temperature contrast between southward-setting cold currents and northward-setting warm currents. Water movement of cold water across the central Sea of Japan is known as the Mid-Japan Sea or Maritime Province Cold Current.

→ Liman Current
→ North Korea Cold Current
→ Tsushima Current
→ Prevailing flow
--- Polar Front

Seafloor topography

Tsushima Island divides Korea Strait into two shallow passages, the Western and Eastern channels. About two percent of the Kuroshio transport enters the region through the strait. Most of this flow passes through the Western Channel before it turns toward the coast of Japan.

JAPAN
Nagoya • Osaka Shikoku Kyūshū Tsushima
Honshū   • Hiroshima   • Pusan   Cheju-do
Sea   of   Japan   SOUTH   Yellow
KOREA   Sea
Seoul
NORTH
KOREA

SCALE 1:10,000,000
Miller Projection
0   200 kilometers
0   200 statute miles
0   200 nautical miles

RUSSIAN

FEDERATION

Sea of Okhotsk

Sakhalin

Zaliv
Terpeniya   Mys Terpeniya

Tatarskiy Proliv
(Tartar Strait)

Kuril

Basin

Ostrov
Moneron   *Zaliv*
Aniva
La Pérouse Strait   Mys Kril'on   Mys Aniva
Rebun-tō   Sōya-wan
Rishiri-tō   Sōya-misaki

Yagishiri-tō
Teuri-tō   Shiretoko-misaki   Nemuro-kaikyō

Hokkaidō   Ostrov
Kunashir
Shakotan-misaki   Nemuro-
Ishikari   wan
-wan   • Sapporo   Kushiro

CHINA
Motsuta-misaki   Akkeshi-wan

• Vladivostok   Uchiura-wan   Erimo-misaki
Okushiri-tō   Hakodate   Esan-misaki
Ō-shima   Esan-misaki
Ko-jima   Shiriya-zaki

Ch'ŏngjin   Tsugaru-kaikyō   Mutsu-wan

Japan   Basin
Henashi-zaki   Aomori

Sea   of   Japan
(East   Sea)   Nyūdō-zaki   • Akita

NORTH   **JAPAN**
KOREA   Kesennuma

Yamato   Bank
◆ P'YŎNGYANG   Awa-shima
Hajiki-zaki   Kinka-san
Yamato   Sadoga-shima   Sendai • Sendai-wan
Basin   Sawasaki-bana   • Niigata
Rokkō-zaki
Ullŭng-do   Notohantō
Toyama-
◆ SEOUL   wan

Shioya-zaki

SOUTH   Kashima-
KOREA   Oki-shōtō   nada
Dōgo   Inubō-zaki   **NATURAL RESOURCES**
Dōzen • Nakano-shima
Chiburi-jima   Kyōga-misaki   Wakasa-
Jizō-zaki   wan   TOKYO ◆   Tōkyō-
Pusan   wan
Kōje-do   Strait   Mi-shima   Kōbe   • Nagoya   Suruga-   Nojima-zaki
Tsushima   nada   Sagami-   Ō-shima
Iki   Awaji-   • Osaka   Iro-zaki   To-shima
shima   Osaka-   Enshū-nada   Kōzu-shima   Nii-jima
Kanmon-Kaikyō   wan   Daiō-zaki   Miyake-jima
Uku-jima   Iki-suidō   Seto   Naikai   Mikura-jima
Ojika-jima   • Fukuoka   Tosa-   Shiono-misaki
Nakadōri-   Bungo-suidō   wan   Hachijō-jima
shima   Okino-   Ashizuri-misaki   Muroto-zaki
Fukue-jima   shima
Gotō-rettō   Kyūshū   Shimo-
Amakusa-Shimo-shima   Koshiki-jima
Amakusa-nada
Kami-Koshiki-jima   Sata-misaki   Fishing
Koshikijima-rettō   Shellfish
Shimo-Koshiki-jima   Yaku-shima   Tanega-shima   Metallic minerals
Noma-misaki

Korea   **Tsushima**
Strait

Shikoku

Nankai   Trough

Yellow
Sea

Cheju-do

East China Sea

Honshū

Hiroshima

Izu-shotō

Longitude east of Greenwich

**BATHYMETRIC
DEPTHS**
Feet | Meters
Sea level | Sea level
656 | 200
1640 | 500
3281 | 1000
6562 | 2000
9842 | 4000
13,123 | 5000
16,404 | 6000
19,685 | 7000
26,246 | 8,000

Japan Trench
Japan Rise

Header row: A B C D E F G H I J K L M

EAST CHINA SEA AND YELLOW SEA

The vast shelf region between Taiwan in the south and Korea in the north comprises two interconnected seas. The region south of a line between Kyushu and Shanghai is known as the East China Sea. It connects with the South China Sea through Taiwan Strait and with the main Pacific basins to the south of Kyushu and through passages between the Ryukyu Islands. The deep, fast-flowing, Kuroshio Current carries warm, saline water along its eastern perimeter. Dilution from the Yangtze River lowers salinity in the west. North of Shanghai the Yellow Sea connects to the Sea of Japan through Korea Strait. Sediment brought from China's loess plateau by the Yellow River (Hwang Ho), which enters the region through the Bo Hai Gulf, gives the Yellow Sea its name. Its wide intertidal mudflats are an important resting place for millions of wading birds during their migration from Siberia and Alaska to the southern hemisphere.

Sediment flow
A true-color satellite image reveals the effect of sediment carried by the Yellow River plume far out into the Bo Hai Sea. Some coastal waters are turbid from tidal current action. Farther south the coastal region is affected by the discharge of the Yangtze River.

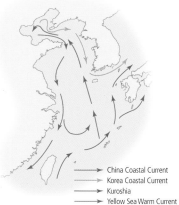

China Coastal Current
Korea Coastal Current
Kuroshia
Yellow Sea Warm Current

Surface currents
The circulation in the East China Sea and Yellow Sea is counterclockwise and follows the coast. A warm current branches off from the Kuroshio and flows into the center of the region. Another off-shoot from the Kuroshio enters the East China Sea from the south.

NATURAL RESOURCES

Fishing
Shellfish
Tourism

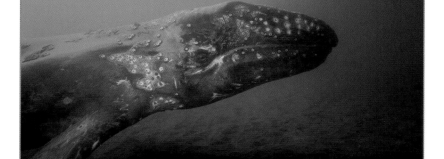

Yangtze River estuary
After flowing east for almost 4,000 miles (6,380 km), the waters of the Yangtze River finally reach the sea at Shanghai. The river's annual sediment load combined with that of the Yellow River makes up more than 10 percent of the total sediment flux to the world's oceans.

Gray whale
The endangered Asian population of gray whales (Eschrichtius robustus), which consists of less than 300 animals, migrates between the Sea of Okhotsk and Korea. Gray whales once also lived in the North Atlantic. Some 21,000 gray whales still migrate in the eastern Pacific between Alaska and California.

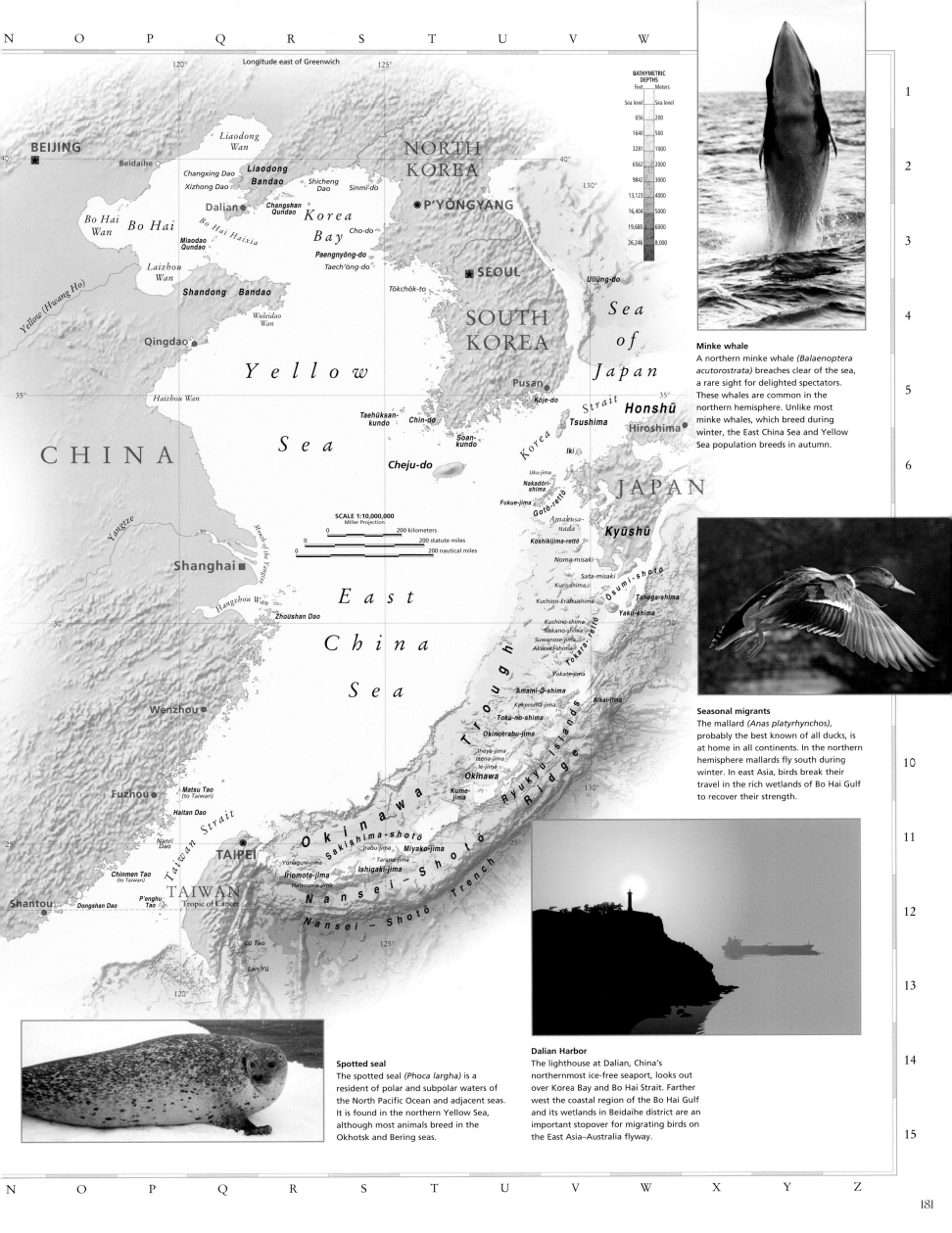

Longitude east of Greenwich

120°   125°

130°

BATHYMETRIC
DEPTHS

Feet	Meters
Sea level	Sea level
656	200
1640	500
3281	1000
6562	2000
9842	3000
13,123	4000
16,404	5000
19,685	6000
26,246	8,000

BEIJING

Beidaihe

Liaodong
Wan

**Liaodong
Bandao**

Changxing Dao

Xizhong Dao

Shicheng
Dao

Sinmi-do

**NORTH
KOREA**

Dalian

Changshan
Qundao

Cho-do

●**P'YŎNGYANG**

Bo Hai
Wan

Bo Hai

Bo Hai Haixia

Miaodao
Qundao

Paengnyŏng-do

Korea
Bay

Laizhou
Wan

Taech'ŏng-do

Shandong Bandao

Wuleidao
Wan

★ SEOUL

Qingdao

**SOUTH
KOREA**

Sea
of
Japan

Ullŭng-do

Haizhou Wan

35°

35°

CHINA

Yellow

Tökchök-to

Pusan

Kŏje-do

Korea Strait

Honshū

Tsushima

Hiroshima

Yellow (Hwang Ho)

Taehŭksan-
kundo

Chin-do

Iki

Korea Strait

Sea

Soan-
kundo

Uku-jima

**Nakadōri-
shima**

Cheju-do

Fukue-jima

Gotō-rettō

JAPAN

Amakusa-
nada

Kyūshū

Koshikijima-rettō

Yangtze

Mouth of the Yangtze

SCALE 1:10,000,000
Miller Projection

0   200 kilometers

0   200 statute miles

0   200 nautical miles

Noma-misaki

Sata-misaki

Ōsumi-shotō

Shanghai

Kuro-shima

Kuchino-Erabushima

Tanega-shima

Kuchino-shima

Yaku-shima

East

Nakano-shima

30°

Suwanose-shima

30°

Akuseki-shima

China

Zhoushan Dao

Hangzhou Wan

Yokate-jima

Sea

Amami-Ō-shima

Kekeroma-shima

Kikai-jima

Wenzhou

Toku-no-shima

Okinawa Trough

Okinoerabu-jima

Iheya-jima

Izena-jima

Ie-jima

Okinawa

Kume-
jima

Ryukyu Islands Ridge

Fuzhou

Matsu Tao
(to Taiwan)

Haitan Dao

Sakishima-shotō

130°

Irabu-jima

Miyako-jima

25°

Nanri
Dao

Yonaguni-jima

Tarana-jima

25°

TAIPEI

Iriomote-jima

Ishigaki-jima

Hateruma-jima

Chinmen Tao
(to Taiwan)

Nansei-Shotō Trench

TAIWAN

Dongshan Dao

P'enghu
Tao

Tropic of Cancer

Shantou

Nansei-Shotō

Taiwan Strait

Lü Tao

125°

Lan Yü

120°

Minke whale
A northern minke whale (*Balaenoptera
acutorostrata*) breaches clear of the sea,
a rare sight for delighted spectators.
These whales are common in the
northern hemisphere. Unlike most
minke whales, which breed during
winter, the East China Sea and Yellow
Sea population breeds in autumn.

Seasonal migrants
The mallard (*Anas platyrhynchos*),
probably the best known of all ducks, is
at home in all continents. In the northern
hemisphere mallards fly south during
winter. In east Asia, birds break their
travel in the rich wetlands of Bo Hai Gulf
to recover their strength.

Spotted seal
The spotted seal (*Phoca largha*) is a
resident of polar and subpolar waters of
the North Pacific Ocean and adjacent seas.
It is found in the northern Yellow Sea,
although most animals breed in the
Okhotsk and Bering seas.

Dalian Harbor
The lighthouse at Dalian, China's
northernmost ice-free seaport, looks out
over Korea Bay and Bo Hai Strait. Farther
west the coastal region of the Bo Hai Gulf
and its wetlands in Beidaihe district are an
important stopover for migrating birds on
the East Asia–Australia flyway.

1
2
3
4
5
6
10
11
12
13
14
15

WESTERN TROPICAL PACIFIC OCEAN

Deep trenches, isolated deep basins, myriad seamounts, and Micronesia's many hundred islands characterize the Western Tropical Pacific. The North Equatorial Countercurrent has its source here and the region is important for water exchange between ocean basins. North of New Guinea the South Equatorial Current and New Guinea Coastal Current combine to feed southern hemisphere water into the countercurrent, forming the Halmahera Eddy in the process. The North Equatorial Current adds northern hemisphere water through the Mindanao Eddy but also directs substantial amounts into the Indonesian seas toward the Indian Ocean. The heavily populated regions in its west, where fishing has been supplemented by aquaculture for centuries, contrast with the pristine conditions of the islands in the east and south. The high water temperatures of the "West Pacific Warm Pool" are the source of cyclones and play a key role in the El Niño–Southern Oscillation phenomenon.

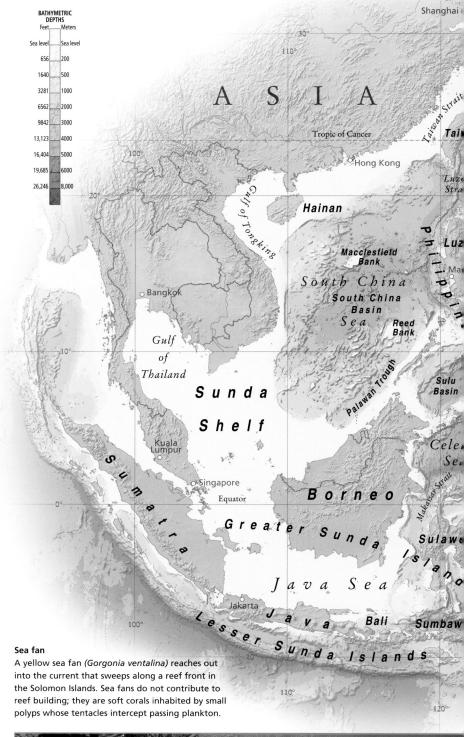

Outrigger
Pacific islanders navigated their vast ocean space in outrigger canoes for centuries, using star constellations, swell patterns, and bird flight to guide them. This Melanesian is on a less challenging voyage; he heads for a nearby village to participate in a village festivity.

Surface currents
The western tropical Pacific plays a key role in the global oceanic circulation. It is the main region of the Pacific where currents transfer water between the two hemispheres, and it provides an opening into the Indonesian seas for water movement from the Pacific to the Indian Ocean.

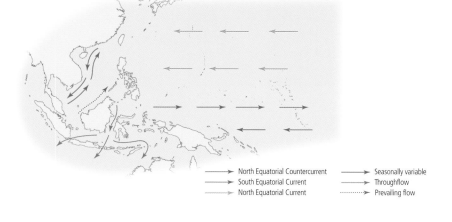

Sea fan
A yellow sea fan (Gorgonia ventalina) reaches out into the current that sweeps along a reef front in the Solomon Islands. Sea fans do not contribute to reef building; they are soft corals inhabited by small polyps whose tentacles intercept passing plankton.

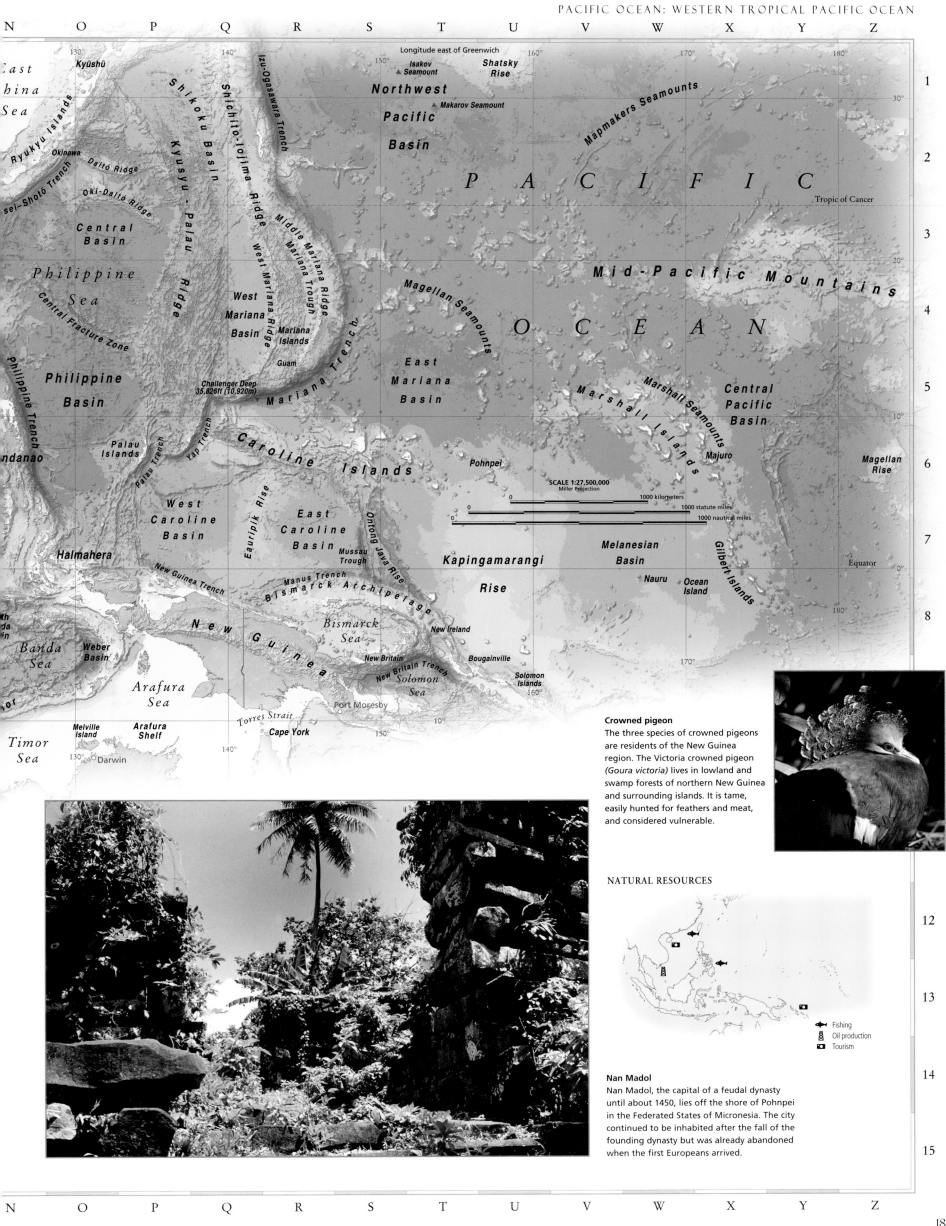

East China Sea

Kyūshū

Ryukyu Islands

Okinawa

Daitō Ridge

sei-Shotō Trench

Oki-Daitō Ridge

Central Basin

Philippine Sea

Central Fracture Zone

Philippine Trench

Philippine Basin

ndanao

Halmahera

Banda Sea

Weber Basin

Arafura Sea

Timor Sea

Melville Island

Arafura Shelf

Darwin

Shikoku Basin

Kyusyu Basin

Shichito-Iojima Ridge

Izu-Ogasawara Trench

Kyusyu - Palau Ridge

West Mariana Ridge

Middle Mariana Ridge

Mariana Trough

Mariana Ridge

West Mariana Basin

Mariana Islands

Guam

Challenger Deep 35,826ft (10,920m)

Mariana Trench

Palau Islands

Palau Trench

Yap Trench

West Caroline Basin

Eauripik Rise

Caroline Islands

East Caroline Basin

Mussau Trough

Ontong Java Rise

New Guinea Trench

Manus Trench

Bismarck Archipelago

New Guinea

Bismarck Sea

New Ireland

New Britain

New Britain Trench

Solomon Sea

Bougainville

Solomon Islands

Port Moresby

Torres Strait

Cape York

Longitude east of Greenwich

Isakov Seamount

Shatsky Rise

Northwest Pacific Basin

Makarov Seamount

Mapmakers Seamounts

P A C I F I C

Tropic of Cancer

Mid-Pacific Mountains

O C E A N

Magellan Seamounts

East Mariana Basin

Marshall Islands

Marshall Seamounts

Central Pacific Basin

Majuro

Magellan Rise

Pohnpei

SCALE 1:27,500,000
Miller Projection

0   1000 kilometers
0   1000 statute miles
                                   1000 nautical miles

Kapingamarangi Rise

Melanesian Basin

Gilbert Islands

Equator

Nauru

Ocean Island

Crowned pigeon

The three species of crowned pigeons are residents of the New Guinea region. The Victoria crowned pigeon (*Goura victoria*) lives in lowland and swamp forests of northern New Guinea and surrounding islands. It is tame, easily hunted for feathers and meat, and considered vulnerable.

NATURAL RESOURCES

Fishing
Oil production
Tourism

Nan Madol

Nan Madol, the capital of a feudal dynasty until about 1450, lies off the shore of Pohnpei in the Federated States of Micronesia. The city continued to be inhabited after the fall of the founding dynasty but was already abandoned when the first Europeans arrived.

SOUTH CHINA SEA

The South China Sea reaches from Taiwan in the north to Singapore in the south. It consists of an isolated deep basin, which is connected with the main Pacific basins through the 8,500 feet (2,600 m) deep Bashi Channel between Taiwan and Luzon, a wide shelf region in the east, and a vast shelf region between Indonesia and Malaysia in the south, where it connects with the Java Sea. Numerous tiny islands, most of them uninhabited and without much vegetation, along with hundreds of coral reefs, are the object of dispute between coastal states. The South China Sea connects with the Indian Ocean through the Strait of Malacca, one of the most important shipping lanes in the world. The strait has a minimum depth of 82 feet (25 m) and is dominated by large tidal currents that produce shifting sandbars 13–23 feet (4–7 m) high at its floor.

THE FACTS	
Area	895,400 square miles (2,319,075 km²)
Average depth	5,419 feet (1,652 m)
Maximum depth	16,456 feet (5,015 m)
Maximum width	840 miles (1,352 km)
Maximum length	1,182 miles (1,902 km)

NATURAL RESOURCES

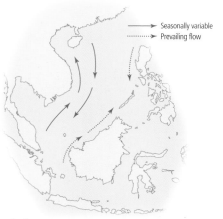

- 🐟 Fishing
- 🦐 Shellfish
- 📷 Tourism

→ Seasonally variable
⋯> Prevailing flow

Surface currents
Currents in the South China Sea are determined by the monsoon. During summer the southwest monsoon pushes water from the Sunda Shelf northward. During winter the northeast monsoon causes southward movement along the Vietnamese coast, but currents along Borneo continue to flow northward.

Halong Bay
The 1,969 limestone islands of Halong Bay in northern Vietnam are a UNESCO World Heritage site and a popular tourist destination. The islands' terrain is too steep for settlements, but the quiet waters between some islands support floating villages.

🐢 Turtle protection
The hawksbill turtle *(Eretmochelys imbricata)* lives in all tropical and subtropical oceans and is the main source of tortoiseshell. In Japan and Southeast Asia it is considered good eating. Hunting has severely reduced its numbers and many countries have banned trade in hawksbills and derived products.

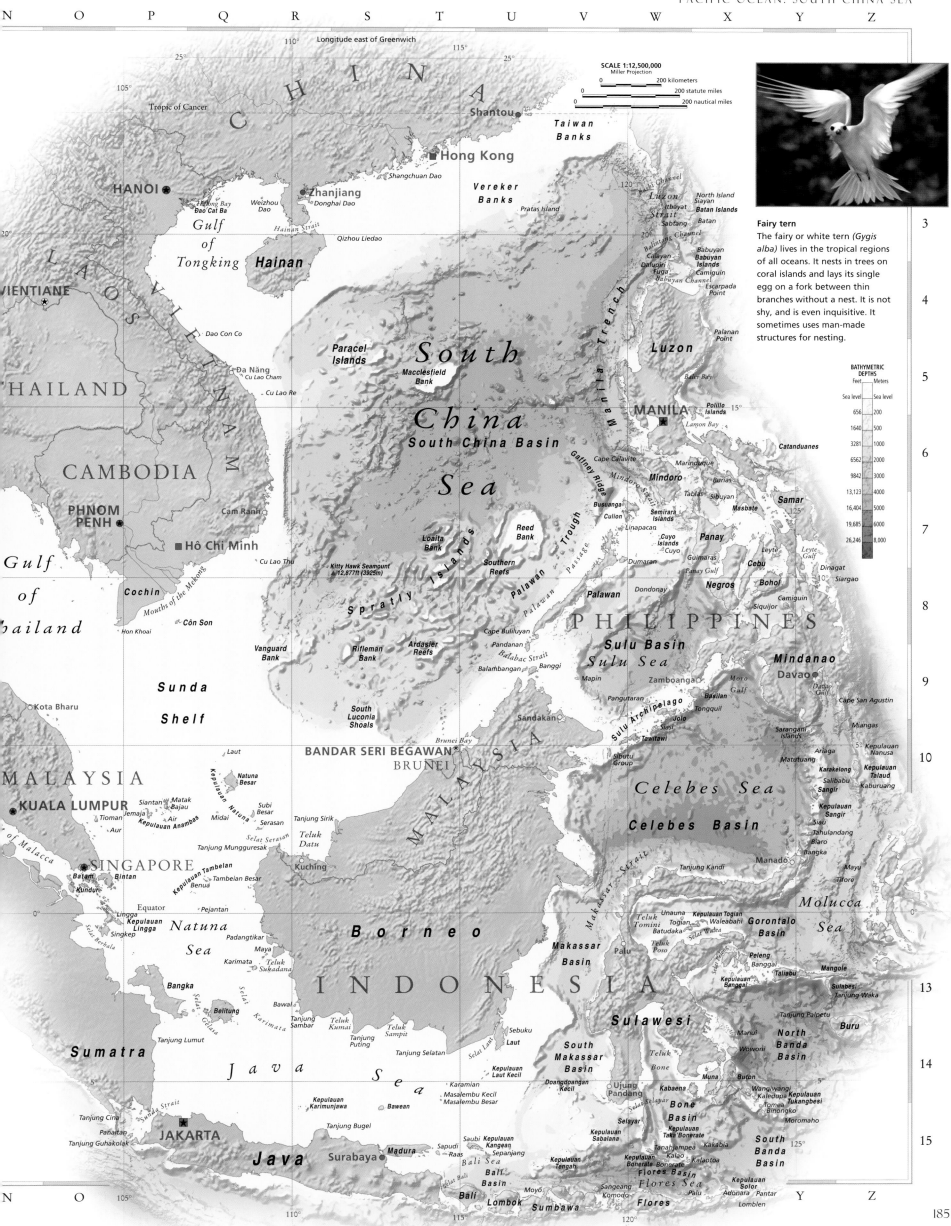

N O P Q R S T U V W X Y Z

Longitude east of Greenwich

SCALE 1:12,500,000
Miller Projection

0   200 kilometers
0   200 statute miles
0   200 nautical miles

Fairy tern
The fairy or white tern (*Gygis alba*) lives in the tropical regions of all oceans. It nests in trees on coral islands and lays its single egg on a fork between thin branches without a nest. It is not shy, and is even inquisitive. It sometimes uses man-made structures for nesting.

BATHYMETRIC DEPTHS

Feet	Meters
Sea level	Sea level
656	200
1640	500
3281	1000
6562	2000
9842	3000
13,123	4000
16,404	5000
19,685	6000
26,246	8,000

CHINA

Tropic of Cancer

HANOI
Ha Long Bay
Dao Cat Ba
Weizhou Dao
Donghai Dao
Zhanjiang
Shangchuan Dao
Hong Kong
Shantou
Taiwan Banks
Vereker Banks
Pratas Island

Gulf of Tongking

Hainan Strait
Hainan
Qizhou Liedao

LAOS

VIENTIANE

Dao Con Co

VIETNAM

THAILAND

Đa Nẵng
Cu Lao Cham
Cu Lao Re

Paracel Islands

Macclesfield Bank

South China Sea

South China Basin

Manila Trench

Luzon Strait
North Island
Siayan
Itbayat
Batan Islands
Batan
Sabtang
Calayan
Daluipiri
Fuga
Babuyan Channel
Babuyan Islands
Camiguin
Escarpada Point

Luzon

Palanan Point

Baler Bay

MANILA
Polillo Islands
Lanson Bay

CAMBODIA

PHNOM PENH

Cam Ranh

Hô Chi Minh

Gulf of Thailand

Cochin

Côn Son

Hon Khoai

Cu Lao Thu

Kitty Hawk Seamount
12,877ft (3925m)

Loaita Bank
Reed Bank
Southern Reefs

Spratly Islands

Palawan Trough

Gaffney Ridge

Cape Calavite
Mindoro Strait
Mindoro
Marinduque
Burias
Tablas
Sibuyan
Masbate
Semirara Islands
Busuanga
Culion
Linapacan
Cuyo Islands
Cuyo
Guimaras
Panay
Cebu
Leyte
Dinagat
Siargao
Leyte Gulf

Samar

Catanduanes

Vanguard Bank

Rifleman Bank

Ardasier Reefs

Cape Buliluyan
Pandanan
Balabac Strait

Palawan

Dumaran
Dondonay
Negros
Bohol
Siquijor
Camiguin

PHILIPPINES

Mindanao
Davao
Davao Gulf
Cape San Agustin

Sunda Shelf

Kota Bharu

South Luconia Shoals

Balambangan
Banggi

Sulu Basin
Sulu Sea
Mapin
Zamboanga
Pangutaran
Basilan
Tongquil
Jolo
Siasi
Tawitawi

Sulu Archipelago

Moro Gulf

Sarangani Islands

Miangas

Of Malacca

MALAYSIA

KUALA LUMPUR

Siantan
Matak
Bajau
Jemaja
Air
Tioman
Aur
Kepulauan Anambas
Midai

Kepulauan Natuna
Natuna Besar
Subi Besar
Serasan
Tanjung Sirik

Tanjung Mungguresak

Sandakan

Brunei Bay

BANDAR SERI BEGAWAN

BRUNEI

MALAYSIA

Sibutu Group

Matutuang
Ariaga
Kepulauan Nanusa
Karakelong
Salibabu
Sangir
Kepulauan Talaud
Kaburuang

Kepulauan Sangir
Siau
Tahulandang
Biaro
Bangka

Celebes Sea

Celebes Basin

SINGAPORE

Batam
Bintan
Kundur

Kepulauan Tambelan
Tambelan Besar
Benua

Selat Serasan

Teluk Datu

Kuching

Mayu
Tifore

Molucca Sea

Equator

Lingga
Kepulauan Lingga
Singkep

Natuna Sea

Padangtikar
Maya
Karimata
Teluk Sukadana

Pejantan

Tanjung Kandi

Manado

Borneo

Teluk Tomini
Unauna
Togian
Batudaka
Kepulauan Togian
Waleabahi

Makassar Strait

Teluk Poso

Gorontalo Basin

Sumatra

Bangka

Belitung

Bawal

Tanjung Sambar

Teluk Kumai

Teluk Sampit

Tanjung Puting

Kepulauan Kangean
Kangean
Sebuku
Laut
Tanjung Selatan

INDONESIA

Makassar Basin

Palu

Selat Tiworo

Palu

Peleng
Banggai
Kepulauan Banggai
Taliabu

Mangole

Sulebesi
Tanjung Waka

Buru

Tanjung Cina

Bangka

Selat Gelasa

Karimata

Tanjung Lumut

JAKARTA

Java Sea

Kepulauan Karimunjawa

Bawean

Tanjung Bugel

Surabaya

Madura

Saubi Kepulauan Sapudi
Raas
Kalao
Masalembu Kecil
Masalembu Besar

Kepulauan Laut Kecil

Doangdoangan Kecil

Ujung Pandang

Kabaena

Sulawesi

South Makassar Basin

Teluk Bone

Muna
Buton

North Banda Basin

Wowoni
Manui

Wangiwangi
Kaledupa
Tomea
Binongko
Kepulauan Tukangbesi

Moromaho

Panaitan
Tanjung Guhakolak

Sunda Strait

Java

Tanjung Selayar
Selat Selayar
Selayar
Kepulauan Sabalana
Kepulauan Taka Bonerate

Bone Basin

Tanahjampea
Kalaotoa
Kakabia

South Banda Basin

Kepulauan Tengah
Kepulauan Bonerate
Bonerate

Selat Bali
Bali Sea
Bali Basin

Moyo
Komodo

Sangeang

Flores Basin
Flores Sea

Bali
Lombok
Sumbawa
Flores

Kepulauan Solor
Solor
Adonara
Pantar
Lomblen

185

GULF OF THAILAND

The Gulf of Thailand is bowl-shaped and shallow. Rainfall exceeds evaporation here and creates a two-layered system, with low-salinity water leaving the gulf at the surface and water of oceanic salinity entering across the sill, 190 feet (58 m) deep, that separates the gulf from the South China Sea. The region is under the influence of the wet southwest monsoon from May to September and under the dry northeast monsoon from November to March. Forty-two islands near its eastern shore are scattered around a region where the gulf is less than 33 feet (10 m) deep; they form the Mu Ko Ang Thong National Park and are protected under international treaties. Turbid water and sediment from rivers support mangrove forests. The gulf also supports important artisanal and commercial fisheries. Oil and gas reserves are under dispute between Malaysia, Thailand, and Vietnam but developed jointly between the parties.

Lettuce coral
A school of anthias (*Pseudanthias tuka*) searches for food in a yellow scroll coral or lettuce coral (*Turbinaria reniformis*), a stony coral species popular for aquaria. Anthias are born female; if a dominant male dies, a female changes into a male to take its place.

Fishing fleet
Thai fishing boats anchor at Ko Samui, Thailand's third-largest island and the second most popular destination for tourists. Although tourism has shaped the face of the island, fishing vessels built from local teak still bring in a fresh catch in the morning.

THE FACTS	
Area	123,553 square miles (320,000 km²)
Average depth	148 feet (45 m)
Maximum depth	262 feet (80 m)
Maximum width	350 miles (563 km)
Maximum length	450 miles (724 km)

NATURAL RESOURCES

- Shellfish
- Tourism
- Oil production
- Gas production

Giant anemone
Anthias swarm around a giant anemone (*Heteractis magnifica*). In locations with good light and a strong, turbulent current, such as the wave zone on a reef front, giant anemones can grow to 3 feet (1 m) in diameter. They feed on vertebrates and invertebrates, including fish and crustaceans.

N O P Q R S T U V W X Y Z

Longitude east of Greenwich

100°

THAILAND

★ BANGKOK

Bight of Bangkok

Ko Khram

MYANMAR

Mali Kyun

Kadan Kyun

Ko Samet

Saganthif Kyun

Ko Chang

Kanmaw Kyun

Ko Kut

Kau-ye Kyun

Kaôh Kŏng

Campbell Island

Bada

Isthmus of Kra

Ao Sawi

Gulf

Chăk Sihanoukville

Kaôh Rŭng

Ko Tao

of

CAMBODIA

PHNOM PENH

105°

Đao Phu Quôc

Đao Vây

Vinh Rach Gia

Phra Thong

Ko Ang Thong

Ko Phangan

Ao Ban Don

Ko Samui

Thailand

Quân Đao Nam Du   Hon Rai

VIETNAM

Đao Thô Chur

ayer Island

Surat Thani

Cua Song-bay-hap

Mui Ca Mau

Côn Son

o Phuket

Ko Yao Yai

Hon Khoai

Ko Lanta

Sunda

BATHYMETRIC DEPTHS

Ko Libong

Feet	Meters
Sea level	Sea level
656	200
1640	500
3281	1000
6562	2000
9842	3000
13,123	4000
16,404	5000
19,685	6000
26,246	8,000

Terutao

Butang Group

Langkawi

Shelf

SCALE 1:5,000,000
Miller Projection

0   100 kilometers

0   100 statute miles

0   100 nautical miles

Kota Bharu

Perak

Perhentian Besar

Redang

105°

Pinang   George Town

5°   5°

MALAYSIA

100°

Tenggul

N O P Q R S T U V W X Y Z

RECREATIONAL DIVING

The warm tropical waters of the Gulf of Thailand attract many diving enthusiasts as well as beginners. Diving resorts are found on several islands, among them the former penal colony of Ko Tao, the center of diving tourism. The best seasons to dive are from January to May and from September to October when winds are light and underwater visibility increases.

When high water submerges the reef and the sun stands high it is time to put on snorkel and mask and marvel at the underwater scenery of corals and fish.

Mu Ko Ang Thong Marine Park
The protected waters of Thailand's Mu Ko Ang Thong Marine Park provide food and shelter for parrotfish, angelfish, butterflyfish and many other reef fish species. More than 50 species of waterbirds inhabit its many islands.

Red fin anthias
The red fin anthias *(Pseudanthias dispar)* is one of the most attractively colored of the many anthias species. In the wild, anthias congregate in swarms of thousands of fish. Within the swarm, males defend small "harems" of females against others.

Surface currents
Currents in the Gulf of Thailand are driven by the monsoon. The southwest monsoon drives a clockwise circulation during summer, the northeast monsoon causes counterclockwise circulation during winter. Due to high local rainfall, water leaving the gulf is generally less saline than water entering it.

→ Summer
→ Winter

1
2
3
6
9
10
11
12
13
14
15

BANDA SEA, CELEBES SEA, AND ADJACENT SEAS

The seas between Indonesia and the Philippines display the most complicated bathymetry of the world's oceans. Shallow sills divide the region into several deep basins. Water from the Pacific is transported through the various seas to the Indian Ocean, giving the region an important role in the global ocean conveyor belt. The "Indonesian Throughflow" enters south of Mindanao, passes through Makassar Strait, and leaves through the various passages between Bali and Timor. Annual rainfall exceeds evaporation by 6.5 feet (2 m), so Pacific water is strongly diluted during its passage and reaches the Indian Ocean with much-reduced salinity. Water renewal in the deep basins is slow, but faster than in the deep basins of the open Pacific due to strong mixing at ridges and sills. In the Weber Basin—at more than 23,000 feet (7,000 m) the deepest location of the region—the transit time is about 60 years.

Satellite view
Sun glint on the Molucca and Banda seas contrasts with the white of clouds that rise over the mountain ranges and highlight the convoluted coastlines of Indonesia's islands. The passage between Mindanao and Halmahera in the upper right is the entry point for the Throughflow.

Flores Island
Flores is one of the islands that form the border between the Pacific and Indian oceans. It carries several volcano craters and experienced a major earthquake and tsunami in 1992. The Throughflow passes through straits to the east and west of the island.

Seafloor topography
The Lesser Sunda Islands form part of the Pacific Ring of Fire and, in 1815, experienced the most violent volcanic eruptions in recent history. The narrow straits between the islands are an important passageway for the Indonesian Throughflow.

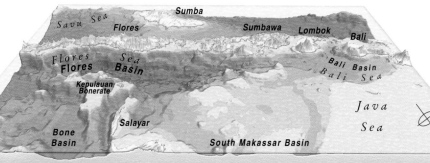

MAKASSAR STRAIT

Makassar Strait is a busy shipping route. Vessels that are too large to go through the Strait of Malacca, between mainland Malaysia and Sumatra, have to pass through this strait and continue through the Lesser Sunda Islands. The strait is shallow on the western side but deeper than 6,500 feet (2,000 m) in the east, where it is connected with the Celebes Sea.

Most of the Indonesian Throughflow passes from the Pacific to the Indian Ocean via Makassar Strait, thus giving this waterway between Borneo and Sulawesi an important role in global ocean circulation.

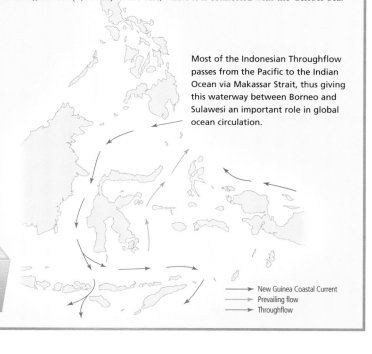

New Guinea Coastal Current
Prevailing flow
Throughflow

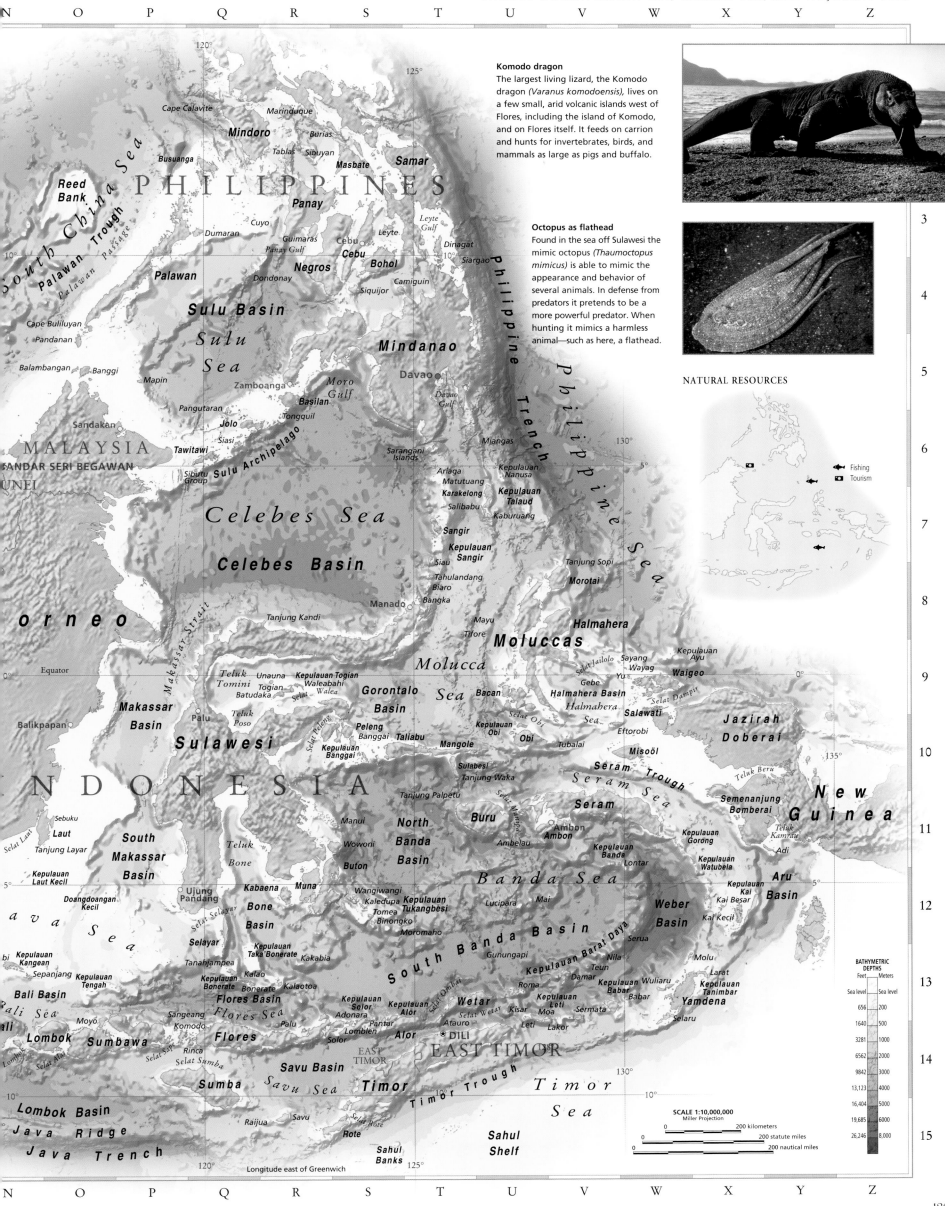

Komodo dragon
The largest living lizard, the Komodo dragon (*Varanus komodoensis*), lives on a few small, arid volcanic islands west of Flores, including the island of Komodo, and on Flores itself. It feeds on carrion and hunts for invertebrates, birds, and mammals as large as pigs and buffalo.

Octopus as flathead
Found in the sea off Sulawesi the mimic octopus (*Thaumoctopus mimicus*) is able to mimic the appearance and behavior of several animals. In defense from predators it pretends to be a more powerful predator. When hunting it mimics a harmless animal—such as here, a flathead.

NATURAL RESOURCES

Fishing
Tourism

SCALE 1:10,000,000
Miller Projection

0   200 kilometers
0   200 statute miles
0   200 nautical miles

BATHYMETRIC DEPTHS

Feet	Meters
Sea level	Sea level
656	200
1640	500
3281	1000
6562	2000
9842	3000
13,123	4000
16,404	5000
19,685	6000
26,246	8,000

PHILIPPINE SEA AND MARIANA TRENCH

The Philippine Sea is an isolated deep ocean region that contains some of the deepest trenches of the world's oceans. The Mariana Trench, the deepest depression in the ocean floor, lies east of the Mariana Islands—just outside the Philippine Sea—where the Pacific plate subducts under the Philippine plate. It was the place of the deepest ever ocean dive, when the bathyscaphe *Trieste* explored the Challenger Deep in 1960. In the west of the region is the Philippine Trench, the second deepest of ocean trenches, formed by subduction of the Philippine plate under the Eurasian plate. A sill depth of less than 9,000 feet (2,700 m) divides the region into the West Mariana Basin and the Philippine Basin. The North Equatorial Current enters the Philippine Sea from the east and continues as the Philippine Current and Kuroshio Current, the western boundary currents of the Subtropical Gyre.

NATURAL RESOURCES

➤ Fishing

Typhoon origins
The warm waters of the Philippine Sea present ideal conditions for the formation of tropical cyclones, known in the region as typhoons. A large pressure difference between the cyclone center and the surrounding ocean produces gale-force winds and torrential rain.

Surface currents
Most of the Philippine Sea experiences westward flow from the North Equatorial Current. The North Equatorial Countercurrent originates in the region and flows eastward near 5°N. Two eddies develop between these currents near Halmahera and Mindanao. The swift, deep-reaching Philippine Current flows northward along the Philippine coast.

→ North Equatorial Countercurrent	→ Philippine Current
→ South Equatorial Current	→ Mindanao Eddy
→ North Equatorial Current	⋯→ Halmahera Eddy

SCALE 1:15,000,000
Miller Projection
0 ____ 250 kilometers
0 ____ 250 statute miles
0 ____ 250 nautical miles

BATHYMETRIC DEPTHS

Feet	Meters
Sea level	Sea level
656	200
1640	500
3281	1000
6562	2000
9842	3000
13,123	4000
16,404	5000
19,685	6000
26,246	8,000

Typhoon winds
A satellite image of winds and rain in Typhoon Nesat of June 2005. Color indicates wind speed, dark purple and light pink showing the strongest winds. White arrows near the center of the typhoon indicate heavy rain.

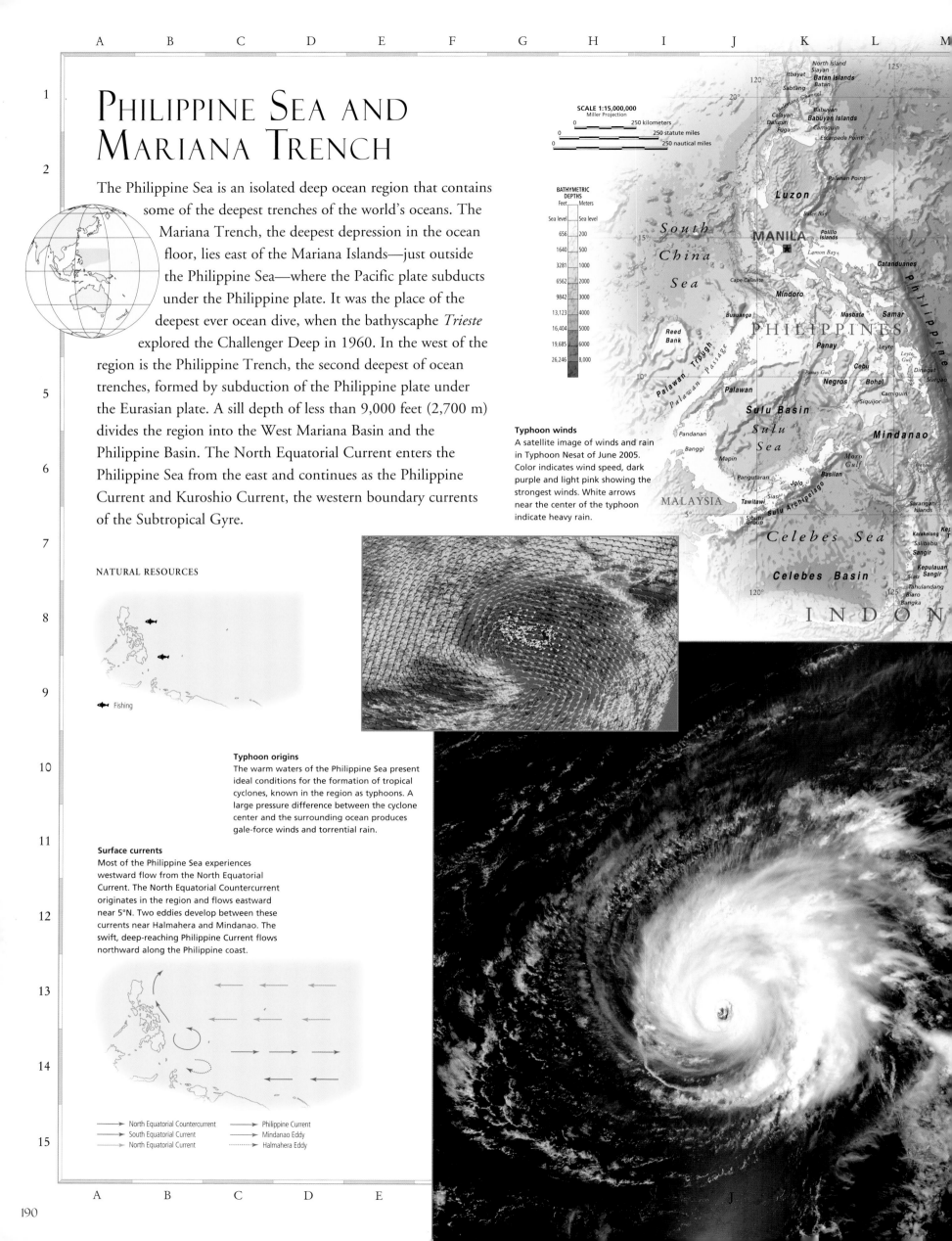

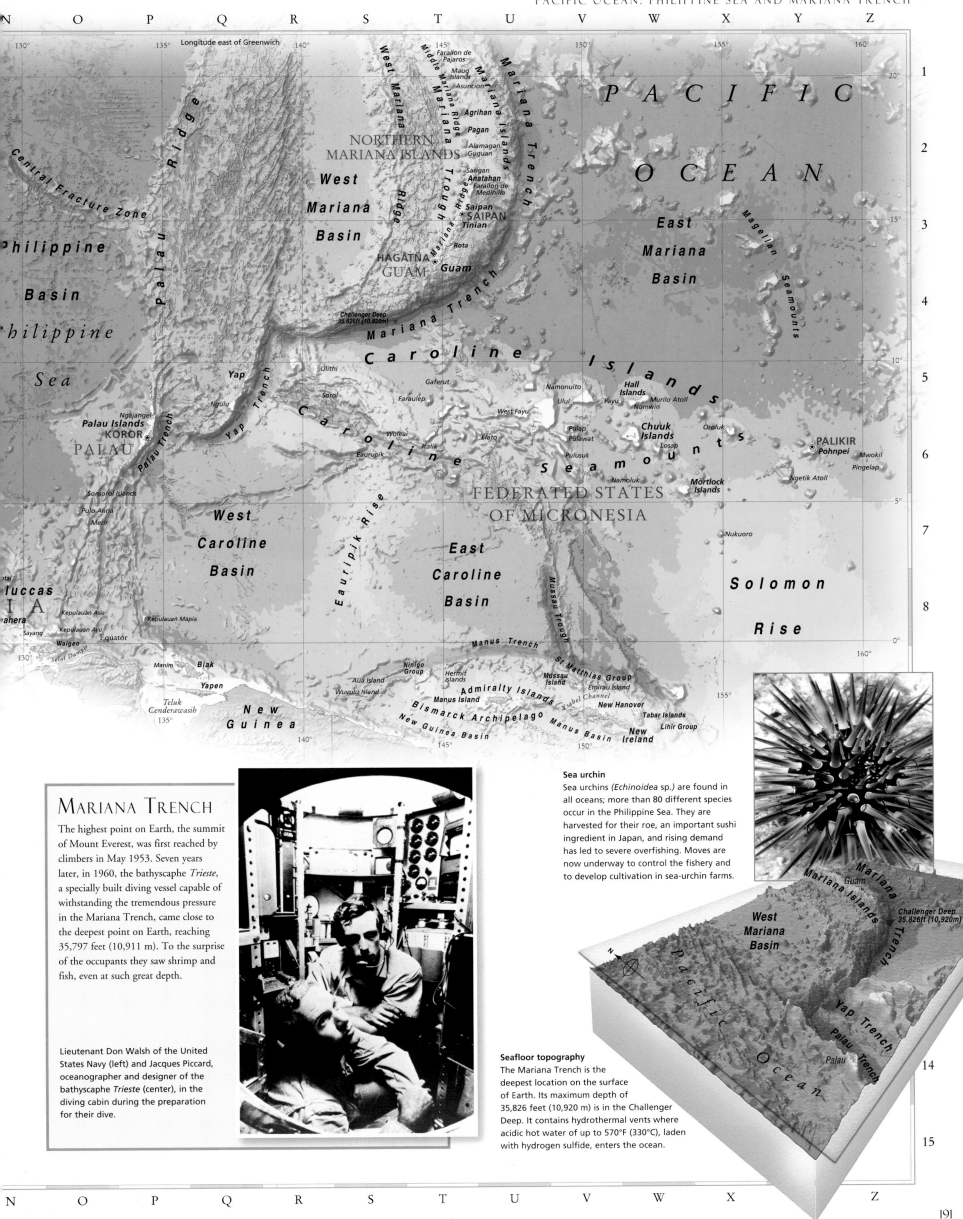

MARIANA TRENCH

The highest point on Earth, the summit of Mount Everest, was first reached by climbers in May 1953. Seven years later, in 1960, the bathyscaphe *Trieste*, a specially built diving vessel capable of withstanding the tremendous pressure in the Mariana Trench, came close to the deepest point on Earth, reaching 35,797 feet (10,911 m). To the surprise of the occupants they saw shrimp and fish, even at such great depth.

Lieutenant Don Walsh of the United States Navy (left) and Jacques Piccard, oceanographer and designer of the bathyscaphe *Trieste* (center), in the diving cabin during the preparation for their dive.

Sea urchin

Sea urchins (*Echinoidea* sp.) are found in all oceans; more than 80 different species occur in the Philippine Sea. They are harvested for their roe, an important sushi ingredient in Japan, and rising demand has led to severe overfishing. Moves are now underway to control the fishery and to develop cultivation in sea-urchin farms.

Seafloor topography

The Mariana Trench is the deepest location on the surface of Earth. Its maximum depth of 35,826 feet (10,920 m) is in the Challenger Deep. It contains hydrothermal vents where acidic hot water of up to 570°F (330°C), laden with hydrogen sulfide, enters the ocean.

SOUTHWESTERN PACIFIC OCEAN

Coral islands, extensive plateaus and deep basins characterize the Southwestern Pacific. Where the Pacific plate subducts under the Australian plate the ocean floor is folded into island chains beside deep trenches. The region's hydrography is determined by the western part of the Subtropical Gyre of the southern hemisphere. The South Equatorial Current enters the Coral Sea from the east; its tropical waters are the source of the East Australian Current. Like all western boundary currents the East Australian Current is fast-flowing and extends to great depth. Loss of water from the Subtropical Gyre to the Indian Ocean through the Indonesian seas means that the East Australian Current transports less water than other western boundary currents, and it often disintegrates into eddies measuring up to 120 miles (200 km) across. The current turns east between the Coral and Tasman seas along the Tasman Front and continues along New Zealand's east coast as the East Auckland Current.

BATHYMETRIC DEPTHS

Feet	Meters
Sea level	Sea level
656	200
1640	500
3281	1000
6562	2000
9842	3000
13,123	4000
16,404	5000
19,685	6000
26,246	8,000

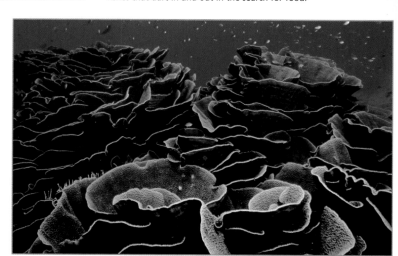

Tropical storm
The tropical southwestern Pacific receives some 10–13 feet (3–4 m) of rain every year. Rainfall is usually heavy and accompanied by strong wind but is localized and short-lived. Here a rainstorm passes over Kimbe Bay in West New Britain, Papua New Guinea.

Fiji
Fiji's 322 islands hold nearly 4,000 square miles (10,000 km²) of reef. In 2000, a crown-of-thorns starfish invasion posed a serious threat. Warm water temperatures in the following years led to extensive bleaching, and the reef area is declining.

Cabbage coral
Shallow reefs with good light conditions and strong current movement are the ideal habitat for the cabbage or lettuce coral (Turbinaria sp.), a favorite species for aquaria. The coral provides good shelter for many reef fishes that dart in and out in the search for food.

Surface currents
South of 45°S the Antarctic Circumpolar Current flows eastward. It has moderate speed but is deep-reaching and carries the largest transport of all currents. The western part of the Subtropical Gyre determines the circulation to the north. At its center currents are mostly weak and variable.

→ Antarctic Circumpolar Current → South Equatorial Current
→ East Auckland Current → South Pacific Current
→ East Australian Current

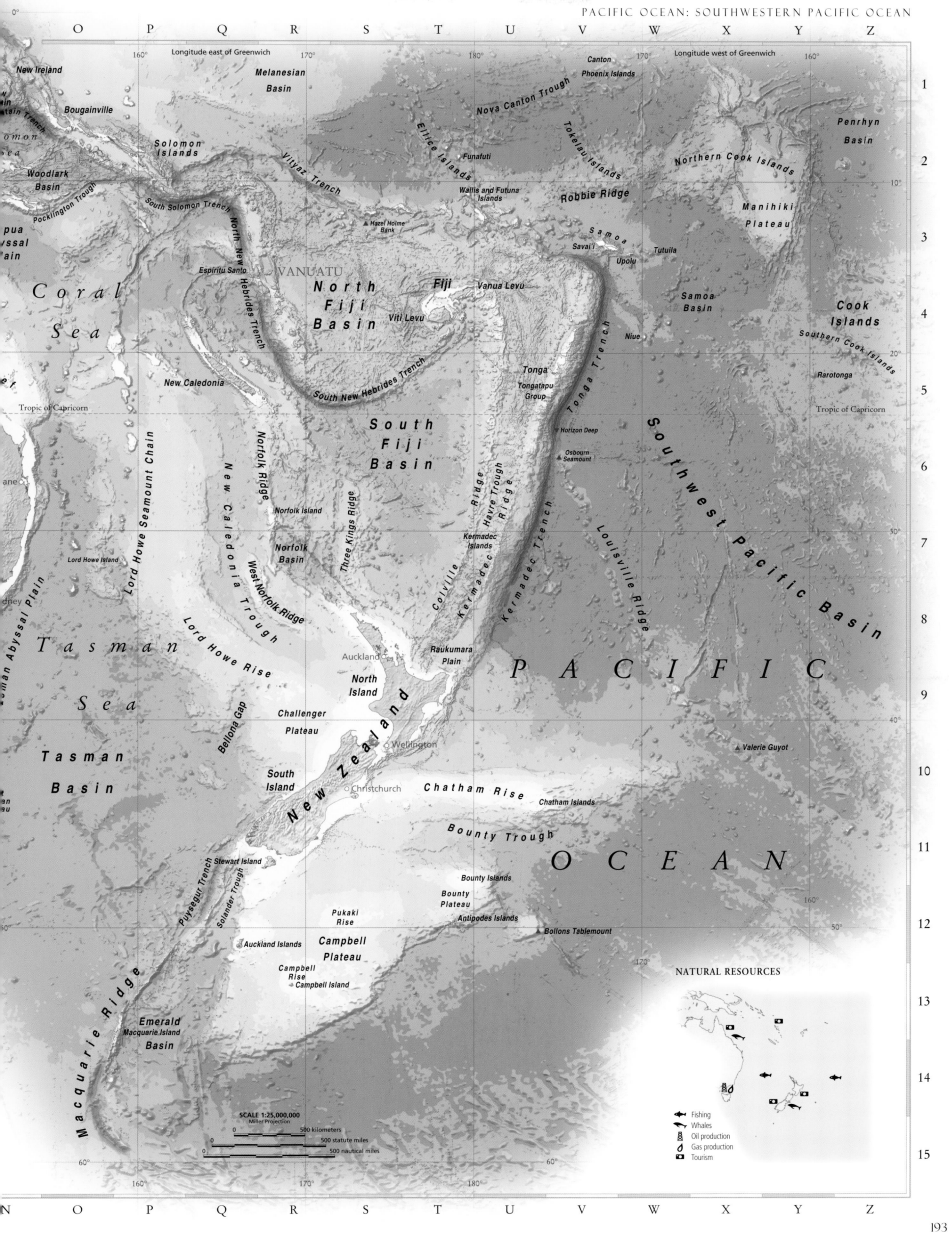

ARAFURA SEA AND GULF OF CARPENTARIA

During the last ice age the Arafura Sea and the Gulf of Carpentaria formed a land bridge between Australia and New Guinea. Today they are shelf seas 150–250 feet (45–80 m) deep. The Arafura Sea adjoins the Indian Ocean where it meets the Timor Sea. In the east it connects with the Coral Sea through Torres Strait, which has a maximum depth of only 36 feet (11 m); large ships following the busy sea lane through the Arafura Sea have to wait for high tide before passing through the strait. Farther west the tidal range along the Australian coast exceeds 26 feet (8 m). The region is rich in marine life. Sea cucumbers are prized by Indonesian fishermen and shrimp fishing is a key industry in the Gulf of Carpentaria. The Morning Glory, a spectacular cloud band stretching from horizon to horizon, occurs along the gulf coast during September and October.

Sunset, Arafura Sea
The sun sets over the Arafura Sea at Mindil Beach in Darwin, Australia. Because the beach slopes gently toward the sea and the tidal range on Australia's north shore reaches up to 26 feet (8 m), the sea retreats a significant distance at low tide.

THE FACTS (ARAFURA SEA)	
Area	250,990 square miles (650,000 km²)
Average depth	230 feet (70 m)
Maximum depth	12,000 feet (3,660 m)
Maximum width	435 miles (700 km)
Maximum length	620 miles (1,000 km)

Starfish
Sea stars or starfish generally have five arms, which they can regenerate as long as at least one arm is still attached to the central disk. This starfish, found off Wessel Island east of Darwin, is regenerating two arms it had lost to predators.

Dugong
The dugong (Dugong dugon), a marine mammal and relative of Atlantic manatees, inhabits the Indo-Pacific region. Most of the population is found in northern Australian waters. This dugong and its calf graze the seagrasses of the Arafura Sea.

Cobourg Peninsula
Separated from Melville Island by Dundas Strait, the Cobourg Peninsula forms part of the northern boundary of Van Diemen Gulf in Australia's far northwest. It is nearly entirely Aboriginal land and has been declared a national park. It comprises coral reefs, wetlands, and rain forest and protects six species of sea turtles.

Surface currents
The prevailing currents in the Arafura Sea and Gulf of Carpentaria are tidal, changing direction twice a day. The wind-driven currents are weak and usually of secondary importance. From November to April this pattern can be disturbed by cyclones and their associated strong currents.

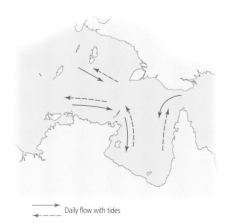

Daily flow with tides

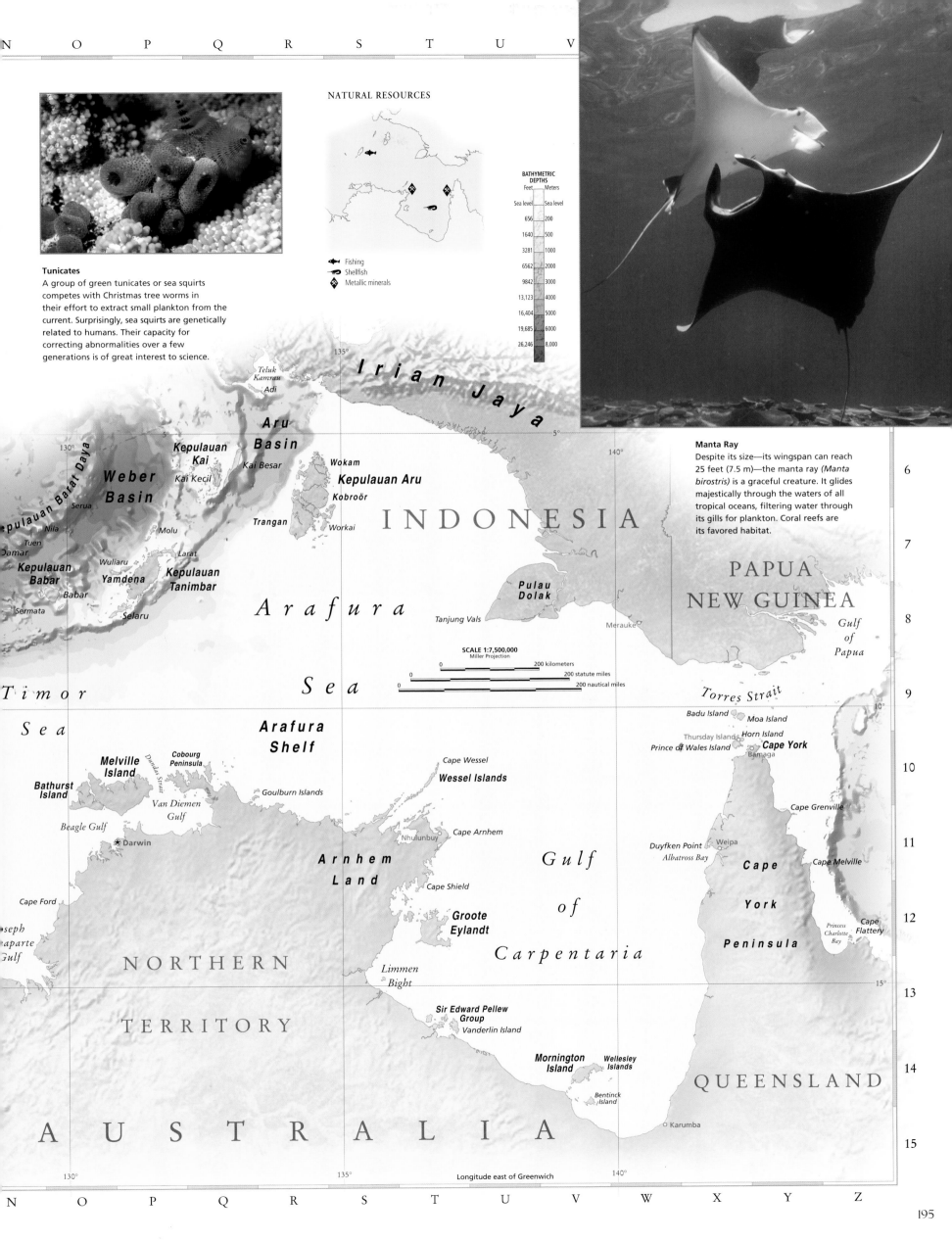

Tunicates
A group of green tunicates or sea squirts competes with Christmas tree worms in their effort to extract small plankton from the current. Surprisingly, sea squirts are genetically related to humans. Their capacity for correcting abnormalities over a few generations is of great interest to science.

NATURAL RESOURCES

BATHYMETRIC DEPTHS

Feet	Meters
Sea level	Sea level
656	200
1640	500
3281	1000
6562	2000
9842	3000
13,123	4000
16,404	5000
19,685	6000
26,246	8,000

- Fishing
- Shellfish
- Metallic minerals

Manta Ray
Despite its size—its wingspan can reach 25 feet (7.5 m)—the manta ray (Manta birostris) is a graceful creature. It glides majestically through the waters of all tropical oceans, filtering water through its gills for plankton. Coral reefs are its favored habitat.

Teluk Kamrau
Adi

Irian Jaya

Aru Basin

Kepulauan Kai
Kai Besar
Kai Kecil

Weber Basin

Wokam
Kepulauan Aru
Kobroör

Trangan
Workai

Kepulauan Barat Daya
Serua
Nila
Tuen
Damar
Molu
Larat
Wuliaru
Kepulauan Babar
Yamdena
Kepulauan Tanimbar
Babar
Sermata
Selaru

INDONESIA

Pulau Dolak

Tanjung Vals
Merauke

PAPUA NEW GUINEA

Gulf of Papua

Arafura Sea

Timor Sea

SCALE 1:7,500,000
Miller Projection
0 200 kilometers
0 200 statute miles
0 200 nautical miles

Torres Strait

Badu Island — Moa Island
Thursday Island — Horn Island
Prince of Wales Island — **Cape York**
Bamaga

Arafura Shelf

Cobourg Peninsula
Melville Island
Bathurst Island

Cape Wessel
Wessel Islands

Cape Grenville

Goulburn Islands

Douglas Strait
Van Diemen Gulf
Beagle Gulf

Cape Arnhem

Duyfken Point — Weipa
Albatross Bay

Darwin

Nhulunbuy

Cape Melville

Arnhem Land

Cape Shield

Gulf of Carpentaria

Cape York Peninsula

Cape Ford

Groote Eylandt

Princess Charlotte Bay
Cape Flattery

Joseph Bonaparte Gulf

NORTHERN

Limmen Bight

Sir Edward Pellew Group
Vanderlin Island

TERRITORY

Mornington Island
Wellesley Islands

QUEENSLAND

Bentinck Island

AUSTRALIA

Karumba

Longitude east of Greenwich

CORAL SEA

Located between tropical Australia and the island arc formed by the Solomon Islands, Vanuatu, New Caledonia, and Norfolk Island in the south, the Coral Sea contains deep trenches in the east, deep basins in the north, part of the Lord Howe Rise in the south, and myriad coral reefs in the north and west. The South Equatorial Current enters it from the east, sending some of its water northward into the New Guinea Coastal Current, while the bulk of the current continues south to provide the source for the East Australian Current. January to April is the cyclone season, when palm trunks and other debris from devastation on land can be found drifting across the Coral Sea. Many marine life species that are endangered elsewhere are still found in healthy numbers in this sea, including reef and hammerhead sharks, manta rays, maori wrasse, and five of the seven species of turtles.

THE FACTS	
Area	1,849,000 square miles (4,788,888 km²)
Average depth	7,870 feet (2,398 m)
Maximum depth	25,134 feet (7,661 m)
Maximum width	1,500 miles (2,414 km)
Maximum length	1,400 miles (2,253 km)

Coral Sea diving
During summer the extremely venomous irukandji or box jellyfish keeps swimmers at bay; contact with its tentacles, which can be 3 feet (1 m) long, can be fatal. But in winter the Coral Sea is a diver's paradise. This diver is attracted by an alcyonarian, one of the soft coral species.

NATURAL RESOURCES

→ Fishing
↘ Whales
▢ Tourism

Reef shark
The non-aggressive whitetip reef shark (*Triaenodon obesus*) is a common shark found around coral reefs in the Indo-Pacific. It is nocturnal in habit; snorkelers often see it resting on the bottom during the day. Here a shark swims past a soft coral tree (*Dendronephtya* sp.).

Norfolk Island
The Norfolk Island Pine (*Araucaria heterophylla*) is adapted to life in an environment exposed to frequent sea spray. Its needles have a protective waxy coating. The tree dominates the scenery of Norfolk Island but has also been planted along the seafront of many cities.

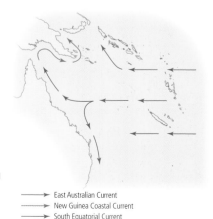

Surface currents
As the westward flowing South Equatorial Current approaches the Great Barrier Reef its flow is mainly directed northward and southward. Water exchange between the Coral Sea and the reef's lagoon is achieved by strong tidal currents that sweep through the narrow channels between individual reefs.

→ East Australian Current
→ New Guinea Coastal Current
→ South Equatorial Current

N

5°

V W X Y Z

Bismarck Sea

New Guinea Basin

New Ireland

Manus Basin

150°

155°

Longitude east of Greenwich

160°

PAPUA NEW GUINEA

New Britain

New Britain Trench

Bougainville

Choiseul

Solomon Islands

SCALE 1:15,000,000
Miller Projection

0   400 kilometers
0   400 statute miles
0   400 nautical miles

BATHYMETRIC DEPTHS
Feet   Meters

1

New Guinea

Solomon Sea

Santa Isabel

Vityas Trench

Sea level   Sea level
656   200
1640   500

Gulf of Papua

Woodlark Island

New Georgia Islands

Malaita

HONIARA

170°

3281   1000
6562   2000

* PORT MORESBY

Woodlark Basin

Guadalcanal

San Cristobel

Santa Cruz Islands

10°

9842   3000
13,123   4000

2

Torres Strait

Louisiade Archipelago

Pocklington Trough

South Solomon Trench

Rennell

Ndeni

North New Hebrides Trench

16,404   5000
19,685   6000

Cape York

Papua Plateau

Indispensable Reefs

Torres Islands

Banks Islands

26,246   8,000

3

Cape York Peninsula

Coral Sea Basin

Papua Abyssal Plain

Coral

Maéwo

North Fiji Basin

4

Osprey Reef

Queensland Plateau

Sea

Espiritu Santo

VANUATU
Pentecost
Ambrym   Epi

15°

Bougainville Reef

Malakula

15°

AUSTRALIA

Holmes Reef   Diane Bank

Flora Reef

Lihou Reef

Mellish Reef

New Hebrides Trench

Éfaté
PORT VILA

5

Cairns

Flinders Reef

Tregrosse Reefs

Erromango

Townsville

Great Barrier Reef

Marion Reef

Isles Chesterfield

Tanna

Isles Loyaute

Anatom

20°

Lifou

20°

6

Frederick Reefs

Lane Downe Bank

Fairway Reef

New Caledonia

Maré

Octocoral
A close view of an octocoral
(*Alcyonaria* sp.) reveals the many polyps on
the coral skeleton. Octocorals form colonies
of greatly different shapes. Most are rooted
to foreign objects, some float freely in the sea.

Kenn Reefs

Wreck Reefs

Nova Bank

NOUMÉA *

Ile des Pins

7

Hervey Bay   Sandy Cape

Argo Bank

Tropic of Capricorn

Kelso Bank

Lord Howe Seamount Chain

Norfolk Ridge

New Caledonia Trough

Cook Fracture Zone

25°

8

Recorder Guyot

Capel Bank

170°

Moreton Seamount

Brisbane

Brisbane Guyot

Gifford Guyot

9

Queensland Guyot

Norfolk Island

Britannia Guyots

Dampier Ridge

Stradbroke Seamount

Middleton Reef

Sea whip
A diver enjoys the clear waters of the Coral
Sea and admires an elegant sea whip or sea fan
(*Gorgonia* sp.). The fan spreads itself across the
prevailing current to maximize chances for its
eight-armed polyps to catch small plankton.

10

Coffs Harbour

30°

Elizabeth Reef

30°

Derwent Hunter Guyot

155°

160°

Lord Howe Island

Rockhampton

150°

145°

165°

Island paradise
The Isle of Pines in the archipelago of New
Caledonia is known for its idyllic environment
and excellent diving conditions. Its tall, slender
New Caledonia pines (*Araucaria columnaris*)
are closely related to the Norfolk Island pine.

N   O   P   Q

GREAT BARRIER REEF

The Great Barrier Reef is the world's biggest single structure made by living organisms. Declared a Marine Park in 1975 and inscribed in the World Heritage list in 1981, it consists of more than 2,900 individual reefs and 900 islands and extends along Australia's east coast for 1,250 miles (2,000 km). The Great Barrier Reef Marine Park Authority manages its use in accordance with several international conventions. At least 400 species of hard and soft corals form the reef. The animal life found here includes more than 1,500 species of fish; 125 species of sharks, stingrays, and skates; 30 species of whales, porpoises, and dolphins; 6 species of turtles; and 17 species of sea snakes. Some 1.5 million birds breed on its islands. Saltwater crocodiles live in mangrove and salt marshes near the coast and most of the world's remaining dugong population is found on the reef where seagrasses are abundant.

THE FACTS	
Area	134,286 square miles (347,800 km²)
Length	1,250 miles (2,000 km)
Maximum width	95 miles (152 km)
Surface water temperature	75°–86°F (24°–30°C)
No. of hard coral species	More than 300
No. of fish species	More than 1,500
No. of sponge species	More than 400
No. of mollusk species	Approximately 4,000
No. of seaweed species	Approximately 500

Above the reef
Australia's Great Barrier Reef is the only living structure on Earth that is visible from space. Here a small seaplane flies low over the reef, giving passengers a sweeping view.

Dwarf minke whale
In the northern Great Barrier Reef dwarf minke whales (*Balaenoptera acutorostrata* subsp.), known for being inquisitive, often meet boats and swimmers during "swim with whales" excursions.

CORAL BLEACHING

One of the main effects of global warming is an increase in ocean water temperatures. This can lead to coral bleaching, the loss of zooxanthellae—a symbiotic algae—from the polyps. A temperature increase of just 2.7–3.6°F (1.5–2°C) above normal can kill coral.

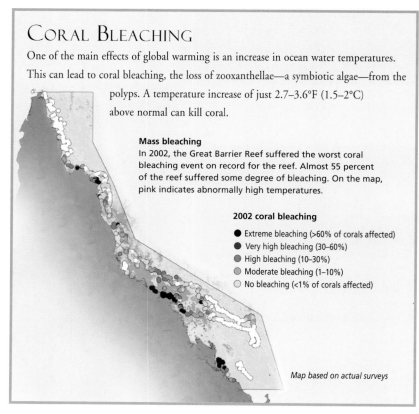

Mass bleaching
In 2002, the Great Barrier Reef suffered the worst coral bleaching event on record for the reef. Almost 55 percent of the reef suffered some degree of bleaching. On the map, pink indicates abnormally high temperatures.

2002 coral bleaching
- ● Extreme bleaching (>60% of corals affected)
- ● Very high bleaching (30–60%)
- ● High bleaching (10–30%)
- ○ Moderate bleaching (1–10%)
- ○ No bleaching (<1% of corals affected)

Map based on actual surveys

Torres Strait

adu Island
Moa Island
Thursday Island
Horn Island
e of Wales Island
Cape York
Bamaga

10°
Eastern Fields

Ashmore Reef

Papua Plateau

Coral Sea

Cape Grenville

Cape York Peninsula

Pandora Entrance

Cape Direction

Princess Charlotte Bay
Cape Melville

Cape Flattery

Lizard Island

Osprey Reef

QUEENSLAND

Cooktown

Bougainville Reef

15°

Cape Tribulation

Trinity Bay
Arlington Reef

Cairns

145°

Holmes Reef

Diane Bank

Flora Reef

Flinders Reef

150°

Tregrosse Reefs

Dunk Island

Hinchinbrook Island

Palm Islands

Halifax Bay
Magnetic Island

Townsville

Marion Reef

20°

Whitsunday Group

AUSTRALIA

Lindeman Island
Cape Conway

Brampton Island
Scawfell Island

Mackay

Middle Island
Percy Isles

Swain Reefs

Frederick Reefs

Saumarez Reefs

Long Island

Broad Sound
Townshend Island

Cape Clinton

Great Keppel Island
Heron Island

Rockhampton

Curtis Island

Tropic of Capricorn

Round Hill Head

Sandy Cape

Hervey Bay

Fraser Island

Recorder Guyot

Double Island Point

Moreton Seamount

BATHYMETRIC DEPTHS

Feet	Meters
Sea level	Sea level
656	200
1640	500
3281	1000
6562	2000
9842	3000
13,123	4000
16,404	5000
19,685	6000
26,246	8,000

→ East Australian Current
→ Great Barrier Reef Undercurrent
→ South Equatorial Current

Surface currents
As the South Equatorial Current approaches the Great Barrier Reef it splits into southward and northward flow. Water exchange with the lagoon occurs through strong tidal mixing in the many passages between the individual reefs. Currents in the lagoon are determined by the wind and river runoff.

Mushroom coral
The solitary mushroom coral (Actinodiscus sp.) feeds at night. It does not form colonies and is not attached to the seabed, although it begins as a small disk attached to rock or dead coral.

Anemonefish in sea anemone
Anemonefish (Amphiprion sp.) are protected by a mucous coating. This allows them to come into contact with the sea anemone's stinging tentacles without being affected.

NATURAL RESOURCES

Whales
Tourism

Crown-of-thorns starfish
The crown-of-thorns starfish (Acanthaster planci) feeds on coral polyps, its venomous spines keeping predators at bay. On the Great Barrier Reef occasional population explosions have damaged entire reefs. Pollution and climate change have been suspected, but the reasons for these outbreaks are still unclear.

Zooxanthellae

Sting cell

Polyp tentacle

Tentacle cross section
Zooxanthellae give corals their color, while sting cells discharge to pierce the skin of prey.

Formation of coral
In reef-building hard coral species, individual polyps secrete a limestone skeleton that partially encloses them. The polyps form communities in a variety of shapes, and their remains form reefs.

Polyp

Limestone skeleton

SCALE 1:6,250,000
Miller Projection
0   200 kilometers
0   200 statute miles
0   200 nautical miles

Longitude east of Greenwich

TASMAN SEA

The Tasman Basin is open to the south but closed in the north and is thus influenced by the Southern Ocean at depth. The dominant surface feature is the fast-flowing and deep East Australian Current, the western boundary current of the South Pacific Subtropical Gyre. Water loss from the gyre through the Indonesian seas reduces its transport, making the East Australian Current the weakest of all western boundary currents. The current follows the Australian coast but turns offshore, north and finally east toward New Zealand, forming the Tasman Front between the Tasman and Coral seas. Southbound ships coming from Asia ride the current but avoid it on their return voyage by staying farther away from the coast. On occasions the East Australian Current disintegrates into a field of eddies that may measure 120 miles (200 km) across. Islands in the Tasman Sea are home to the little penguin, the smallest of the world's 17 penguin species.

Yellow-eyed penguins
Yellow-eyed penguins *(Megadyptes antipodes)* are the rarest of the world's penguins. They breed on the South Island and islands to the south of New Zealand and share their range with the little or fairy penguin *(Eudyptula minor)*, a species also found in Australia.

NATURAL RESOURCES

- Fishing
- Whales
- Oil production
- Gas production
- Tourism

THE FACTS	
Area	1,545,000 square miles (4,001,530 km²)
Average depth	9,023 feet (2,750 m)
Maximum depth	17,000 feet (5,182 m)
Maximum width	1,400 miles (2,253 km)
Maximum length	1,243 miles (2,000 km)

East Australian Current
A satellite image of seawater temperature—warm is red–orange, cold is green–blue, clouds are white—shows the East Australian Current as a band of warm water flowing south along the continental shelf. At 35°S it turns away from the coast and flows toward New Zealand.

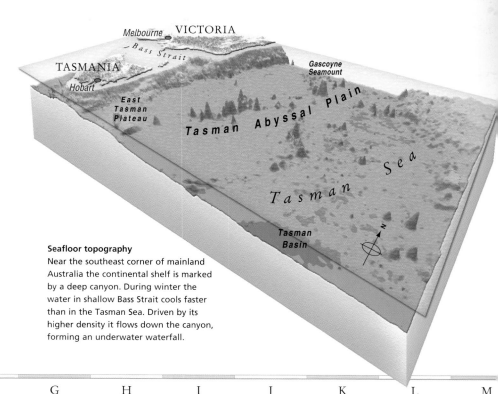

Seafloor topography
Near the southeast corner of mainland Australia the continental shelf is marked by a deep canyon. During winter the water in shallow Bass Strait cools faster than in the Tasman Sea. Driven by its higher density it flows down the canyon, forming an underwater waterfall.

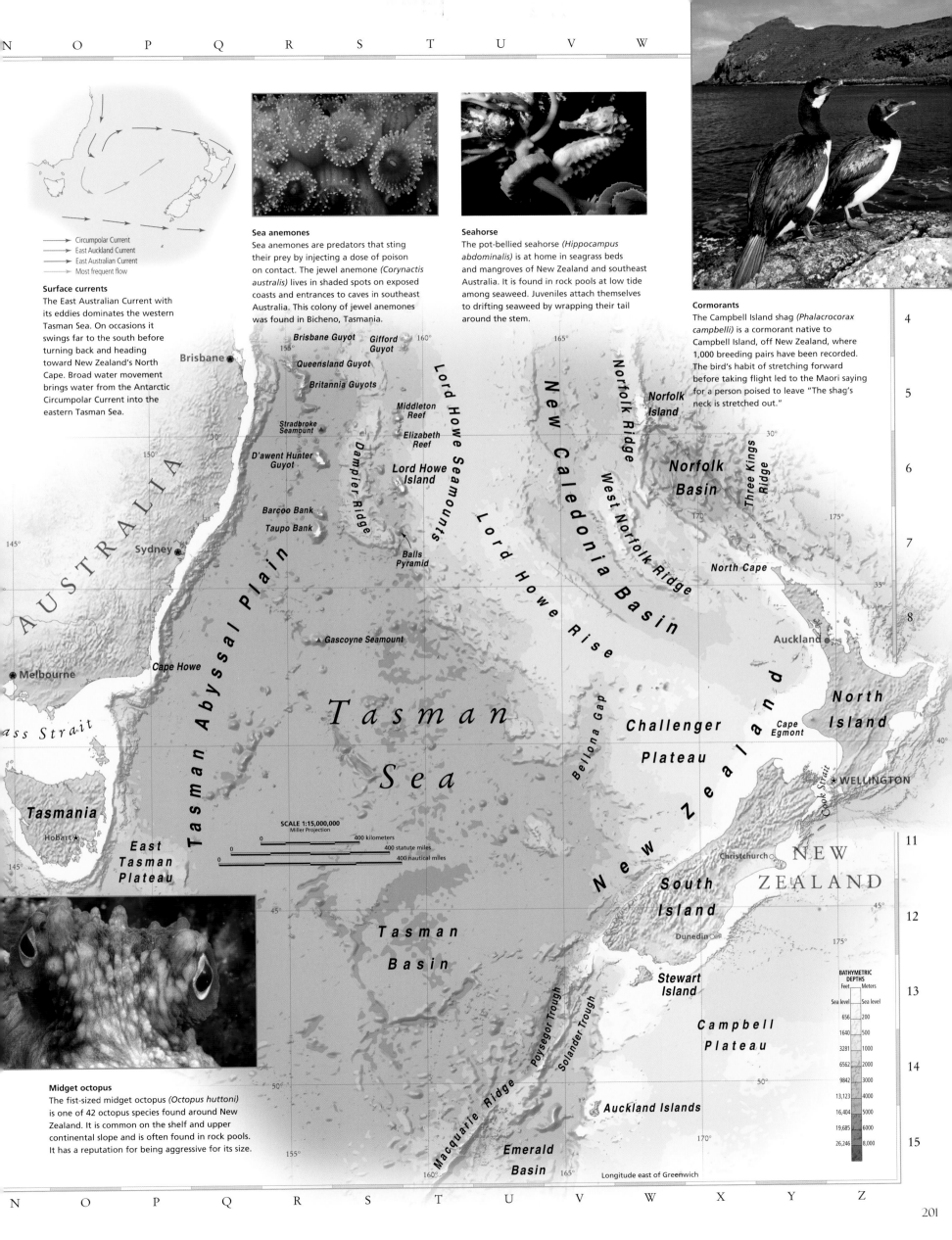

Surface currents

Circumpolar Current
East Auckland Current
East Australian Current
Most frequent flow

Surface currents
The East Australian Current with its eddies dominates the western Tasman Sea. On occasions it swings far to the south before turning back and heading toward New Zealand's North Cape. Broad water movement brings water from the Antarctic Circumpolar Current into the eastern Tasman Sea.

Sea anemones
Sea anemones are predators that sting their prey by injecting a dose of poison on contact. The jewel anemone (Corynactis australis) lives in shaded spots on exposed coasts and entrances to caves in southeast Australia. This colony of jewel anemones was found in Bicheno, Tasmania.

Seahorse
The pot-bellied seahorse (Hippocampus abdominalis) is at home in seagrass beds and mangroves of New Zealand and southeast Australia. It is found in rock pools at low tide among seaweed. Juveniles attach themselves to drifting seaweed by wrapping their tail around the stem.

Cormorants
The Campbell Island shag (Phalacrocorax campbelli) is a cormorant native to Campbell Island, off New Zealand, where 1,000 breeding pairs have been recorded. The bird's habit of stretching forward before taking flight led to the Maori saying for a person poised to leave "The shag's neck is stretched out."

Midget octopus
The fist-sized midget octopus (Octopus huttoni) is one of 42 octopus species found around New Zealand. It is common on the shelf and upper continental slope and is often found in rock pools. It has a reputation for being aggressive for its size.

Map labels:

AUSTRALIA
Brisbane
Sydney
Cape Howe
Melbourne
Bass Strait
Tasmania
Hobart
East Tasman Plateau

Brisbane Guyot
Gifford Guyot
Queensland Guyot
Britannia Guyots
Middleton Reef
Stradbroke Seamount
Elizabeth Reef
D'awent Hunter Guyot
Lord Howe Island
Barcoo Bank
Taupo Bank
Balls Pyramid
Dampier Ridge
Lord Howe Seamounts
Lord Howe Rise
Gascoyne Seamount

Tasman Abyssal Plain
Tasman Sea
Tasman Basin

New Caledonia Basin
Norfolk Ridge
West Norfolk Ridge
Norfolk Island
Norfolk Basin
Three Kings Ridge
North Cape
Bellona Gap
Challenger Plateau
Cape Egmont
North Island
Auckland
NEW ZEALAND
WELLINGTON
Cook Strait
Christchurch
South Island
Dunedin
New Zealand
Stewart Island
Campbell Plateau
Macquarie Ridge
Poysegor Trough
Solander Trough
Auckland Islands
Emerald Basin

SCALE 1:15,000,000
Miller Projection
400 kilometers
400 statute miles
400 nautical miles

Longitude east of Greenwich

BATHYMETRIC DEPTHS

Feet	Meters
Sea level	Sea level
656	200
1640	500
3281	1000
6562	2000
9842	3000
13,123	4000
16,404	5000
19,685	6000
26,246	8,000

CAMPBELL PLATEAU AND CHATHAM RISE

The Campbell Plateau, the Chatham Rise, and New Zealand once formed a microcontinent that separated from Antarctica. Today the major part of the Campbell Plateau is 1,200–3,000 feet (350–900 m) deep but breaks the surface in several places to form groups of islands and rises to 270 feet (82 m) in the Campbell Rise. The plateau steers the Antarctic Circumpolar Current along its flanks, isolating the region from cold polar waters. The smaller Chatham Rise is the shallower of the two, with depths of 600–1,800 feet (180–550 m), rising to 168 feet (51 m) at Mernoo Bank and breaking the surface at the Chatham Islands. The East Auckland Current brings warm subtropical water from the north and creates the Subtropical Front over the Chatham Rise. Mixing of subtropical and subantarctic water increases the productivity of the region; the Chatham Rise provides 60 percent of New Zealand's fish catch.

John Dory
The deep-sea predator John Dory (*Zeus faber*) is found at about 330 feet (100 m) along all coastal shelves except the Pacific east coast. A good table fish, it has been fished since the 1950s and supports a major commercial trawl fishery in New Zealand.

White Island
White Island, an active volcano in the Bay of Plenty off New Zealand's North Island, is known to Maori as Whakaari. It is 1.2 miles (2 km) wide and 1,053 feet (321 m) high. It was mined for sulfur until a landslide killed all 10 workers in 1914.

Sulfur
White Island has some of the most acidic lakes in the world. Runoff from lake water produces colorful sulfur deposits that create an eerie scenery on the mountain's flanks. An eruption in 2000 created a new crater and turned the earlier crater into a lake.

NATURAL RESOURCES

➤ Fishing
➤ Whales
▣ Tourism

Snares crested penguin
Snares crested penguin (*Eudyptes robustus*) breeds on The Snares, an island group off New Zealand's South Island. Its restricted distribution makes it a vulnerable species; the current population is estimated at around 30,000 breeding pairs. It feeds mainly on krill but occasionally takes squid and small fish.

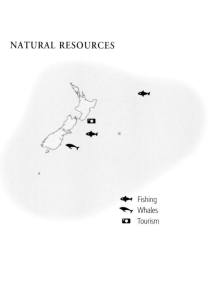

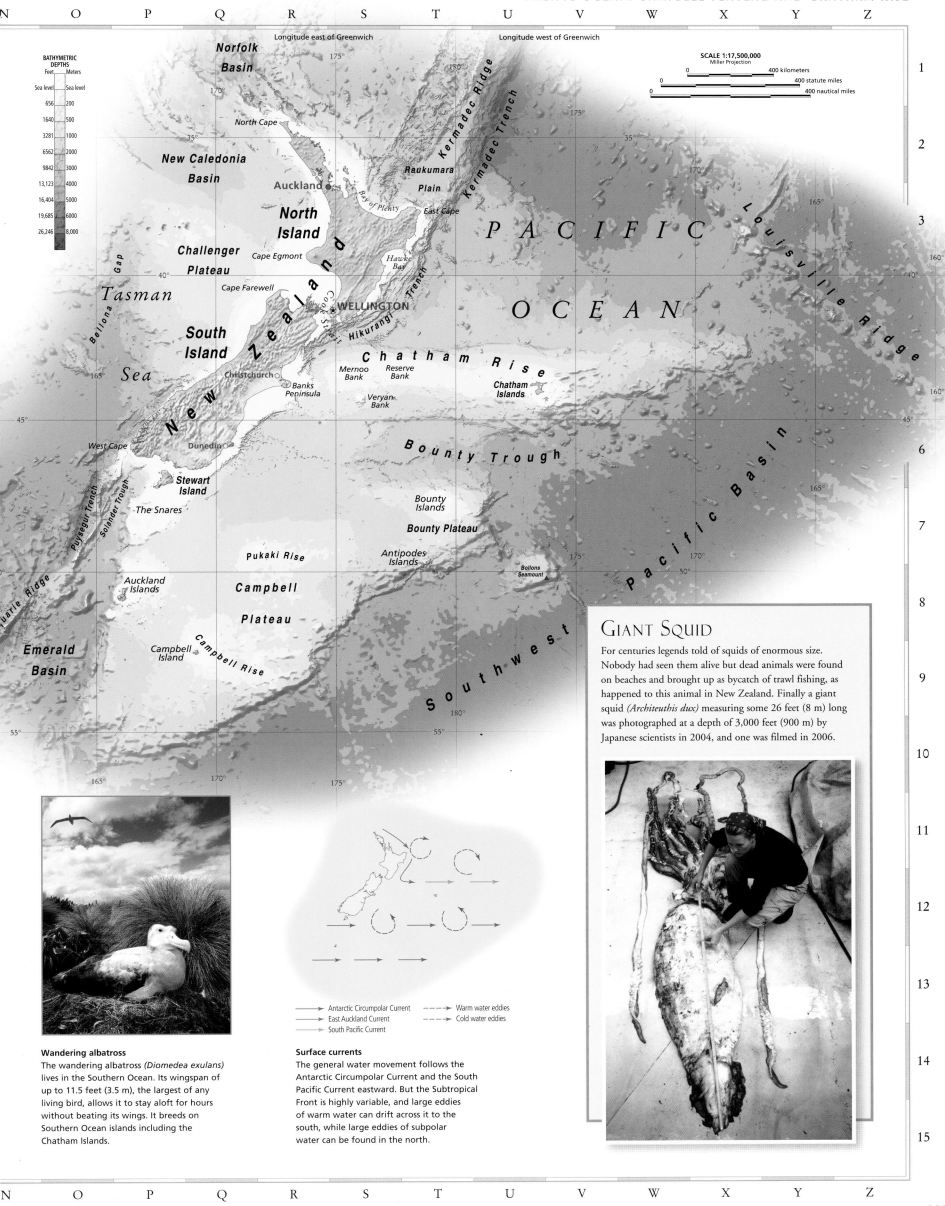

BATHYMETRIC DEPTHS

Feet	Meters
Sea level	Sea level
656	200
1640	500
3281	1000
6562	2000
9842	4000
13,123	4000
16,404	5000
19,685	6000
26,246	8,000

SCALE 1:17,500,000
Miller Projection

0   400 kilometers

0   400 statute miles

0   400 nautical miles

Norfolk Basin

New Caledonia Basin

North Cape

Auckland

North Island

Challenger Plateau

Cape Egmont

Tasman

Challenger Gap

Bellona Gap

Bay of Plenty

Raukumara Plain

East Cape

Kermadec Ridge

Kermadec Trench

Hawke Bay

PACIFIC

OCEAN

Louisville Ridge

Cape Farewell

Cook Strait

WELLINGTON

Hikurangi Trench

New Zealand

South Island

Sea

Christchurch

Banks Peninsula

Mernoo Bank

Veryan Bank

Reserve Bank

Chatham Rise

Chatham Islands

West Cape

Dunedin

Bounty Trough

Pacific Basin

Puysegur Trench

Solander Trough

Stewart Island

The Snares

Bounty Islands

Bounty Plateau

...uarie Ridge

Auckland Islands

Pukaki Rise

Antipodes Islands

Bollons Seamount

Campbell Plateau

Southwest

Emerald Basin

Campbell Island

Campbell Rise

Plateau

GIANT SQUID

For centuries legends told of squids of enormous size. Nobody had seen them alive but dead animals were found on beaches and brought up as bycatch of trawl fishing, as happened to this animal in New Zealand. Finally a giant squid *(Architeuthis dux)* measuring some 26 feet (8 m) long was photographed at a depth of 3,000 feet (900 m) by Japanese scientists in 2004, and one was filmed in 2006.

Wandering albatross

The wandering albatross *(Diomedea exulans)* lives in the Southern Ocean. Its wingspan of up to 11.5 feet (3.5 m), the largest of any living bird, allows it to stay aloft for hours without beating its wings. It breeds on Southern Ocean islands including the Chatham Islands.

Antarctic Circumpolar Current
East Auckland Current
South Pacific Current
Warm water eddies
Cold water eddies

Surface currents

The general water movement follows the Antarctic Circumpolar Current and the South Pacific Current eastward. But the Subtropical Front is highly variable, and large eddies of warm water can drift across it to the south, while large eddies of subpolar water can be found in the north.

Eastern Tropical Pacific Ocean

Most of the seafloor in the eastern tropical Pacific Ocean is a featureless plain, but deep trenches mark its eastern rim. Water in the Panama Basin is so stagnant that heating from Earth's interior raises its temperature by 0.5°F (0.3°C). The first chemosynthetic ecosystem around a hydrothermal vent was discovered in 1977 at the junction of the East Pacific Rise and the Galapagos Rift. Westward water movement dominates the region, interrupted by the eastward flowing North Equatorial Countercurrent. From August to February increased friction between the South Equatorial Current and the North Equatorial Countercurrent generates eddy-like disturbances in the flow field that are visible in satellite images. Upwelling along the equator supports an important tuna fishery. The region contains some of the smallest nation states in the world. Kiritimati (Christmas Island), the world's largest coral island, is home to several million seabirds, and the waters of the uninhabited Phoenix Islands form the world's largest marine protected area.

Sunfish
The sunfish (Mola mola), a resident of tropical and temperate waters, has a stocky body that ends just behind the vertical fins but can grow to 10 feet (3 m). It feeds on jellyfish and likes to sunbathe, lying sideways, flat at the sea surface.

BATHYMETRIC DEPTHS

Feet	Meters
Sea level	Sea level
656	200
1640	500
3281	1000
6562	2000
9842	3000
13,123	4000
16,404	5000
19,685	6000
26,246	8,000

NATURAL RESOURCES

- Fishing
- Shellfish
- Mining
- Oil production
- Tourism

Fanning Island
Tabuaeran, also known as Fanning Island, is one of 32 atolls that belong to the island nation of Kiribati. The atolls, dispersed over 1.35 million square miles (3.5 million km²), are home to more than 100,000 people. If the sea level rises, most of these low-lying islands will disappear.

Guadalupe fur seal
The Guadalupe fur seal (Arctocephalus townsendi) was once common along the Californian and Mexican coast. It was hunted and disappeared from southern California by 1825. When hunting was banned in 1894 there were fewer than 100 animals left. Now 10,000 animals breed on Guadalupe again.

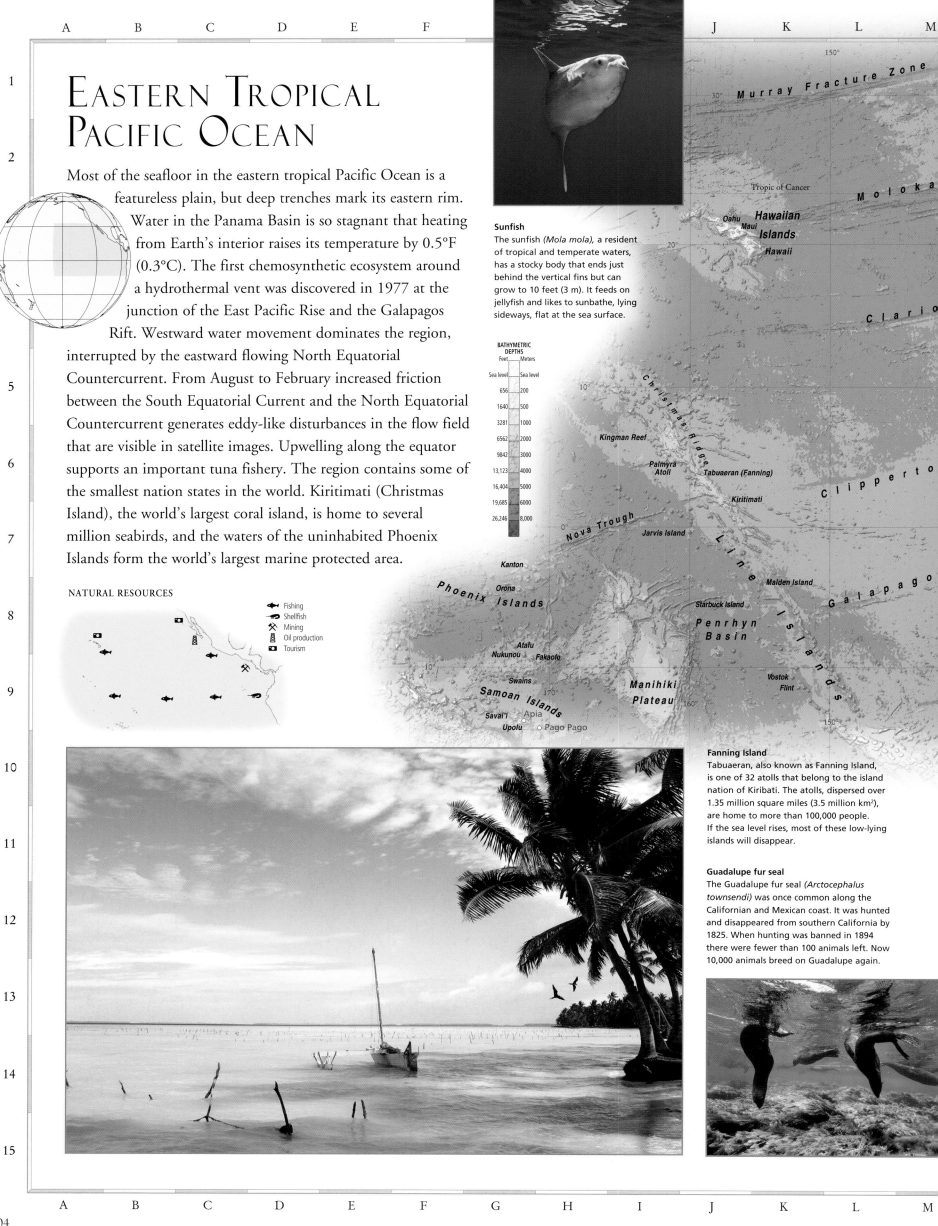

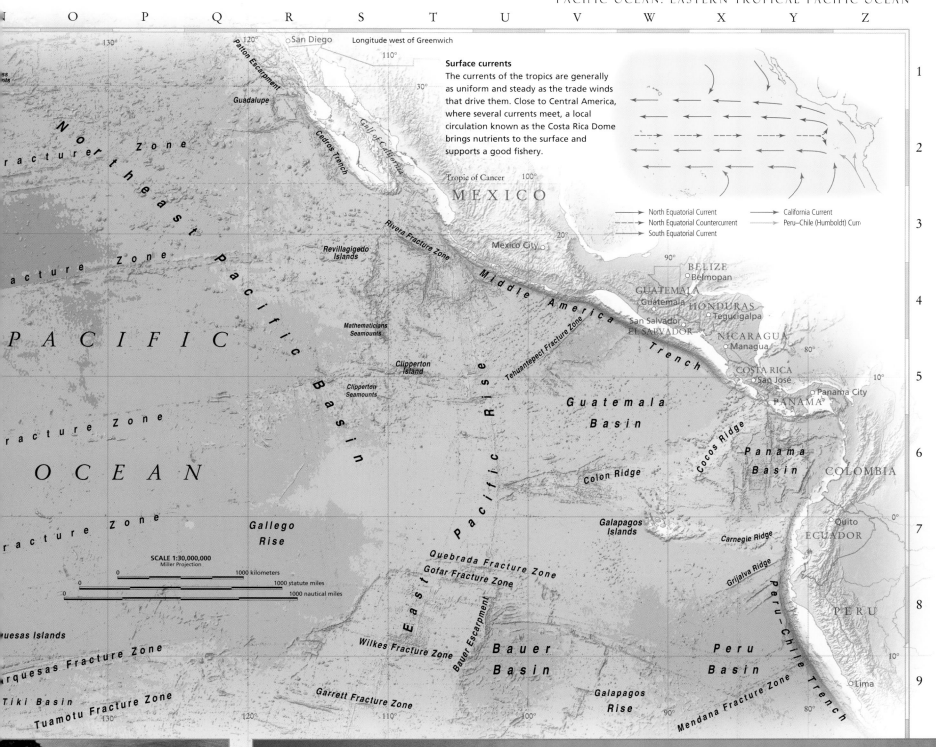

Surface currents
The currents of the tropics are generally as uniform and steady as the trade winds that drive them. Close to Central America, where several currents meet, a local circulation known as the Costa Rica Dome brings nutrients to the surface and supports a good fishery.

→ North Equatorial Current   → California Current
‑‑→ North Equatorial Countercurrent   → Peru–Chile (Humboldt) Curr
→ South Equatorial Current

SCALE 1:30,000,000
Miller Projection
1000 kilometers
1000 statute miles
1000 nautical miles

Map labels: San Diego, Longitude west of Greenwich, Patton Escarpment, Guadalupe, Gulf of California, Cedros Trench, Northeast Fracture Zone, Fracture Zone, Rivera Fracture Zone, Revillagigedo Islands, Tropic of Cancer, MEXICO, Mexico City, Middle America Trench, BELIZE, Belmopan, GUATEMALA, Guatemala, HONDURAS, Tegucigalpa, San Salvador, EL SALVADOR, NICARAGUA, Managua, COSTA RICA, San José, PANAMA, Panama City, Mathematicians Seamounts, Clipperton Island, Clipperton Seamounts, Tehuantepec Fracture Zone, Guatemala Basin, Cocos Ridge, Panama Basin, COLOMBIA, PACIFIC OCEAN, Fracture Zone, East Pacific Rise, Colon Ridge, Galapagos Islands, Carnegie Ridge, Quito, ECUADOR, Gallego Rise, Quebrada Fracture Zone, Gofar Fracture Zone, Grijalva Ridge, Peru–Chile Trench, PERU, Marquesas Islands, Marquesas Fracture Zone, Wilkes Fracture Zone, Bauer Escarpment, Bauer Basin, Peru Basin, Tiki Basin, Tuamotu Fracture Zone, Garrett Fracture Zone, Galapagos Rise, Mendana Fracture Zone, Lima

Brown booby
Brown boobies *(Sula leucogaster)* live in the tropical Atlantic and Pacific, where they dive-hunt for fish and squid. Cocos Island, on the western Cocos Ridge, is one of their favorite nesting places. The island has been a World Heritage site since 1997.

Sailfish
Two sailfish *(Istiophorus platypteros)* cruise the tropical waters off the Mexican coast. Sailfish are among the fastest fish in the ocean. Their sail-like dorsal fin is usually folded but can be spread to make the fish look larger in case of danger, and during hunting.

GULF OF CALIFORNIA

Where the East Pacific Rise comes to the surface in Baja
California Peninsula it creates a narrow sea with a rich
and unique ecosystem, the Gulf of California, also
known as the Sea of Cortez. Whales, rays, whale
sharks, turtles, and many other migratory species are
regular visitors to the region. There are resident
populations of whales, sea lions, and elephant seals.

The more than 800 species of fishes support the major
part of Mexico's fishery. There are more than 900 islands in the
gulf and, of these, 244 are on UNESCO's World Heritage list
and provide a sanctuary for hundreds of bird species. West of
the peninsula and farther north, coastal upwelling creates one of
the richest ecosystems in the world's oceans. Its once-vast schools
of sardines disappeared through overfishing half a century ago,
but sea otters still float among giant kelp, seaweed that grows
10 inches (27 cm) a day to reach 160 feet (50 m) at maturity.

KELP FORESTS

Kelp occurs worldwide where the water temperature does not exceed 68°F (20°C). It
requires high nutrient supply, mixing from wave action, and light. In the Californian
upwelling region giant kelp *(Macrocystis pyrifera)* grows into dense forests and provides
habitat for many marine creatures. Supported by gas-filled bladders its fronds grow
straight up to the surface, where they form a dense canopy.

THE FACTS

Area	62,000 square miles (160,580 km²)
Average width	95 miles (153 km)
Maximum width (at mouth)	200 miles (320 km)
Maximum length	750 miles (1,200 km)

NATURAL RESOURCES

- Fishing
- Whales
- Tourism

Sea lions
The highly intelligent Californian sea lion
(Zalophus californianus) is a common sight at
Moss Landing in Monterey Bay. Sea lions feed
on squid and fish and have learned to wait
for prey near fish ladders. During the non-
breeding season males and juveniles migrate
north along the coast.

Surface currents
In the California Current region upwelling
produces low sea-surface temperatures and
frequent fog. Currents in the Gulf of California
vary with the seasons. In the inner gulf, which
has a tidal range of up to 30 feet (9 m),
currents are dominated by tidal movement.

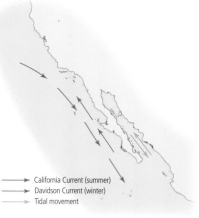

→ California Current (summer)
→ Davidson Current (winter)
→ Tidal movement

Blue whale

From December to March, blue whales (*Balaenoptera musculus*) in the Gulf of California are often accompanied by young calves. Many bear scars from encounters with killer whales. Along the northern Californian coast, blue whale populations have found new feeding grounds and are on the increase.

Monterey Bay

Once the center of an important sardine fishery, Monterey Bay is now part of the Monterey Bay National Marine Sanctuary. Famous for its kelp forests, it is home to many species of marine mammals. The old sardine cannery in Moss Landing now houses a world-renowned aquarium.

Californian sea otter

The endangered Californian sea otter (*Enhydra lutris*) forages for sea urchins, mollusks and crustaceans, which it dislodges and opens using small rocks as tools. It spends nearly its entire life in the ocean and wraps itself in kelp to avoid floating away while resting.

BATHYMETRIC DEPTHS

Feet	Meters
Sea level	Sea level
656	200
1640	500
3281	1000
6562	2000
9842	3000
13,123	4000
16,404	5000
19,685	6000
26,246	8,000

SCALE 1:10,000,000
Millér Projection

0   200 kilometers
0   200 statute miles
0   200 nautical miles

Longitude west of Greenwich

GALAPAGOS ISLANDS

The Galapagos Archipelago was formed over a volcanic hot spot and contains some of the most active volcanoes in the world. Declared a World Heritage site in 1978, the islands are also home to 40,000 people. Their unique ecosystem gave Charles Darwin the observational material for his work *On the Origin of Species*. Lacking mammal predators, island life is characterized by reptiles, among them giant tortoises, and land and sea iguanas. Among the many nesting birds are the blue-footed and red-footed boobies. The 13 main islands, 6 smaller islands, and 107 rocks and islets form an obstacle in the South Equatorial Current that produces a wake 600 miles (1,000 km) long. Upwelling in the wake brings cold water and nutrients to the surface, which leads to high productivity and provides ideal conditions for the Galapagos penguin, the world's northernmost penguin species and the only one to cross the equator.

Red rock crab
The red rock crab *(Grapsus grapsus)* is common along the Pacific coast of Central and South America and on the Galapagos Islands. It walks on tiptoe and can run in any direction. Its quick movement and fast reaction time have given it the name "Sally Lightfoot."

Galapagos sea lions
The Galapagos sea lion *(Zalophus wollebaeki)* is at home on the Galapagos Islands and on the Isla de la Plata off the coast of Ecuador. It is a social animal that loves to play, sunbathe, and perform acrobatics in the surf. It is always popular with visitors.

MARINE IGUANA

Among the many unique lifeforms encountered by Charles Darwin on his visit to the Galapagos, the marine iguana *(Amblyrhynchus cristatus)* is certainly the most specially adapted creature. It grazes on algae in cold water, yet being cold-blooded it can remain under water for only half an hour before it has to return to the shore. There it basks in the sun to raise its body temperature again.

Rocky shores
Red rock crabs live in swarms among rocks in the turbulent wave zone just above the limit of the sea spray, where they feed on algae and clean up carcasses.

Peru/Chile (Humboldt) Current
Equatorial Undercurrent (subsurface)
South Equatorial Current

Surface currents
The waters around the Galapagos Islands are highly productive. Their position on the equator places the islands in the equatorial upwelling region. The wake of the South Equatorial Current in the west brings nutrients to the surface.

Darwin called marine iguanas "disgusting clumsy lizards." They may be clumsy on land, but in the water they are graceful swimmers. This iguana soaks up the sun to prepare for its next dive.

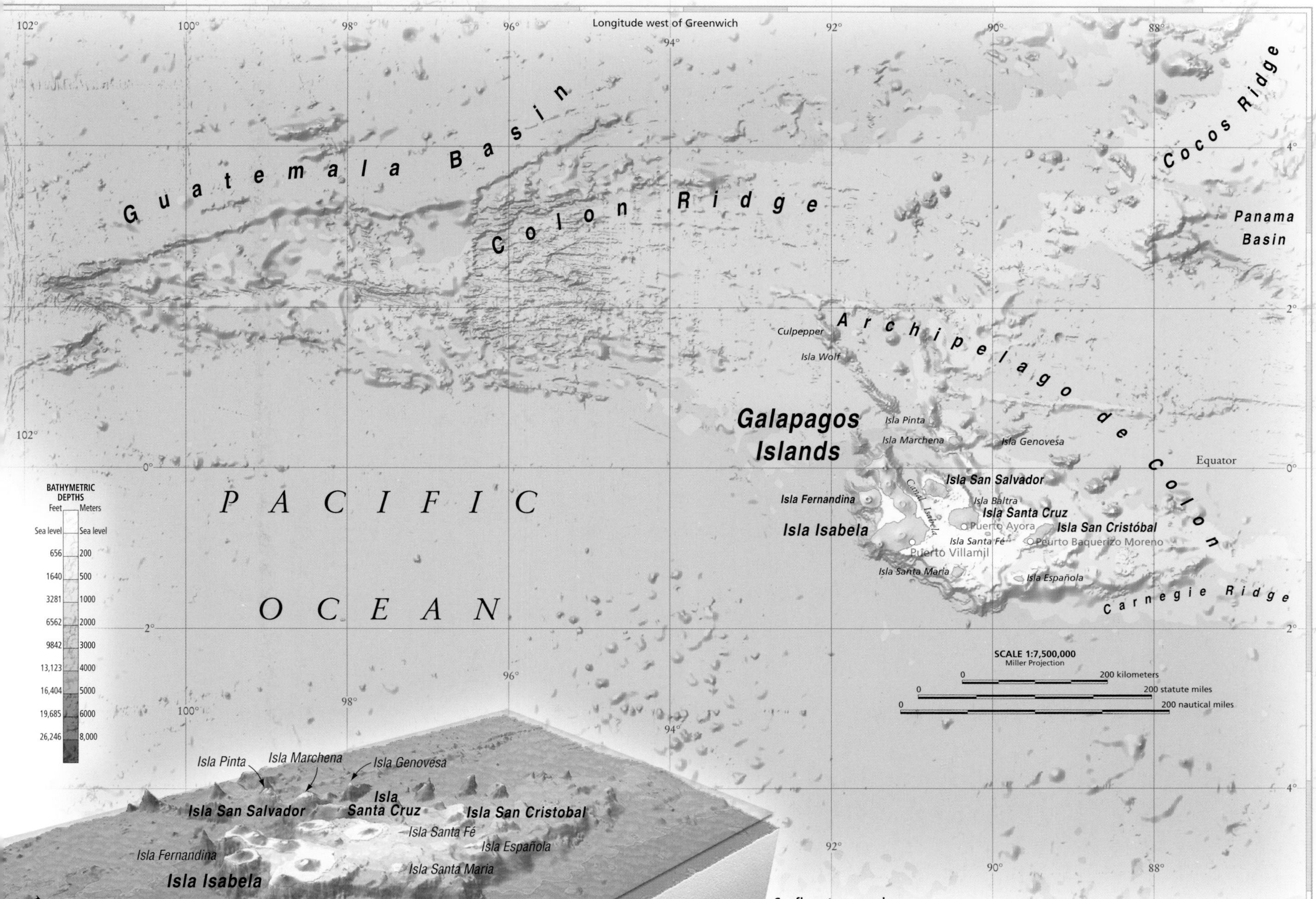

N O P Q R S T U V W X Y Z

Longitude west of Greenwich

102° 100° 98° 96° 94° 92° 90° 88°

Guatemala Basin

Colon Ridge

Cocos Ridge

Panama Basin

Archipelago de Colon

Culpepper
Isla Wolf

Galapagos Islands

Isla Pinta
Isla Marchena
Isla Genovesa

Isla Fernandina
Isla Baltra
Isla San Salvador
Isla Santa Cruz
Puerto Ayora
Isla Isabela
Isla Santa Fé
Isla San Cristóbal
Puerto Baquerizo Moreno
Puerto Villamil
Isla Santa María
Isla Española

Equator

Carnegie Ridge

PACIFIC

OCEAN

BATHYMETRIC DEPTHS

Feet	Meters
Sea level	Sea level
656	200
1640	500
3281	1000
6562	2000
9842	3000
13,123	4000
16,404	5000
19,685	6000
26,246	8,000

SCALE 1:7,500,000
Miller Projection

0 ———— 200 kilometers
0 ———— 200 statute miles
0 ———— 200 nautical miles

Isla Pinta Isla Marchena Isla Genovesa
Isla San Salvador
Isla Santa Cruz
Isla Santa Fé
Isla San Cristobal
Isla Fernandina
Isla Española
Isla Isabela
Isla Santa Maria

Galapagos Islands

Pacific Ocean

N

Seafloor topography

The Galapagos Islands share a common shelf area. At 1,300 feet (400 m) the archipelago presents a single large obstacle to the passing current. Only the smaller islands in the north have sunk deep enough to be separated from the main shelf by deep channels.

Blue-footed boobies

Spreading their wings and stomping their feet on the ground, a pair of blue-footed boobies (Sula nebouxii) performs the typical courtship dance. These birds are also found along the American coast from Ecuador to northern California.

NATURAL RESOURCES

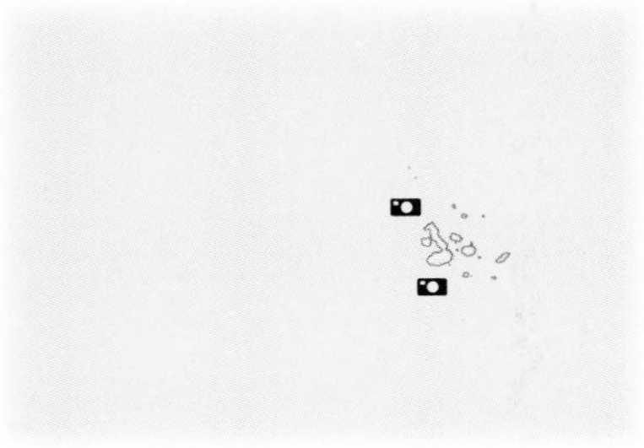

■ Tourism

N O P Q R S T U V W X Y Z

SOUTHEASTERN PACIFIC OCEAN

Few shipping lanes cross the southeastern Pacific and the region remains one of the least explored of the world's oceans. It encompasses most of the Subtropical Gyre of the southern hemisphere, with the South Pacific Current in the south, the Peru–Chile or Humboldt Current in the east, and the South Equatorial Current in the north. Its waters are low in nutrients, their deep blue contrasting with the white sands and green vegetation of the islands. Coastal upwelling along the coast of Chile and Peru supports the largest fishery in the world and feeds the millions of seabirds responsible for rich guano deposits. Disruption of the upwelling during El Niño years causes mass mortality among fish and birds, and social upheaval in fishing villages and towns. High evaporation in the region of the Polynesian Islands increases the salinity of the surface water, causing it to sink to 650 feet (200 m).

EASTER ISLAND

Isolated in the vast South Pacific, Easter Island, a World Heritage site, is located 2,237 miles (3,600 km) west of mainland Chile. Between 1250 and 1500 its Polynesian inhabitants, the Rapanui, created hundreds of large monolithic statues called moai. In the 18th and 19th centuries all moai were overthrown, probably during conflict between clans. Some 50 statues have been re-erected.

Great barracuda
The great barracuda *(Sphyraena barracuda),* a voracious predator of all tropical oceans, grows to 6 feet (1.8 m) in length. It lies in wait in reefs and ambushes its prey, attacking with short bursts of speed up to 25 mph (40 km/h).

Atacama coast
Nowhere can the contrast between land and sea be greater than along the coasts of Peru and Chile. The Atacama desert, the driest on Earth, borders the coast and is nearly devoid of life. In the sea, upwelling provides nutrients for the oceans' richest fishing grounds.

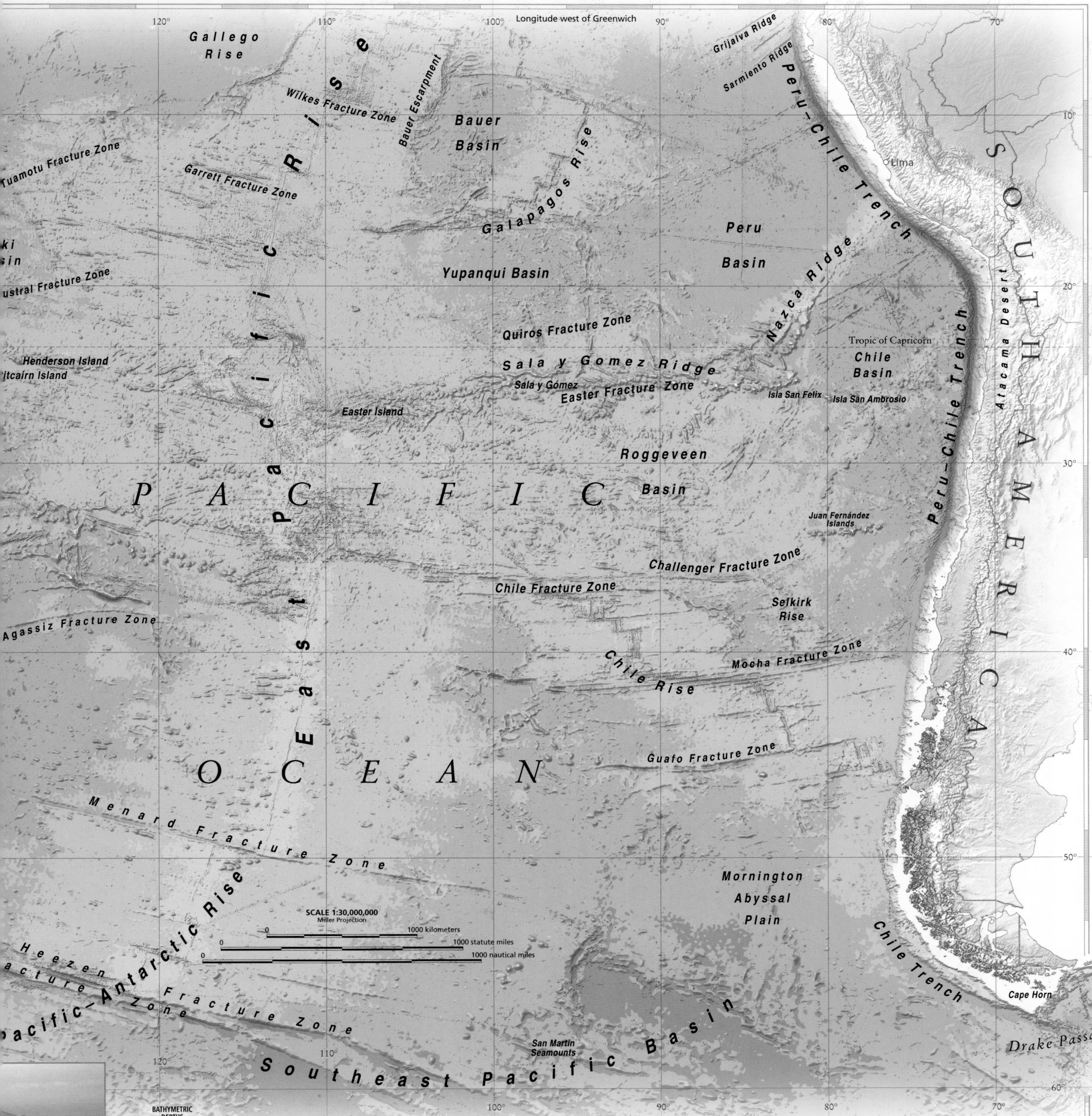

N O P Q R S T U V W X Y Z

120° 110° 100° Longitude west of Greenwich 90° 80° 70°

Gallego Rise

Grijalva Ridge

Sarmiento Ridge

Wilkes Fracture Zone

Bauer Escarpment

Bauer Basin

o Lima

Peru–Chile Trench

S O U T H

Tuamotu Fracture Zone

Garrett Fracture Zone

Galapagos Rise

Peru Basin

ki sin

ustral Fracture Zone

Yupanqui Basin

Nazca Ridge

Atacama Desert

Quiros Fracture Zone

Tropic of Capricorn

Chile Basin

Henderson Island
itcairn Island

Sala y Gomez Ridge

Sala y Gómez

Easter Fracture Zone

Isla San Felix

Isla San Ambrosio

Easter Island

A M E R I C A

Roggeveen Basin

P A C I F I C

Juan Fernández Islands

Challenger Fracture Zone

Chile Fracture Zone

Selkirk Rise

Agassiz Fracture Zone

E a s t   P a c i f i c   R i s e

Chile Rise

Mocha Fracture Zone

O C E A N

Guafo Fracture Zone

Menard Fracture Zone

Pacific–Antarctic Rise

Mornington Abyssal Plain

Chile Trench

SCALE 1:30,000,000
Miller Projection

0   1000 kilometers
0   1000 statute miles
0   1000 nautical miles

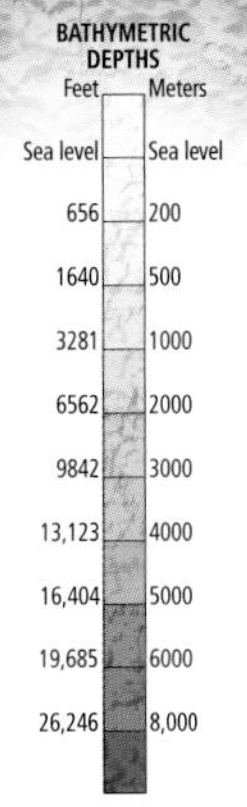

Heezen Fracture Zone

Cape Horn

Drake Passage

120° 110° 100° 90° 80° 70° 60°

San Martin Seamounts

Southeast Pacific Basin

BATHYMETRIC DEPTHS
Feet   Meters

Sea level   Sea level
656   200
1640   500
3281   1000
6562   2000
9842   3000
13,123 4000
16,404 5000
19,685 6000
26,246 8000

NATURAL RESOURCES

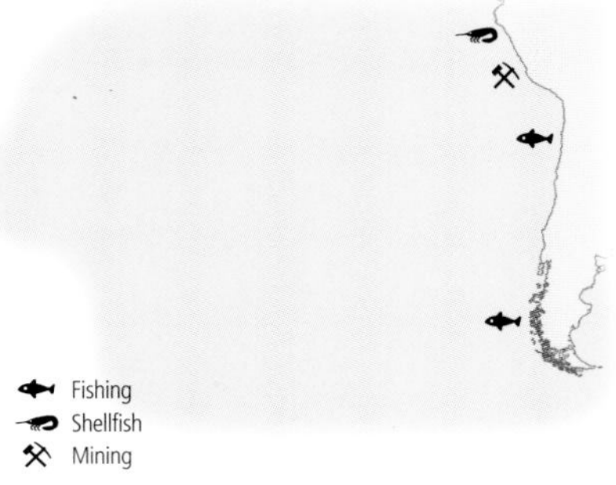

↠ Fishing
◗ Shellfish
⚒ Mining

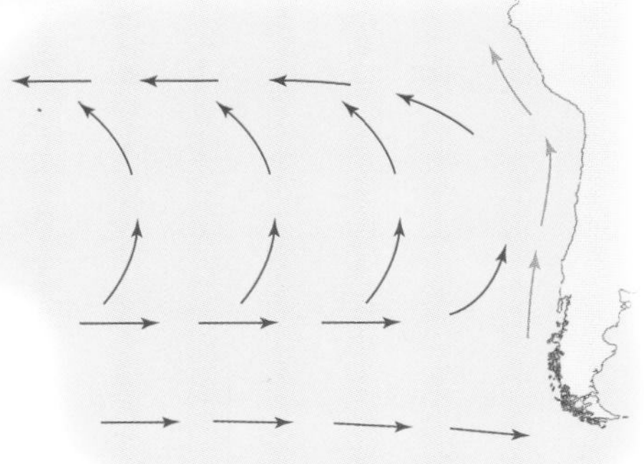

Surface currents
Easter Island marks the center of the eastern Subtropical Gyre, where currents are generally weak. The prevailing current direction near the island is northward, from the South Pacific Current in the south toward the South Equatorial Current in the north. Currents here are, however, highly variable.

→ Circumpolar Current
→ Peru–Chile (Humboldt) Current
→ South Equatorial Current
→ South Pacific Current

POLYNESIAN ISLANDS

Several hot spots created the many island chains of the South Pacific. Young islands such as Tahiti have volcanic cones surrounded by fringing reefs. As the islands drift away from their place of formation they sink back into the ocean crust while their coral fringes grow into barrier reefs, as seen at Bora Bora. Eventually the islands disappear into the sea, leaving coral atolls such as the Tuamotus as their legacy. Located in the center of the South Pacific Subtropical Gyre the islands are surrounded by ocean of low productivity, which keeps the big fishing fleets away; but their reefs support a diverse ecosystem that provides for the island communities, whose diet depends on fish. Few shipping lines cross the region. Cyclones are a rare occurrence, and the fresh breezes that moderate the region's temperature make it a preferred tourist destination. Cruise vessels of various sizes operate a busy schedule around the islands.

School of bannerfish
A school of longfin bannerfish (*Heniochus acuminatus*) moves through the lagoon of Rangiroa Atoll in the Tuamotu Islands. Bannerfish, also known as butterflyfish, occur in several species on reefs of the Indian and Pacific oceans with water temperatures of 77–82°F (25–28°C).

THREE TYPES OF VOLCANIC ISLANDS

The Leeward Islands (south to north) demonstrate the development from volcano to atoll. Huahine, Raiatea, and Tahaa are tall volcanic islands with fringing reefs. Bora Bora's volcano has started to sink, a lagoon has opened around the island, and the reef has become a barrier reef. At Tupai the island has sunk below the surface, leaving an atoll with reef and an enclosed lagoon.

Coral trout
A coral trout (*Cephalopholis miniata*) hovers in a coral niche among cup corals, sponges, soft corals, feather stars, and sea fans. The abundance of sedentary plankton-feeders is an indication that the area is bathed in plankton-rich current. Coral trout are common in reefs of the tropical Pacific.

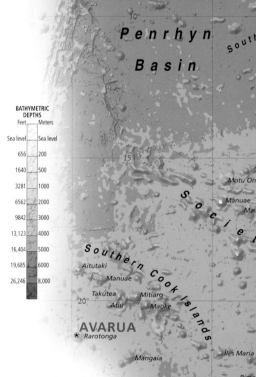

BATHYMETRIC DEPTHS

Feet	Meters
Sea level	Sea level
656	200
1640	500
3281	1000
6562	2000
9842	3000
13,123	4000
16,404	5000
19,685	6000
26,246	8,000

Central Line Islands
Starbuck Island
Tongareva
Penrhyn Basin
South
Motu One
Manuae
Mau
Soc ie t
Aitutaki
Southern Cook Islands
Manuae
Takutea   Mitiaro
Mauke
Atiu
AVARUA
Rarotonga
Iles Maria
Mangaia
Rimat
COOK
Tropic of Capricorn
ISLANDS
Southwest Pacific Basin

NATURAL RESOURCES

Fishing
Tourism

212

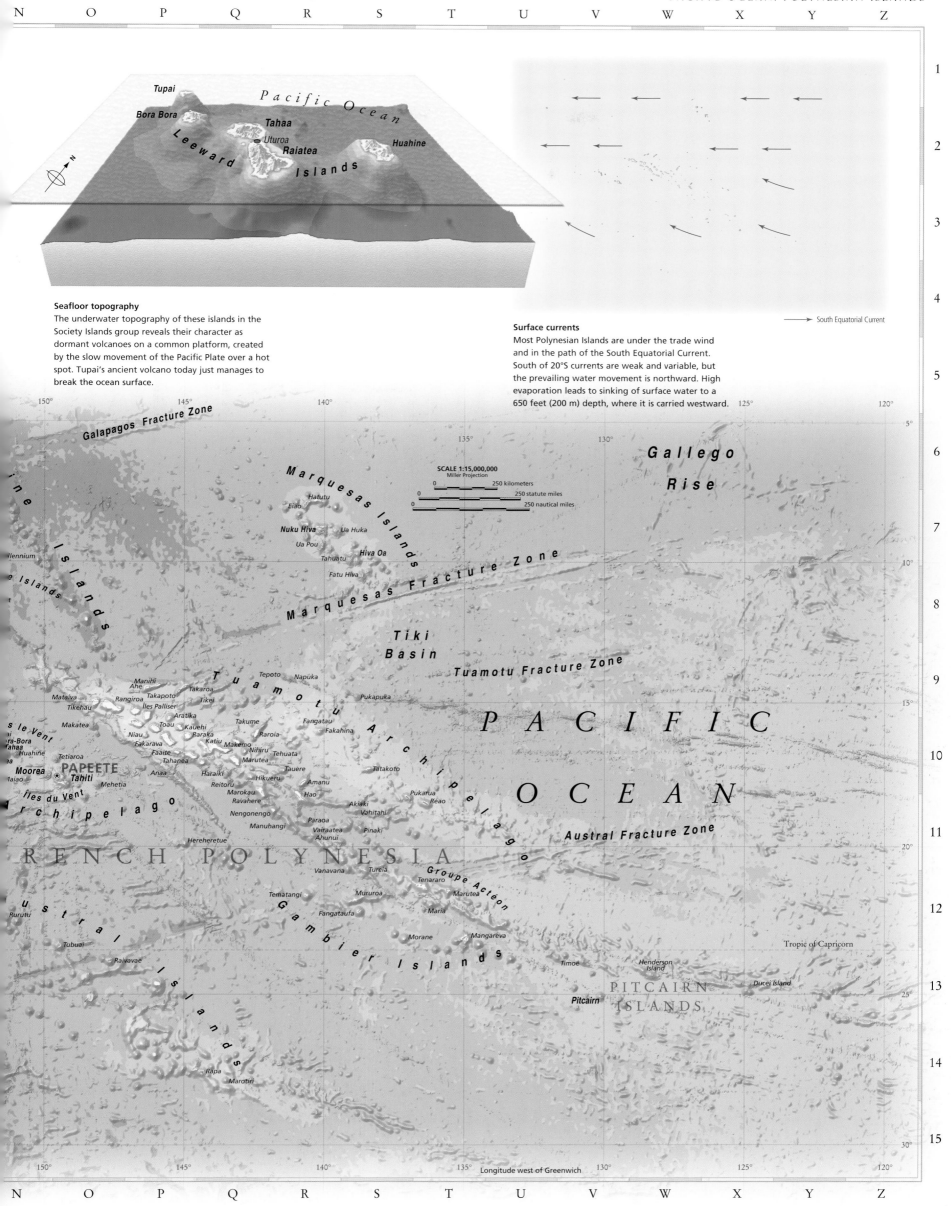

Seafloor topography

The underwater topography of these islands in the Society Islands group reveals their character as dormant volcanoes on a common platform, created by the slow movement of the Pacific Plate over a hot spot. Tupai's ancient volcano today just manages to break the ocean surface.

Surface currents

Most Polynesian Islands are under the trade wind and in the path of the South Equatorial Current. South of 20°S currents are weak and variable, but the prevailing water movement is northward. High evaporation leads to sinking of surface water to a 650 feet (200 m) depth, where it is carried westward.

→ South Equatorial Current

SCALE 1:15,000,000
Miller Projection
0   250 kilometers
0   250 statute miles
0   250 nautical miles

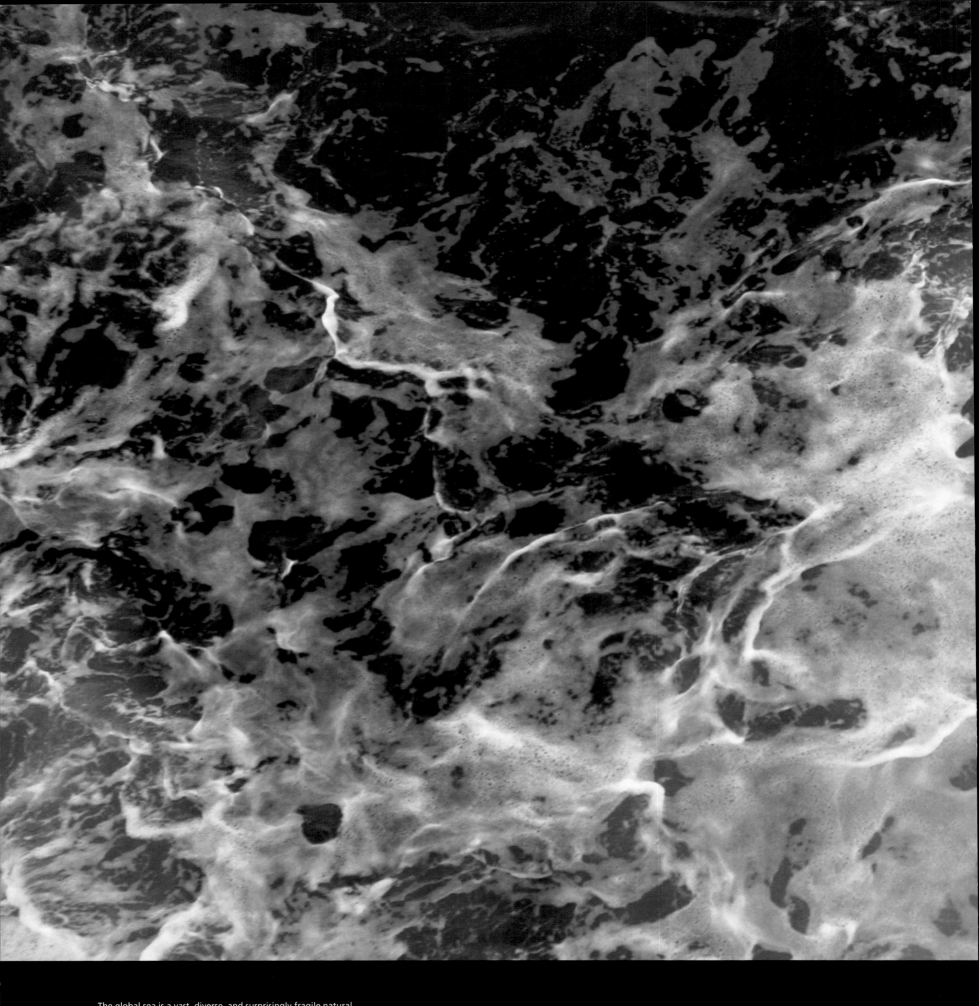

The global sea is a vast, diverse, and surprisingly fragile natural
world. Despite centuries of marine exploration and avid human
use of marine resources, the depths continue to reveal new
wonders, pose new challenges, and spark the imagination
and curiosity of each new generation.

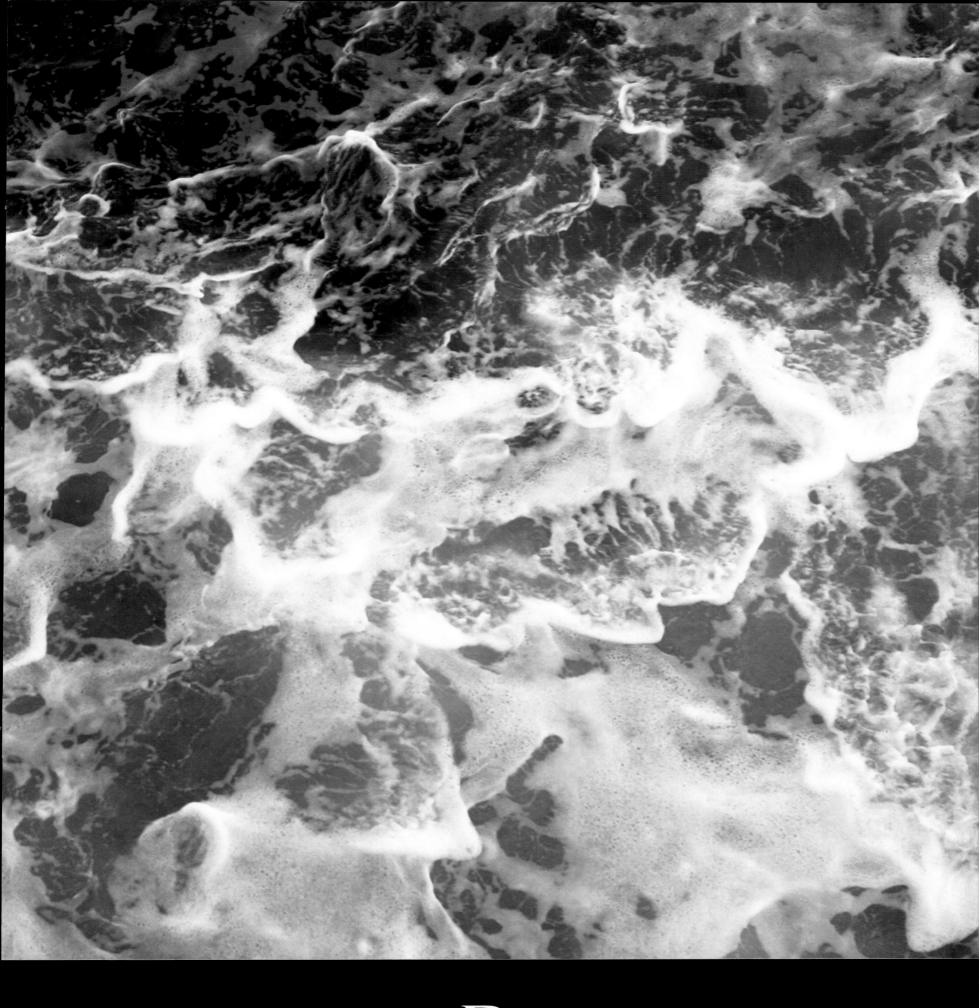

REFERENCE

OCEAN FACT FILE

Names of oceans and seas	Area square miles (km²)	Average depth feet (m)	Greatest known depth: feet (m)	Length miles (km)	Width miles (km)	Volume cubic miles (km³)	
Planet Earth				(Equatorial circ.)*	(Polar circ.)*		
Planet Earth	196,930,000 (510,000,000)	–	–	24,902 (40,077)*	24,820 (39,942)*	–	
The Continents (29.2% area of Earth)	57,510,000 (148,940,000)	–	–	–	–	–	
The World Ocean (70.8% area of Earth)	139,420,000 (361,060,000)	12,430 (3,790)	36,201 (11,034)	–	–	329,070,000 (1,370,740,000)	
The three main ocean basins							
Pacific Ocean including marginal seas and Pacific section of the Southern Ocean	69,380,000 (179,680,000)	13,220 (4,030)	36,201 (11,034)	10,106 (16,264)	to 11,185 (to 18,000)	173,770,000 (723,840,000)	
Atlantic Ocean including marginal seas (Black, Mediterranean, Caribbean etc), the Arctic Ocean and the Atlantic section of the Southern Ocean	41,110,000 (106,460,000)	10,920 (3,330)	27,493 (8,380)	13,360 (21,500)	to 4,909 (7,900)	85,200,000 (354,900,000)	
Indian Ocean including marginal seas and the Indian Ocean section of the Southern Ocean	28,930,000 (74,920,000)	12,790 (3,890)	24,460 (7,455)	6,351 (10,220)	to 6,338 (10,200)	70,100,000 (292,000,000)	
The oceans							
Pacific Ocean, including marginal seas	65,590,000 (169,852,000)	13,127 (4,001)	36,201 (11,034)	8,637 (13,900)	to 11,185 (18,000)	163,100,000	(679,614,000)
Atlantic Ocean, including marginal seas	33,560,000 (86,915,000)	11,828 (3,605)	28,233 (8,605)	8,774 (14,120)	to 4,909 (7,900)	75,200,000	(313,352,500)
Indian Ocean, including marginal seas	26,980,000 (69,876,000)	12,645 (3,854)	24,460 (7,455)	5,841 (9,400)	to 6,338 (10,200)	64,720,000	(269,302,000)
Southern Ocean, including marginal seas	7,850,000 (20,327,000)	14,450 (4,500)	23,736 (7,235)	to 13,360 (21,500)	249–1,678 (400–2,700)	21,950,000	(91,471,500)
Arctic Ocean, including marginal seas	5,440,000 (14,090,000)	4,690 (1,430)	18,456 (5,625)	to 3,107 (5,000)	to 1,988 (3,200)	4,100,000	(17,000,000)

THE OCEANS AND SUBDIVISIONS IHO 23-4th: Limits of Oceans and Seas, Special Publication 23, 4th Edition June 2002, published by the International Hydrographic Bureau of the International Hydrographic Organization.

IHO	Names of oceans and seas	Area square miles (km²)	Average depth feet (m)	Greatest known depth: feet (m)	Length miles (km)	Width miles (km)	Volume cubic miles (km³)
	North Atlantic Ocean and subdivisions						
1	North Atlantic Ocean	–	–	28,233 (8,605)	4,636 (7,460)	to 4,909 (7,900)	–
1.1	Skaggerak	12,970 (33,600)	1,312 (400)	1,969 (600)	150 (240)	80–90 (130–145)	3,225 (13,440)
1.2	North Sea	222,100 (575,200)	308 (94)	2,165 (660)	621 (1,000)	93–373 (150–600)	12,974 (54,069)
1.3	Inner Seas (off West Coast Scotland)	4,630 (12,000)	82 (25)	266 (81)	174 (280)	43–62 (70–100)	72 (300)
1.4	Irish Sea	40,000 (100,000)	125 (38)	576 (175)	130 (210)	150 (240)	912 (3,800)
1.5	Bristol Channel	1,160 (3,000)	36 (11)	98 (30)	93 (150)	3–24 (5–40)	8 (33)
1.6	Celtic Sea	61,780 (160,000)	180 (55)	236 (72)	249 (400)	249 (400)	2,112 (8,800)
1.7	English Channel	34,700 (89,900)	272 (83)	394 (120)	249 (400)	21–112 (31–180)	1,726 (7,192)
1.7.1	Dover Strait	950 (2,450)	46 (14)	180 (55)	43 (70)	18–25 (30–40)	8 (34)
1.8	Bay of Biscay	86,000 (223,000)	7,874 (2,400)	15,525 (4,735)	317 (510)	342 (550)	128,419 (535,200)
1.9	Gulf of Guinea	324,360 (840,000)	12,796 (3,900)	16,405 (5,000)	435 (700)	746 (1,200)	786,064 (3,276,000)
1.10	Caribbean Sea	1,049,500 (2,718,200)	8,685 (2,647)	25,218 (7,686)	1,678 (2,700)	360–840 (600–1,400)	1,726,430 (7,195,075)
1.11	Gulf of Mexico	615,000 (1,592,800)	4,874 (1,486)	12,425 (3,787)	1,100 (1,770)	800 (1,287)	567,929 (2,366,901)
1.12	Straits of Florida	48,270 (125,000)	1,148 (350)	1,641 (500)	311 (500)	155 (250)	10,498 (43,750)
1.13	Bay of Fundy	3,600 (9,300)	328 (100)	656 (200)	94 (151)	32 (52)	223 (930)
1.14	Gulf of St Lawrence	62,530 (162,000)	197 (60)	656 (200)	280 (450)	261 (420)	2,332 (9,720)
1.15	Labrador Sea	222,030 (575,000)	6,562 (2,000)	12,468 (3,800)	to 870 (1,400)	to 492 (820)	275,938 (1,150,000)
	Other subdivisions of the North Atlantic Ocean						
–	Bay of Campeche	65,640 (170,000)	1,476 (450)	10,499 (3,200)	441 (710)	205 (330)	18,356 (76,500)
–	Block Island Sound	190 (500)	59 (18)	66 (20)	20 (32)	10 (16)	2 (9)
–	Cabot Strait	1,450 (3,750)	1,148 (350)	3,281 (1,000)	155 (250)	60–372 (100–320)	315 (1,313)
–	Canarias Sea	90,360 (234,000)	5,906 (1,800)	6,562 (2,000)	373 (600)	249 (400)	101,065 (421,200)
–	Cape Cod Bay	830 (2,150)	82 (25)	115 (35)	31 (50)	27 (43)	13 (54)
–	Chaleur Bay	1,680 (4,350)	82 (25)	164 (50)	90 (145)	15–25 (24–40)	26 (109)
–	Chesapeake Bay	5,800 (15,000)	23 (7)	80 (24)	193 (311)	3–25 (5–40)	25 (105)
–	Delaware Bay	970 (2,500)	23 (7)	70 (21)	52 (84)	6–25 (10–40)	4 (18)
–	Denmark Strait	54,060 (140,000)	3,281 (1,000)	8,203 (2,500)	300 (483)	180 (290)	33,592 (140,000)
–	Gulf of Cadiz	14,480 (37,500)	1,969 (600)	3,281 (1,000)	93 (150)	200 (320)	5,399 (22,500)
–	Gulf of Venezuela	10,190 (26,400)	8,203 (2,500)	9,843 (3,000)	75 (120)	150 (240)	15,836 (66,000)
–	Gulf of Honduras	30,890 (80,000)	2,953 (900)	8,203 (2,500)	249 (400)	9–240 (15–400)	17,276 (72,000)
–	Gulf of Maine	90,700 (235,000)	492 (150)	1,237 (377)	323 (520)	280 (450)	8,458 (35,250)
–	Long Bay	4,630 (12,000)	49 (15)	131 (40)	78 (125)	62 (100)	43 (180)
–	Long Island Sound	1,180 (3,056)	82 (25)	328 (100)	90 (145)	3–20 (5–32)	18 (76)
–	Massachusetts Bay	820 (2,123)	115 (35)	295 (90)	31 (50)	26 (42)	18 (74)
–	Mona Passage	8,500 (22,000)	656 (200)	3,281 (1,000)	112 (180)	68–87 (110–145)	1,056 (4,400)
–	Nantucket Sound	1,000 (2,600)	59 (18)	131 (40)	43 (70)	25 (40)	11 (47)
–	North Channel	2,320 (6,000)	328 (100)	656 (200)	124 (200)	11–36 (18–60)	144 (600)
–	Onslow Bay	5,790 (15,000)	66 (20)	164 (50)	103 (165)	62 (100)	72 (300)
–	Rhode Island Sound	580 (1,500)	23 (7)	33 (10)	25 (40)	24 (38)	3 (11)
–	Saint George's Channel	4,250 (11,000)	148 (45)	203 (62)	99 (160)	47 (76)	119 (495)

IHO	Names of oceans and seas	Area square miles (km²)	Average depth feet (m)	Greatest known depth: feet (m)	Length miles (km)	Width miles (km)	Volume cubic miles (km³)
Other subdivisions of the North Atlantic Ocean (continued)							
–	Sargasso Sea	1,448,020 (3,750,000)	16,405 (5,000)	21,005 (6,402)	1,864 (3,000)	994 (1,600)	4,498,990 (18,750,000)
–	Windward Passage	3,480 (9,000)	3,281 (1,000)	5,545 (1,690)	68 (110)	50 (80)	2,160 (9,000)
–	Yucatan Channel	16,600 (43,000)	3,281 (1,000)	6,693 (2,040)	135 (217)	124 (200)	10,318 (43,000)
Baltic Sea and subdivisions (North Atlantic Ocean)							
2	Baltic Sea	163,000 (422,200)	180 (55)	1,380 (421)	795 (1,280)	24–324 (40–540)	5,572 (23,221)
2.1	Central Baltic Sea	46,340 (120,000)	164 (50)	656 (200)	373 (600)	186 (300)	1,440 (6,000)
2.2	Gulf of Bothnia	45,200 (117,000)	200 (60)	965 (295)	450 (725)	48–150 (80–240)	1,684 (7,020)
2.2.1	Bothnian Sea	19,110 (49,500)	246 (75)	656 (200)	205 (330)	48–132 (80–220)	891 (3,713)
2.2.2	Bay of Bothnia	9,270 (24,000)	246 (75)	656 (200)	249 (400)	9–75 (15–125)	432 (1,800)
2.3	Gulf of Finland	11,600 (30,000)	85 (26)	377 (115)	249 (400)	12–80 (19–130)	187 (780)
2.4	Sound Sea	25,100 (65,000)	82 (25)	164 (50)	186 (300)	137 (220)	390 (1,625)
2.5	Gulf of Riga	7,000 (18,000)	131 (40)	144 (44)	109 (175)	24–72 (40–120)	173 (720)
2.6	The Sound	390 (1,000)	131 (40)	164 (50)	68 (110)	3–9 (5–14)	10 (40)
2.7	The Great Belt	460 (1,200)	85 (26)	164 (50)	47 (75)	9–12 (15– 20)	7 (31)
2.8	The Little Belt	420 (1,100)	85 (26)	164 (50)	37 (60)	9–24 (15– 40)	7 (29)
2.9	Kattegat	9,840 (25,485)	84 (26)	164 (50)	137 (220)	37–88 (60–142)	159 (663)
Other subdivisions of the Baltic Sea (North Atlantic Ocean)							
–	Gulf of Gdansk	1,660 (4,296)	180 (55)	197 (60)	62 (100)	43 (70)	57 (236)
–	Kiel Bay	970 (2,500)	131 (40)	131 (40)	50 (80)	22 (35)	24 (100)
–	Mecklenburger Bay	1,000 (2,600)	131 (40)	125 (38)	47 (75)	18–27 (30–45)	25 (104)
–	Pomeranian Bay	930 (2,400)	66 (20)	164 (50)	43 (70)	31 (50)	12 (48)
Mediterranean Sea and subdivisions (North Atlantic Ocean)							
3.1	Mediterranean Sea	969,000 (2,510,000)	4,920 (1,500)	16,897 (5,150)	2,500 (4,000)	497 (800)	860,636 (3,586,790)
3.1.1	Mediterranean Sea, Western Basin	328,220 (850,000)	-	12,000 (3,658)	1,250 (2,000)	497 (800)	-
3.1.1.1	Strait of Gibraltar	290 (750)	1,200 (365)	3,117 (950)	36 (58)	8 (13)	66 (274)
3.1.1.2	Alboran Sea	18,530 (48,000)	1,969 (600)	3,872 (1180)	249 (400)	48–120 (80–200)	6,910 (28,800)
3.1.1.3	Balearic Sea	123,560 (320,000)	2,461 (750)	4,987 (1,520)	497 (800)	120–420 (200–700)	57,587 (240,000)
3.1.1.4	Ligurian Sea	13,510 (35,000)	4,265 (1,300)	9,300 (2,850)	155 (250)	106 (170)	10,918 (45,500)
3.1.1.5	Tyrrhenian Sea	46,340 (120,000)	9,515 (2,900)	11,897 (3,626)	475 (760)	60–300 (97–483)	83,501 (348,000)
3.1.2	Mediterranean Sea, Eastern Basin	640,990 (1,660,000)	-	16,897 (5,150)	1,250 (2,000)	497 (800)	-
3.1.2.1	Adriatic Sea	52,220 (135,250)	1,457 (444)	4,035 (1,324)	497 (800)	99 (160)	14,409 (60,051)
3.1.2.2	Strait of Sicily	19,310 (50,000)	328 (100)	1,969 (600)	311 (500)	93 (150)	1,200 (5,000)
3.1.2.3	Ionian Sea	104,260 (270,000)	12,796 (3,900)	16,000 (4,900)	373 (600)	120–360 (200–600)	252,663 (1,053,000)
3.1.2.4	Aegean Sea	83,000 (214,000)	1,969 (600)	11,627 (3,543)	380 (611)	186 (399)	30,809 (128,400)
3.2	Sea of Marmara	4,430 (11,474)	1,620 (494)	4,446 (1,355)	175 (280)	50 (80)	1,360 (5,668)
3.3	Black Sea	196,000 (508,000)	4,062 (1,240)	7,365 (2,245)	730 (1,175)	160 (260)	151,147 (629,920)
3.4	Sea of Azov	14,500 (37,555)	23 (7)	45 (13)	210 (340)	85 (135)	63 (263)
Other subdivisions of the Mediterranean Sea (North Atlantic Ocean)							
–	Dardanelles	100 (250)	180 (55)	300 (92)	38 (61)	0.75–4 (1.2–6.5)	3.3 (13.8)
–	Gulf of Lion	11,580 (30,000)	246 (75)	276 (84)	93 (150)	60–138 (100–230)	540 (2,250)
–	Gulf of Venice	2,010 (5,200)	98 (30)	128 (39)	60 (95)	37 (60)	37 (156)
–	Bosporus	40 (105)	98 (30)	408 (124)	19 (30)	2.3 (3.7)	0.8 (3.2)
–	Sea of Crete	27,800 (72,000)	6,562 (2,000)	10,000 (3,294)	249 (400)	130 (210)	34,552 (144,000)
–	Thracian Sea	3,480 (9,000)	246 (75)	328 (100)	93 (150)	50 (80)	162 (675)
Southern Atlantic Ocean and subdivisions							
4	South Atlantic Ocean	–	–	27,651 (8,428)	4,139 (6,660)	to 4,680 (to 7,800)	–
4.1	River Plate	12,740 (33,000)	20 (6)	70 (21)	186 (300)	9 to 120 (15 to 200)	48 (198)
4.2	Scotia Sea	348,000 (900,000)	11,500 (4,500)	27,651 (8,428)	870 (1,400)	497 (800)	755,830 (3,150,000)
4.3	Drake Passage	308,910 (800,000)	11,000 (3,400)	15,600 (4,800)	497 (800)	621 (1,000)	652,653 (2,720,000)
Other subdivisions of the South Atlantic Ocean							
–	San Jorge Gulf	15,450 (40,000)	115 (35)	262 (80)	99 (160)	137 (220)	336 (1,400)
–	San Matias Gulf	6,950 (18,000)	98 (30)	230 (70)	99 (160)	24–90 (40–150)	130 (540)
–	Strait of Magellan	2,240 (5,800)	66 (20)	98 (30)	350 (560)	2–20 (3–32)	28 (116)
Indian Ocean and subdivisions							
5	Indian Ocean	26,500,000 (68,600,000)	12,644 (3,854)	23,376 (7,125)	5,800 (9,400)	6,300 (10,200)	64,720,000 (269,302,104)
5.1	Mozambique Channel	432,470 (1,120,000)	8,531 (2,600)	9,843 (3,000)	1,000 (1,600)	250–600 (400–950)	698,723 (2,912,000)
5.2	Gulf of Suez	4,050 (10,500)	82 (25)	295 (90)	180 (290)	15–35 (24–56)	63 (263)

IHO	Names of oceans and seas	Area square miles (km²)	Average depth feet (m)	Greatest known depth: feet (m)	Length miles (km)	Width miles (km)	Volume cubic miles (km³)
Indian Ocean and subdivisions (continued)							
5.3	Gulf of Aqaba	1,480 (3,840)	2,625 (800)	6,070 (1,850)	99 (160)	12–17 (19–27)	737 (3,072)
5.4	Red Sea	169,100 (438,000)	1,608 (490)	9,974 (3,040)	1,398 (2,250)	220 (355)	51,602 (215,058)
5.5	Gulf of Aden	205,000 (530,000)	4,922 (1,500)	17,586 (5,360)	920 (1,480)	300 (480)	190,757 (795,000)
5.6	Persian Gulf	96,911 (251,000)	164 (50)	344 (119)	615 (989)	35 (56)	1,957 (8,155)
5.7	Strait of Hormuz	4,630 (12,000)	213 (65)	2,953 (900)	99 (160)	35–60 (55–95)	187 (780)
5.8	Gulf of Oman	65,640 (170,000)	3,937 (1,200)	9,843 (3,000)	350 (560)	200 (320)	48,949 (204,000)
5.9	Arabian Sea	1,500,000 (3,900,000)	9,022 (2,750)	15,262 (4,652)	to 1,243 (2,000)	1,490 (2,400)	2,533,521 (10,558,708)
5.10	Lakshadweep Sea	289,600 (750,000)	7,874 (2,400)	14,765 (4,500)	to 932 (1,500)	to 620 (1,000)	431,903 (1,800,000)
5.11	Gulf of Mannar	11,740 (30,400)	3,281 (1,000)	5,906 (1,800)	99 (160)	80–170 (130–275)	7,294 (30,400)
5.12	Palk Strait and Palk Bay	5,780 (14,960)	98 (30)	295 (90)	85 (136)	40–85 (64–137)	108 (449)
5.13	Bay of Bengal	838,613 (2,172,000)	8,500 (2,600)	15,400 (4,694)	1,300 (2,090)	1,000 (1,610)	1,355,648 (5,649,800)
5.14	Andaman Sea	308,000 (797,700)	2,854 (870)	12,392 (3,777)	750 (1,200)	400 (645)	166,522 (693,999)
5.15	Timor Sea	235,000 (615,000)	459 (140)	10,800 (3,300)	609 (980)	435 (700)	20,659 (86,100)
5.15.1	Joseph Bonaparte Gulf	19,310 (50,000)	197 (60)	328 (100)	99 (160)	225 (360)	720 (3,000)
5.16	Arafura Sea	250,990 (650,000)	230 (70)	12,000 (3,660)	to 620 (1,000)	to 435 (700)	10,918 (45,500)
5.16.1	Gulf of Carpentaria	120,000 (310,000)	164 (50)	230 (70)	544 (875)	120–390 (200–650)	3,719 (15,500)
5.17	Great Australian Bight	366,830 (950,000)	7,218 (2,200)	14,765 (4,500)	1,740 (2,800)	to 620 (1,000)	501,487 (2,090,000)
Other subdivisions of the Indian Ocean							
–	Gulf of Bahrain	3,280 (8,500)	98 (30)	131 (40)	106 (170)	12–57 (20–95)	61 (255)
–	Strait of Tiran	440 (1,150)	262 (80)	400 (122)	31 (50)	16 (25)	22 (92)
South China and Eastern Archipelagic Seas (Pacific Ocean)							
6	South China & Eastern Archipelagic Seas	–	–	–	–	–	–
6.1	South China Sea	895,400 (2,319,000)	5,419 (1,652)	16,456 (5,016)	to 1,182 (1,970)	to 840 (1,400)	919,231 (3,830,988)
6.2	Gulf of Tonkin	46,340 (120,000)	246 (75)	230 (70)	311 (500)	150 (250)	2,160 (9,000)
6.3	Gulf of Thailand	123,553 (320,000)	148 (45)	262 (80)	450 (724)	350 (563)	3,455 (14,400)
6.4	Natuna Sea	135,150 (350,000)	148 (45)	328 (100)	559 (900)	60–390 (100–650)	3,779 (15,750)
6.5	Malacca Strait	25,000 (65,000)	90 (27)	656 (200)	497 (800)	40–155 (65–249)	421 (1,755)
6.6	Singapore Strait	1,000 (2,600)	131 (40)	164 (50)	65 (105)	10–18 (16–30)	25 (104)
6.7	Sunda Strait	4,440 (11,500)	131 (40)	164 (50)	103 (165)	16–70 (26–110)	110 (460)
6.8	Java Sea	167,000 (433,000)	151 (46)	689 (210)	900 (1,450)	261 (420)	4,779 (19,918)
6.9	Makassar Strait	81,090 (210,000)	2,625 (800)	6,562 (2,000)	497 (800)	80–230 (130–370)	40,311 (168,000)
6.10	Bali Sea	15,830 (41,000)	197 (60)	1,805 (550)	311 (500)	75 (120)	590 (2,460)
6.11	Flores Sea	93,000 (240,000)	6,890 (2,100)	16,860 (5,140)	435 (700)	108–360 (180–600)	120,933 (504,000)
6.12	Sumba Strait	6,490 (16,800)	328 (100)	2,461 (750)	130 (210)	36–60 (60–100)	403 (1,680)
6.13	Savu Sea	41,000 (105,000)	8,859 (2,700)	11,385 (3,470)	404 (650)	155 (250)	68,025 (283,500)
6.14	Aru Sea	30,890 (80,000)	6,562 (2,000)	11,484 (3,500)	311 (500)	78–102 (130–170)	38,391 (160,000)
6.15	Banda Sea	181,000 (470,000)	14,765 (4,500)	24,409 (7,440)	652 (1,050)	228–330 (380–550)	507,486 (2,115,000)
6.16	Gulf of Bone	12,740 (33,000)	6,562 (2,000)	9,843 (3,000)	186 (300)	36–102 (60–170)	15,836 (66,000)
6.17	Ceram Sea	31,280 (81,000)	7,218 (2,200)	11,484 (3,500)	360 (580)	68–120 (110–200)	42,758 (178,200)
6.18	Gulf of Berau	4,250 (11,000)	230 (70)	328 (100)	137 (220)	12–42 (20–70)	185 (770)
6.19	Halmahera Sea	28,570 (74,000)	2,461 (750)	3,281 (1,000)	186 (300)	186 (300)	13,317 (55,500)
6.20	Molucca Sea	77,000 (200,000)	9,187 (2,800)	15,780 (4,810)	373 (600)	150–258 (250–430)	134,370 (560,000)
6.21	Gulf of Tomini	23,170 (60,000)	3,937 (1,200)	4,922 (1,500)	261 (420)	60–123 (100–205)	17,276 (72,000)
6.22	Celebes Sea	110,000 (280,000)	13,780 (4,200)	20,406 (6,220)	420 (675)	520 (837)	282,177 (1,176,000)
6.23	Sulu Sea	100,000 (260,000)	11,484 (3,500)	18,400 (5,600)	490 (790)	375 (603)	218,351 (910,000)
Other subdivisions of the South China and Eastern Archipelagic Seas							
–	Luzon Sea	81,090 (210,000)	2,953 (900)	9,843 (3,000)	466 (750)	217 (350)	45,350 (189,000)
–	Luzon Strait	46,340 (120,000)	2,953 (900)	6,562 (2,000)	217 (350)	249 (400)	25,914 (108,000)
–	Karimata Strait	52,130 (135,000)	492 (150)	656 (200)	280 (450)	120–228 (200–380)	4,859 (20,250)
–	Yapen Strait	6,180 (16,000)	3,281 (1,000)	3,281 (1,000)	155 (250)	40 (65)	3,839 (16,000)
–	Cenderawasih Bay	18,150 (47,000)	2,297 (700)	3,281 (1,000)	174 (280)	54–252 (90–420)	7,894 (32,900)
North Pacific Ocean and subdivisions							
7	North Pacific Ocean	–	–	36,201 (11,034)	4,499 (7,240)	to 10,800 (18,000)	–
7.1	Philippine Sea	1,776,230 (4,600,000)	19,700 (6,000)	34,578 (10,539)	to 1,800 (3,000)	to 1,200 (2,000)	6,622,513 (27,600,000)
7.2	Taiwan Strait	21,240 (55,000)	197 (60)	230 (70)	286 (460)	100–174 (160–280)	792 (3,300)
7.3	East China Sea	284,000 (735,800)	574 (175)	8,913 (2,717)	684 (1,100)	435 (700)	30,897 (128,765)
7.4	Yellow Sea	180,000 (466,200)	131 (40)	338 (103)	600 (960)	435 (700)	4,475 (18,648)

IHO	Names of oceans and seas	Area square miles (km²)	Average depth feet (m)	Greatest known depth: feet (m)	Length miles (km)	Width miles (km)	Volume cubic miles (km³)
North Pacific Ocean and subdivisions (continued)							
7.4.1	Bo Hai	30,890 (80,000)	82 (25)	164 (50)	217 (350)	72–192 (120–320)	480 (2,000)
7.4.2	Liaodong Gulf	8,110 (21,000)	82 (25)	164 (50)	112 (180)	75 (120)	126 (525)
7.5	Inland Sea of Japan	8,500 (22,000)	121 (37)	197 (60)	233 (375)	6–105 (10–175)	195 (814)
7.6.1	Tatar Strait	23,940 (62,000)	246 (75)	3,281 (1,000)	311 (500)	78 (125)	1,116 (4,650)
7.7	Sea of Okhotsk	613,800 (1,589,700)	2,749 (838)	12,001 (3,658)	to 1,020 (1,700)	to 780 (1,300)	319,649 (1,332,169)
7.8	Bering Sea	884,900 (2,291,900)	5,075 (1,547)	15,659 (4,773)	1,490 (2,397)	990 (1,593)	850,746 (3,545,569)
7.8.1	Gulf of Anadyr	37,070 (96,000)	246 (75)	492 (150)	200 (320)	250 (400)	1,728 (7,200)
7.9	Bering Strait	29,350 (76,000)	133 (40)	164 (50)	236 (380)	60–180 (100–300)	729 (3,040)
7.10	Gulf of Alaska	592,000 (1,533,000)	8,203 (2,500)	16,405 (5,000)	to 1,200 (2,000)	to 240 (400)	919,594 (3,832,500)
7.11	Coastal Waters of Southeast Alaska and British Colombia	13,900 (36,000)	9,843 (3,000)	12,468 (3,800)	932 (1,500)	to 99 (160)	25,914 (108,000)
7.12	Gulf of California	62,000 (160,580)	3,937 (1,200)	10,000 (3,050)	750 (1,200)	200 (320)	44,054 (183,600)
7.13	Gulf of Panama	8,570 (22,200)	246 (75)	328 (100)	99 (160)	115 (185)	400 (1,665)
Other subdivisions of the North Pacific Ocean							
–	Amurskiy Liman	2,160 (5,600)	82 (25)	164 (50)	87 (140)	12–39 (20–65)	34 (140)
–	Bristol Bay	18,530 (48,000)	82 (25)	164 (50)	200 (320)	to 180 (300)	288 (1,200)
–	Cheju Strait	3,860 (10,000)	246 (75)	328 (100)	103 (165)	37 (60)	180 (750)
–	Gulf of Tehuantepec	12,160 (31,500)	984 (300)	3,281 (1,000)	326 (525)	75 (120)	2,267 (9,450)
–	Gulf of Santa Catalina	3,670 (9,500)	394 (120)	656 (200)	68 (110)	62 (100)	274 (1,140)
–	Hecate Strait	7,920 (20,500)	1,476 (450)	3,281 (1,000)	160 (257)	40–60 (64–129)	2,214 (9,225)
–	Strait of La Perouse	4,830 (12,500)	246 (75)	328 (100)	130 (210)	27–51 (45–85)	225 (938)
–	Korea Bay	13,900 (36,000)	98 (30)	164 (50)	165 (265)	121 (195)	259 (1080)
–	Korea Strait	2,510 (6,500)	295 (90)	328 (100)	62 (100)	30–48 (50–80)	140 (585)
–	Queen Charlotte Sound	7,410 (19,200)	1,575 (480)	3,281 (1,000)	124 (200)	75 (120)	2,211 (9,216)
–	Sakhalin Gulf	2,900 (7,500)	98 (30)	164 (50)	47 (75)	36–96 (60–160)	54 (225)
–	Santa Barbara Channel	2,320 (6,000)	1,312 (400)	1,641 (500)	75 (120)	31 (50)	576 (2,400)
–	San Pedro Channel	770 (2,000)	394 (120)	656 (200)	28 (45)	28 (45)	58 (240)
–	Sea of Japan	377,600 (978,000)	5,748 (1,752)	12,276 (3,742)	1,740 (2,800)	to 540 (900)	411,137 (1,713,456)
–	Strait of Georgia	1,450 (3,750)	328 (100)	1,200 (370)	138 (222)	17 (28)	90 (375)
–	Strait of Juan de Fuca	1,310 (3,400)	394 (120)	900 (275)	80–100 (130–160)	16 (25)	98 (408)
–	Gulf of Shelikhova	69,500 (180,000)	410 (125)	1,624 (495)	420 (670)	185 (300)	5,399 (22,500)
South Pacific Ocean and subdivisions							
8	South Pacific Ocean	–	–	35,704 (10,882)	4,139 (6,660)	to 10,800 (18,000)	–
8.1	Bismarck Sea	194,227 (503,000)	6,600 (2,000)	8,200 (2,500)	497 (800)	249 (400)	241,386 (1,006,000)
8.2	Solomon Sea	278,019 (720,000)	14,765 (4,500)	29,988 (9,140)	621 (1,000)	497 (800)	777,425 (3,240,000)
8.3	Coral Sea	1,849,000 (4,788,888)	7,870 (2,398)	25,134 (7,661)	1,400 (2,250)	1,500 (2,414)	2,758,421
8.3.1	Torres Strait	10,430 (27,000)	246 (75)	328 (100)	130 (210)	80 (130)	486 (2,025)
8.3.2	Great Barrier Reef	134,286 (347,800)	197 (60)	328 (100)	1,250 (2,000)	30–95 (50–152)	3,599 (15,000)
8.3.3	Gulf of Papua	14,670 (38,000)	213 (65)	328 (100)	95 (150)	225 (360)	593 (2,470)
8.4	Tasman Sea	1,545,000 (4,001,530)	9,023 (2,750)	17,000 (5,182)	1,243 (2,000)	1,400 (2,253)	2,639,407
8.4.1	Bass Strait	28,950 (75,000)	210 (60)	262 (80)	224 (360)	150 (240)	1,080 (4,500)
Other subdivisions of the South Pacific Ocean							
–	Bay of Plenty	3,090 (8,000)	328 (100)	820 (250)	99 (160)	37 (60)	192 (800)
–	Cook Strait	2,120 (5,500)	420 (128)	3,445 (1,050)	81 (130)	14 (23)	169 (704)
–	Foveaux Strait	970 (2,500)	98 (30)	164 (50)	43 (70)	22 (35)	18 (75)
–	Gulf of Guayaquil	5,410 (14,000)	82 (25)	197 (60)	124 (200)	87 (140)	84 (350)
Arctic Ocean and subdivisions							
9	Arctic Ocean	5,440,000 (14,090,000)	4,690 (1,430)	18,455 (5,625)	to 3,100 (5,000)	to 2,000 (3,200)	4,834,603 (20,148,700)
9.1	East Siberian Sea	361,000 (936,000)	328 (100)	510 (155)	777 (1,250)	497 (800)	22,459 (93,600)
9.2	Laptev Sea	250,900 (649,800)	1,896 (578)	9,774 (2,980)	528 (850)	497 (800)	90,120 (375,584)
9.3	Kara Sea	340,000 (880,000)	417 (127)	2,034 (620)	932 (1,500)	559 (900)	26,816 (111,760)
9.4	Barents Sea	542,000 (1,405,000)	750 (229)	1,969 (600)	808 (1,300)	650 (1,050)	77,201 (321,745)
9.5	White Sea	36,680 (95,000)	200 (60)	1,115 (340)	261 (420)	249 (400)	1,368 (5,700)
9.6	Greenland Sea	353,320 (915,000)	4,750 (1,450)	16,000 (4,800)	808 (1,300)	621 (1,000)	318,349 (1,326,750)
9.7	Norwegian Sea	328,220 (850,000)	5,254 (1,600)	13,020 (3,970)	870 (1,400)	684 (1,100)	326,327 (1,360,000)
9.8	Iceland Sea	111,980 (290,000)	3,701 (1,128)	9,843 (3,000)	404 (650)	280 (450)	78,491 (327,120)
9.9	Davis Strait	115,840 (300,000)	1,476 (450)	4,922 (1,500)	404 (650)	200–400 (322–644)	32,393 (135,000)

IHO	Names of oceans and seas	Area square miles (km²)	Average depth feet (m)	Greatest known depth: feet (m)	Length miles (km)	Width miles (km)	Volume cubic miles (km³)
Arctic Ocean and subdivisions (continued)							
9.10	Hudson Strait	37,070 (96,000)	1,641 (500)	3,090 (942)	497 (800)	40–150 (65–240)	11,517 (48,000)
9.11	Hudson Bay	475,800 (1,232,300)	420 (128)	600 (183)	590 (950)	590 (950)	37,848 (157,734)
9.12	Baffin Bay	266,000 (689,000)	6,234 (1,900)	7,000 (2,100)	900 (1,450)	68–400 (110–650)	314,113 (1,309,100)
9.13	Lincoln Sea	57,920 (150,000)	2,461 (750)	9,394 (2,863)	249 (400)	236 (380)	26,994 (112,500)
9.14	Northwestern Passages	–	492 (150)	656 (200)	–	–	–
9.15	Beaufort Sea	184,000 (476,000)	3,239 (1,004)	15,360 (4,682)	684 (1100)	404 (650)	114,671 (477,904)
9.16	Chukchi Sea	225,000 (582,000)	253 (77)	7,218 (2,200)	559 (900)	435 (700)	10,753 (44,814)
Other subdivisions of the Arctic Ocean							
–	Fox Basin	55,600 (144,000)	492 (150)	656 (200)	280 (450)	249 (400)	5,183 (21,600)
–	James Bay	30,890 (80,000)	164 (50)	230 (70)	275 (443)	135 (217)	960 (4,000)
–	Kane Basin	7,720 (20,000)	492 (150)	656 (200)	124 (200)	62 (100)	720 (3,000)
–	Pechora Sea	34,750 (90,000)	20 (6)	689 (210)	249 (400)	162 (260)	130 (540)
–	Wandel Sea	28,960 (75,000)	1,148 (350)	1,955 (596)	186 (300)	155 (250)	6,299 (26,250)
Southern Ocean and subdivisions							
10	Southern Ocean	7,850,000 (20,327,000)	14,750 (4,500)	23,736 (7,235)	to 12,900 (21,500)	240–1,620 (400–2,700)	21,948,232 (91,471,500)
10.1	Weddell Sea	1,080,000 (2,800,000)	13,124 (4,000)	16,405 (5,000)	to 1,200 (to 2,000)	to 1,200 (2,000)	2,687,397 (11,200,000)
10.2	Lazarev Sea	185,350 (480,000)	11,484 (3,500)	13,124 (4,000)	497 (800)	373 (600)	403,109 (1,680,000)
10.3	Riiser-Larsen Sea	260,640 (675,000)	12,468 (3,800)	13,124 (4,000)	559 (900)	404 (650)	615,462 (2,565,000)
10.4	Cosmonauts Sea	386,140 (1,000,000)	14,108 (4,300)	16,405 (5,000)	621 (1,000)	621 (1,000)	1,031,768 (4,300,000)
10.5	Cooperation Sea	386,140 (1,000,000)	9,515 (2,900)	13,124 (4,000)	621 (1,000)	621 (1,000)	695,844 (2,900,000)
10.6	Davis Sea	347,520 (900,000)	6,562 (2,000)	9,843 (3,000)	621 (1,000)	559 (900)	431,903 (1,800,000)
10.6.1	Tryoshnikova Gulf	34,750 (90,000)	6,562 (2,000)	9,843 (3,000)	280 (450)	to 240 (400)	43,190 (180,000)
10.7	Mawson Sea	96,530 (250,000)	6,562 (2,000)	9,843 (3,000)	311 (500)	311 (500)	119,973 (500,000)
10.8	Dumont d'Urville Sea	185,350 (480,000)	5,906 (1,800)	13,124 (4,000)	497 (800)	373 (600)	207,313 (864,000)
10.9	Somov Sea	100,400 (260,000)	6,562 (2,000)	6,562 (2,000)	404 (650)	249 (400)	124,772 (520,000)
10.10	Ross Sea	370,000 (960,000)	656 (200)	2,625 (800)	684 (1,100)	621 (1,000)	46,070 (192,000)
10.10.1	McMurdo Sound	3,860 (10,000)	3,281 (1,000)	3,281 (1,000)	92 (148)	46 (74)	2,399 (10,000)
10.11	Amundsen Sea	297,330 (770,000)	6,562 (2,000)	9,843 (3,000)	684 (1,100)	435 (700)	369,517 (1,540,000)
10.12	Bellingshausen Sea	173,760 (450,000)	6,562 (2,000)	9,843 (3,000)	435 (700)	404 (650)	215,952 (900,000)
10.13	Drake Passage	308,910 (800,000)	11,000 (3,400)	15,600 (4,800)	497 (800)	621 (1,000)	652,653 (2,720,000)
10.14	Bransfield Strait	26,260 (68,000)	1,148 (350)	1,641 (500)	249 (400)	106 (170)	5,711 (23,800)
Inland Seas (salt lakes not seas)							
–	Caspian Sea	152,239 (394,299)	591 (180)	3,104 (946)	746 (1,200)	102–270 (170–450)	17,030 (70,974)
–	Aral Sea	13,000 (33,800)	52 (16)	223 (68)	266 (428)	176 (284)	130 (541)
–	Dead Sea	394 (1,020)	313 (96)	1,310 (399)	48 (78)	10 (15)	23 (97)
–	Salton Sea	344 (890)	30 (9)	51 (16)	30 (48)	10 (16)	2 (8)
–	Sea of Galilee	64 (166)	79 (24)	157 (48)	13 (21)	7 (11)	1 (4)
Largest subdivisions of the oceans by surface area							
8.3	Coral Sea	1,849,000 (4,790,000)	7,870 (2,400)	25,134 (7,661)	1,400 (2,250)	1,500 (2,414)	2,758,421 (11,496,000)
7.1	Philippine Sea	1,776,230 (4,600,000)	19,700 (6,000)	34,578 (10,539)	to 1,800 (3,000)	to 1,200 (2,000)	6,622,513 (27,600,000)
8.4	Tasman Sea	1,545,000 (4,000,000)	9,023 (2,750)	17,000 (5,200)	1,243 (2,000)	1,400 (2,250)	2,639,407 (11,000,000)
5.9	Arabian Sea	1,491,000 (3,862,000)	8,970 (2,734)	16,405 (5,000)	to 1,243 (2,000)	to 1,320 (2,200)	2,533,521 (10,558,708)
–	Sargasso Sea	1,448,020 (3,750,000)	16,405 (5,000)	21,005 (6,402)	1,864 (3,000)	994 (1,600)	4,498,990 (18,750,000)
10.1	Weddell Sea	1,080,000 (2,800,000)	13,124 (4,000)	16,405 (5,000)	to 1,200 (2,000)	to 1,200 (2,000)	2,687,397 (11,200,000)
1.10	Caribbean Sea	1,049,500 (2,718,200)	8,685 (2,647)	25,218 (7,686)	1,678 (2,700)	360–840 (600–1,400)	1,726,430 (7,195,075)
3.1	Mediterranean Sea	969,000 (2,510,000)	4,688 (1,429)	16,897 (5,150)	2,500 (4,000)	500 (800)	860,636 (3,586,790)
6.1	South China Sea	895,400 (2,319,075)	5,419 (1,652)	16,456 (5,015)	to 1,182 (1,902)	to 840 (1,352)	919,231 (3,830,988)
7.8	Bering Sea	884,900 (2,291,880)	5,075 (1,547)	15,659 (4,773)	990 (1,593)	1,490 (2,397)	850,746 (3,545,569)
5.13	Bay of Bengal	839,000 (2,173,000)	8,500 (2,600)	15,400 (4,694)	1,056 (1,700)	994 (1,600)	1,355,648 (5,649,800)
1.11	Gulf of Mexico	615,000 (1,592,800)	4,874 (1,486)	12,425 (3,787)	1,100 (1,770)	800 (1,287)	567,929 (2,366,901)
7.7	Sea of Okhotsk	611,000 (1,582,483)	2,818 (859)	11,063 (3,742)	1,530 (2,463)	932 (1,500)	319,649 (1,332,169)
7.10	Gulf of Alaska	592,000 (1,533,273)	7,976 (2,431)	16,500 (5,029)	1,200 (2,000)	240 (400)	919,594 (3,832,500)
9.4	Barents Sea	542,000 (1,405,000)	750 (229)	2,000 (600)	800 (1,300)	650 (1,050)	77,201 (321,745)
9.11	Hudson Bay	475,800 (1,232,300)	420 (128)	600 (183)	590 (950)	590 (950)	37,848 (157,734)
5.1	Mozambique Channel	432,470 (1,120,000)	8,531 (2,600)	10,000 (3,000)	1,000 (1,600)	250–600 (400–950)	698,723 (2,912,000)
10.4	Cosmonauts Sea	386,140 (1,000,000)	14,108 (4,300)	16,405 (5,000)	621 (1,000)	621 (1,000)	1,031,768 (4,300,000)
10.5	Cooperation Sea	386,140 (1,000,000)	9,515 (2,900)	13,124 (4,000)	621 (1,000)	621 (1,000)	695,844 (2,900,000)

IHO	Names of oceans and seas	Area square miles (km²)	Average depth feet (m)	Greatest known depth: feet (m)	Length miles (km)	Width miles (km)	Volume cubic miles (km³)
	Largest subdivisions of the oceans by surface area (continued)						
–	Sea of Japan	377,600 (977,979)	5,748 (1,751)	12,276 (3,742)	1,740 (2,800)	to 540 (900)	411,137 (1,713,456)
10.10	Rose Sea	370,000 (960,000)	656 (200)	2,625 (800)	684 (1,100)	621 (1,000)	46,070 (192,000)
5.17	Great Australian Bight	366,830 (950,000)	7,218 (2,200)	14,765 (4,500)	1,740 (2,800)	to 620 (1,000)	501,487 (2,090,000)
9.1	East Siberian Sea	361,000 (936,000)	328 (100)	510 (155)	777 (1,250)	497 (800)	22,459 (93,600)
9.6	Greenland Sea	353,320 (915,000)	4,750 (1,450)	16,000 (4,800)	808 (1,300)	621 (1,000)	318,349 (1,326,750)
4.2	Scotia Sea	348,000 (900,000)	11,500 (3,500)	27,651 (8,428)	870 (1,400)	497 (800)	755,830 (3,150,000)
10.6	Davis Sea	347,520 (900,000)	6,562 (2,000)	9,843 (3,000)	621 (1,000)	559 (900)	431,903 (1,800,000)
9.3	Kara Sea	340,000 (880,000)	417 (127)	2,034 (620)	932 (1,500)	559 (900)	26,816 (111,760)
9.7	Norwegian Sea	328,220 (850,000)	5,254 (1,600)	13,020 (3,970)	870 (1,400)	684 (1,100)	326,327 (1,360,000)
1.9	Gulf of Guinea	324,360 (840,000)	12,796 (3,900)	16,405 (5,000)	435 (700)	746 (1,200)	786,064 (3,276,000)
10.13 + 4.3	Drake Passage	308,910 (800,000)	11,000 (3,400)	15,600 (4,800)	497 (800)	621 (1,000)	652,653 (2,720,000)
5.14	Andaman Sea	308,000 (797,700)	2,854 (870)	12,392 (3,777)	750 (1,200)	400 (645)	166,522 (693,999)
10.11	Amundsen Sea	297,330 (770,000)	6,562 (2,000)	9,843 (3,000)	684 (1,100)	435 (700)	369,517 (1,540,000)
5.10	Lakshadweep Sea	289,600 (750,000)	7,874 (2,400)	14,765 (4,500)	to 932 (1,500)	to 620 (1,000)	431,903 (1,800,000)
7.3	East China Sea	284,000 (735,800)	574 (175)	8,913 (2,717)	684 (1,100)	435 (700)	30,897 (128,765)
8.2	Solomon Sea	278,019 (720,000)	14,765 (4,500)	29,988 (9,140)	621 (1,000)	497 (800)	777,425 (3,240,000)
9.12	Baffin Bay	266,000 (689,000)	6,234 (1,900)	7,000 (2,100)	900 (1,450)	70–400 (110–650)	314,113 (1,309,100)
10.3	Riiser-Larsen Sea	260,640 (675,000)	12,468 (3,800)	13,124 (4,000)	559 (900)	404 (650)	615,462 (2,565,000)
5.16	Arafura Sea	250,990 (650,000)	230 (70)	12,000 (3,660)	to 620 (1,000)	to 435 (700)	10,918 (45,500)
9.2	Laptev Sea	250,900 (649,800)	1,896 (578)	9,774 (2,980)	528 (850)	497 (800)	90,120 (375,584)
5.15	Timor Sea	235,000 (615,000)	459 (140)	10,800 (3,300)	609 (980)	435 (700)	20,659 (86,100)
9.16	Chukchi Sea	225,000 (582,000)	253 (77)	7,218 (2,200)	559 (900)	435 (700)	10,753 (44,814)
1.2	North Sea	222,100 (575,200)	308 (94)	2,165 (660)	621 (1,000)	93–373 (150–600)	12,974 (54,069)
1.15	Labrador Sea	222,030 (575,000)	6,562 (2,000)	12,468 (3,800)	to 870 (1,400)	to 492 (820)	275,938 (1,150,000)
5.5	Gulf of Aden	205,000 (530,000)	4,922 (1,500)	17,586 (5,360)	920 (1,480)	300 (480)	190,757 (795,000)
8.1	Bismarck Sea	194,227 (503,000)	6,600 (2,000)	8,200 (2,500)	497 (800)	249 (400)	241,386 (1,006,000)
10.2	Lazarev Sea	185,350 (480,000)	11,484 (3,500)	13,124 (4,000)	497 (800)	373 (600)	403,109 (1,680,000)
10.8	Dumont d'Urville Sea	185,350 (480,000)	5,906 (1,800)	13,124 (4,000)	497 (800)	373 (600)	207,313 (864,000)
9.15	Beaufort Sea	184,000 (476,000)	3,239 (1,004)	15,360 (4,682)	684 (1,100)	404 (650)	114,671 (477,904)
6.15	Banda Sea	181,000 (470,000)	14,765 (4,500)	24,409 (7,440)	652 (1,050)	228–330 (380–550)	507,486 (2,115,000)
7.4	Yellow Sea	180,000 (466,200)	131 (40)	338 (103)	600 (960)	435 (700)	4,475 (18,648)
10.12	Bellingshausen Sea	173,760 (450,000)	6,562 (2,000)	9,843 (3,000)	435 (700)	404 (650)	215,952 (900,000)
5.4	Red Sea	169,100 (438,000)	1,611 (491)	9,974 (3,040)	1,200 (1,930)	190 (305)	51,602 (215,058)
6.8	Java Sea	167,000 (433,000)	151 (46)	689 (210)	900 (1,450)	260 (420)	4,779 (19,918)
2	Baltic Sea	163,000 (422,200)	180 (55)	1,380 (421)	795 (1,280)	324 (540)	5,572 (23,221)

UNESCO Marine Heritage sites

UNESCO World Heritage sites are designated as part of the United Nations International World Heritage Programme. All have exceptional natural or cultural features. Like other natural areas recognized by UNESCO, marine sites must possess remarkable natural beauty or have extraordinary ecological importance; many meet both these criteria. To date nearly 900 sites in 145 nations have been designated including a growing number of marine coastal areas that are endangered by development, pollution, or other threats.

1	Península Valdés, Argentina	20	Gulf of California, Mexico, Islands, and Protected Areas
2	Great Barrier Reef, Australia	21	Sian Ka'an, Mexico
3	Shark Bay, Australia	22	West Norwegian Fjords, Norway
4	Macquarie Island, Australia	23	El Vizcaino Whale Sanctuary, Mexico
5	Belize Barrier Reef Reserve System	24	New Zealand Sub-Antarctic Islands
6	Lord Howe Island Group, Australia	25	Tewahipounamu, Southwest New Zealand
7	Brazilian Atlantic Islands	26	Coiba National Park, Panama
8	Cocos Island National Park, Costa Rica	27	Tubbataha Reef Marine Park, Philippines
9	Area de Conservacion, Guanacaste, Costa Rica	28	Natural System of Wrangel Island Reserve, Russian Federation
10	Desembarco de Granma National Park, Cuba	29	Pitons Management Area, St Lucia
11	Ilulissat Ice Fjord, Denmark	30	Aldabra Atoll, Seychelles
12	Galapagos Islands, Ecuador	31	East Rennell, Solomon Islands
13	High Coast/Kvarken Archipelago, Finland & Sweden	32	Dorset & East Devon Coast, UK
		33	Giants Causeway and Causeway Coast, UK
14	The lagoons of New Caledonia	34	Gough and Inacccessible Islands, UK
15	Gulf of Porto, Corsica	35	Henderson Island, UK
16	Isole Aolie (Aeolian Islands), Italy	36	Hawaii Volcanoes National Park, Hawaii, USA
17	Surtsey, Iceland		
18	Shiretoko, Hokkaido, Japan	37	Ha Long Bay, Vietnam
19	MacDonald and Heard Islands, Australia	38	Socotra Archipelago, Yemen

Glossary

Abyssal plain

The flat area of an ocean basin between the continental slope and the mid-ocean ridge.

Abyssal zone

Ocean depths between 13,120 and 19,680 feet (4,000 and 6,000 m).

Adaptation

A change in an animal's behavior or body that allows it to survive and breed in new conditions.

Algae

Simple plants that are found as single cells or as seaweeds.

Antarctic circle

The line of latitude at 66°33'S marking the northern limit of the Antarctic region.

Aphotic zone

The part of the ocean where no surface light can penetrate.

Archipelago

A group of islands or an area that contains many small islands.

Arctic circle

The line of latitude at 66°33'N marking the southern limit of where the sun does not set in June or rise at December solstices.

Ascidian

The sea squirts—a group of invertebrates that produce a larvae with a primitive backbone.

Astrolabe

An early navigation instrument that was the forerunner of the sextant.

Atoll

A coral reef that has formed around a central lagoon.

Austral

Relating to the southern hemisphere.

AUV

Autonomous Underwater Vehicle—an unmanned, self-contained submersible.

Backwash

The water retreating down the shore after an incoming wave.

Baleen plates

Plates with frayed edges made out of keratin, the same material as hair and fingernails. Found in the mouths of certain whales instead of teeth, they are used for filter feeding.

Bar

A submerged or emerged mound of sand, gravel, or shell material built on the ocean floor in shallow water by waves and currents.

Barrier island

A ridge of sand, or gravel, that lies parallel to a coast.

Barrier reef

A coral reef around islands or along continental coasts, separated from the land by a deep lagoon.

Bathymetry

Study of the depth contours of all or part of an undersea area.

Bathypelagic zone

The ocean between 656 and 13,120 feet (200 and 4,000 m) deep.

Bathyscaphe

The earliest form of manned submersible.

Bay

A recess in the shore or an inlet of a sea between two capes or headlands, not as large as a gulf but larger than a cove.

Beach

The region of the shore where loose material, sand, mud, or pebbles, are deposited between high and low watermarks.

Benthic zone

The upper layers of the seabed and the water layer immediately above the seabed.

Berm

A horizontal ridge of sand or shingle running parallel to the shore, at the limit of wave action.

Biodiversity

The variety of plant and animal species found in a habitat on land or in the sea.

Bioluminescence

The generation of light by living organisms using the enzyme luciferin.

Bivalve

A mollusk, such as an oyster or a mussel, that has two shells that are joined at a hinge.

Bloom

The sudden increase in phytoplankton numbers, usually associated with seasonal changes.

Brash ice

Accumulations of floating ice made up of fragments not more than 6.6 feet (2 m) across; the wreckage of other forms of ice.

Cap rock

A hard, impervious rock that forms a layer above another rock and, as a result, seals it.

Carapace

The upper part of the shell of a turtle or tortoise.

Cephalopod

An advanced group of molluscs that includes the squids, octopuses, and cuttlefish.

Cetaceans

Whales and dolphins.

Channel

A body of water that connects two larger bodies of water (like the English Channel). A channel is also a part of a river or harbor that is deep enough to let ships sail through.

Chronometer

A watch or clock able to maintain its accuracy on long sea voyages.

Coelenterates

Gelatinous invertebrates with radial symmetry and sting cells.

Cold seep

Cold seawater, rich in methane, hydrogen sulphide, and hydrocarbons issuing from the seafloor.

Comet

A small astronomical body composed of ice and dust that orbits the Sun on an elongated path.

Continental drift

The theory that the present distribution of continents is the result of the fragmentation of one or more pre-existing supercontinents that have drifted apart.

Continental rise

The gently sloping base of the continental slope.

Continental shelf

The shallow, gently sloping edge of a continental landmass where it meets the sea.

Continental slope

The steeply inclined edge of continental plate below the continental shelf.

Copepod

One of a number of tiny freshwater and marine crustaceans.

Coral bleaching

The loss of color affecting coral reefs when the algae that live in them are killed or forced out.

Coriolis effect

The apparent tendency of a freely moving object to follow a curved path in relation to the rotating surface of Earth, similar to the apparent path of a ball thrown from a merry-go-round. Movement is to the right in the northern hemisphere and to the left in the southern hemisphere.

Crustaceans

Invertebrates with jointed limbs and hard chalky shells, such as lobsters, crabs, shrimps, and copepods.

Crustal plate

A segment of Earth's surface. Continental plates are about 25 miles (40 km) thick and oceanic plates 3.1 miles (5 km) thick.

Current

A flow of water in the sea, generated by wind, tidal movements, or thermohaline circulation.

Cyclone

An intense tropical wind system around a low pressure center with winds that move counterclockwise in the northern hemisphere, and clockwise in the southern hemisphere. Maximum sustained winds of 74 miles per hour (120 km/h) or greater. Also known as hurricanes or typhoons.

Deep-sea hydrothermal vent

A spring of superheated, mineral-rich water found on some ridges deep in the ocean.

Deep-sea trench

A long, narrow, steep-sided depression in the seafloor. Trenches occur at subduction zones, where one crustal plate sinks beneath another.

Density

The mass of a substance for a given volume.

Delta

A layer of sediment deposited at the mouth of a slow-moving river and protruding beyond the coastline.

Diatom

One of many kinds of tiny algae in marine and freshwater environments.

Dinoflagellate

One of many kinds of one-celled aquatic and mostly microscopic organisms bearing two dissimilar flagellae (long whip-like structures that let them turn, maneuver, and spin around), and having characteristics of both plants and animals.

Dune

An accumulation of windblown sand often found above the high tide mark on sand shores.

Ebb tide

The period of tide between high water and low water. A falling tide.

Echinoderms

Exclusively marine invertebrates with five-way symmetry and a water vascular system, including starfish, sea cucumbers and brittle stars.

Echiurans

A group of soft-bodied non-segmented worms found from the shore down to the bottom of ocean trenches.

Echolocation

The use of sound by whales and dolphins to sense objects.

Ecosystem

An interacting system of organisms and the environment to which they are adapted.

Eddy

A circular movement in the water produced by flows around obstructions or by interacting currents.

El Niño

The periodic warming of the surface waters in the east Pacific Ocean that stops upwelling of nutrients.

Endemic

A species, or other taxon, found only in one habitat or region.

Erosion

The wearing away of land by the action of natural forces. On a beach, the carrying away of beach material by wave action, tidal currents, littoral currents, or wind.

Estuary

A semi-enclosed area of water where the salinity departs strongly from ocean salinity, either from mixing with river water or from excessive evaporation.

Euphotic zone

The upper layers where there is sufficient light for photosynthesis.

Fast ice

Ice that is anchored to the shore or ocean bottom and does not move with the winds or currents.

Fetch

The distance over water in which waves are generated by a wind having a rather constant direction and speed.

Filter feeder

An animal that obtains food by straining small prey from seawater.

Flood tide

The period of tide between low water and high water. A rising tide.

Fossil fuels

Carbon-based materials, such as oil, coal, and natural gas, formed from the fossils of ancient plants and animals, and burned to produce energy and electricity.

Frazil ice

Frazil ice, a form of sea ice, refers to small ice crystals that form in the surface water when it reaches freezing temperature.

Fringing reef

A coral reef that forms around the shore of an island and gradually extends out to sea.

Gas bladder

The gas-filled buoyancy organ found in most bony fish.

Ghost net

A fishing net that has become detached from the vessel that set it and so floats freely in the sea where it may entangle marine life.

Gill

A structure used by aquatic animals to exchange dissolved gases and salts between their body fluids and the surrounding water.

Glacier

A mass of ice that moves over the underlying surface.

Global ocean conveyor belt

A circulation pattern that is driven by the sinking of cold water of high salinity in the North Atlantic and connects all oceans. Water moves into the Antarctic at depth and from there into the Indian and Pacific oceans, from where it returns to the North Atlantic at intermediate depth.

Gondwana

The southern supercontinent fragment comprising New Zealand, Antarctica, Australia, South America, Africa, and India. It existed as a separate landmass from 650 million years ago and began to break up only 130 million years ago.

Greenhouse effect

The warming of the lower layers of the atmosphere caused by the trapping of solar radiation by carbon dioxide and other gases.

Gulf

Part of the ocean or sea that is partly surrounded by land, usually on three sides; it is usually larger than a bay.

Gulf stream

The strong western boundary current flowing up the east coast of North America.

Guyot

A flat-topped seamount.

Gyre

A circular motion in a body of water.

Hadal zone

The ocean zone below 19,680 feet (6,000 m).

Headland

An area of high elevation more resistant to erosion than surrounding areas and less susceptible to flooding. Headlands can supply sand and gravel to beaches.

Hermatypic coral

Species living in tropical waters able to secrete sufficient calcium carbonate to form reefs.

High tide

The maximum elevation reached by each rising tide.

Holdfast

The multi-branched structure anchoring seaweeds to hard surfaces.

Holoplankton

Animals that live out their entire lifecycles floating in the water column.

Hot spot

In volcanology, local areas of high volcanic activity that do not occur at the edges of tectonic plates.

Hurricane

The name used for cyclones in the Atlantic and eastern Pacific oceans.

Hydrological cycle

The endless cycling of water between land, ocean, and atmosphere.

Hydrothermal vent

A spring of superheated, mineral rich water found on some ocean ridges.

Ice age

A cold phase in the climatic history of Earth during which large areas of land were covered by ice.

Ice sheet

The largest type of glacier.

Ice shelf

An area of floating ice, once part of a glacier, that is still attached to land.

Iceberg

A floated piece of ice broken off from glacier or ice sheet.

Intertidal zone

The area of a seashore that is washed by tides. It is covered by water at high tide and exposed to the air at low tide.

Invertebrate

A multicellular animal without a true backbone.

Kelps

A group of large fast-growing brown seaweeds.

Krill

A shrimp-like crustacean abundant in polar waters that is the principal food of baleen whales.

La Niña

Periods of unusually cold ocean temperatures in the equatorial Pacific that occur between El Niño events. An episode of La Niña brings these conditions for a minimum of five months.

Lagoon

A shallow body of water, as a pond or lake, usually connected to the sea.

Latitude
A measure of north-south location, relative to the equator at 0°.

Laurasia
One of the two continents that formed when the supercontinent Pangea separated. It includes Europe, North America, and Asia (not India). Similarity of plants and animals of these countries is explained by this former connection.

Littoral zone
The seashore between high and low tide marks.

Longitude
A measure of east-west location relative to the Prime Meridian (0°) that runs through the Greenwich Observatory, London, UK.

Longshore drift
The movement of beach material parallel to the coastline by combined wind and wave action.

Lophophore
The brush-like feeding organ of sea mats, horseshoe worms, and lamp shells.

Low tide
The minimum elevation reached by each falling tide.

Magma
Molten rock found below Earth's crust that is ejected by volcanoes and emerges at ocean ridges as lava.

Mangrove
Flowering shrubs and trees tolerant of salt water, found on low-lying tropical coasts and estuaries.

Mantle
The layer of Earth between the crust and the core.

Mariculture
The intensive cultivation of marine organisms in coastal areas in cages or on land in seawater ponds.

Medusa
The free-living bell or disc-like form of many coelenterates.

Meroplankton
The young stages of marine organisms that spend time in the plankton, before developing into non-planktonic adults.

Mid-ocean ridge
A region of the ocean floor where magma rises to the surface to create new ocean floor on either side of a central rift valley.

Migration
The movement of an animal from one place to another, often over long distances. Sea turtles, whales, seabirds, and many fish migrate through and above Earth's oceans.

Mollusks
A group of soft-bodied non-segmented invertebrates that includes sea snails, bivalves, and cephalopods.

Navigation
The science of position fixing and course plotting, using astronomical and other observations.

Neap tides
Tides with much smaller ranges than spring tides, that occur while the gravitational pulls of the Moon and the Sun on the oceans work against each other.

Neritic zone
The zone from high tide to the continental shelf break.

Nilas ice
A smooth thin sheet of sea ice formed of frazil sea ice crystals.

Ocean
One of the five great bodies of seawater defined by continental margins, the equator, and other arbitrary divisions.

Ocean desert
An ocean region devoid of nutrients and therefore of particularly high water clarity.

Oceanography
The scientific study of all aspects of the oceans.

Ore
A mineral or rock that contains a particular metal in a concentration that is high enough to make its extraction commercially viable. Hematite and iron ore are examples.

Osmoregulation
The regulation of the concentration of body fluids by aquatic animals.

Overfishing
The commercial fishing of natural populations so that breeding does not replenish what is removed.

Ozone
A gas that absorbs most of the harmful ultraviolet rays from the Sun and also prevents some heat loss from Earth; it occurs naturally in a thin layer in the stratosphere and is also an ingredient in photochemical smog.

Ozone layer
The thin layer of ozone gas, located roughly 15 miles (24 km) above Earth's surface, which shields us from ultraviolet rays generated by the Sun.

Pack ice
Sea ice that forms around the permanent ice sheets of polar regions in winter and which thins and retreats in summer.

Pancake ice
Uneven plate shapes of sea ice that occur when seawater movement disturbs newly melded ice crystals or nilas ice.

Pangea
The ancient supercontinent that once contained all of Earth's continents. It began to break up about 200 million years ago into Gondwana and Laurasia.

Pelagic zone
The water column above the benthic zone.

Photophores
Light-producing organs, especially common in deep-sea fish.

Photosynthesis
The biological conversion of carbon dioxide and water into sugars using solar energy.

Phytoplankton
Single-celled algae and other photosynthetic organisms floating in the surface layers of the oceans.

Piedmont glacier
A lobe of ice that forms when a valley glacier emerges from the mountain and spreads out on to the plain.

Pinnipeds
Seals, walruses, and sea lions.

Plastron
The bottom part of the shell of a turtle or tortoise.

Plate tectonics
The processes by which the plates that form Earth's surface are formed, moved, and destroyed.

Polar regions
The cold zones between the poles and either the Arctic or Antarctic circles.

Pollutant
A harmful substance or heat energy introduced into an ecosystem by human activities.

Polychaete
A group of marine segmented worms.

Polynesia
A large group of Pacific islands extending from The Hawaiian Islands south to New Zealand and east to Easter Island.

Polynyas
Areas of open water surrounded by sea ice, often of large extent that makes them navigable. Also spelled polynia.

Polyp
The sedentary body form of coelenterates, notably corals.

Predator
An animal that feeds by capturing and eating other animals.

Primary production
The biological conversion of inorganic carbon (carbon dioxide) into living material (organic carbon).

Projection
The system used to translate the three-dimensional form of Earth onto a two-dimensional map.

Radar
Radio Detection and Ranging, the use of pulsed radio waves to follow moving objects by analysing changes in reflected radio signals.

Remote sensing
The use of airborne or satellite sensors to map Earth's surface in space and time.

Reverse osmosis
The use of pressure to force water through semi-permeable membrane, leaving behind any dissolved salts. Used to obtain fresh water from seawater.

Roaring Forties
Areas of ocean either side of the equator between 40° and 50° N or S latitude, noted for high winds and rough seas.

Rogue wave
A single, unusually high wave created by the constructive interference of two or more smaller waves.

ROV
A Remotely Operated Vehicle, an unmanned submersible controlled and powered from the surface by an umbilical cord.

Salt marsh
An area of soft, wet land periodically covered by salt water, in temperate zones generally treeless with characteristic salt-tolerant plants such as reeds and samphire.

Sandbar
A low ridge of sand in shallow water close to a shore.

Scuba
Self-Contained Underwater Breathing Apparatus. The combination of a pressure compensated regulator or demand valve and high pressure compressed air cylinders for diving without an air supply from the surface.

Sea
A division of an ocean or a large body of salt water partially enclosed by land. The term is also used for large, usually saline, lakes that lack a natural outlet, such as the Caspian Sea and the Aral Sea. The term is used in a less geographically precise manner as synonymous with ocean.

Sea ice
Ice that forms when the surface of the ocean freezes.

Sea stack
A rocky tower or spire close to shore that has formed due to the erosion of a nearby headland by wave action, or by the collapse of a natural rock arch.

Seamount
A steep sided circular or elliptical projection from the seafloor that is more than 0.6 of a mile (1 km) in height.

Seasonality
The timing of major biological events cued by changes in light intensity and water temperature associated with the seasons in temperate latitudes.

Seawall
A vertical, wall-like coastal-engineering structure built parallel to the beach or duneline and usually located at the back of the beach or the seaward edge of the dune.

Sediment
Fine organic or mineral particles deposited on the seafloor, originating from the weathering of rocks and transported, suspended in, or deposited by air, water, or ice, or by other natural agents such as chemical precipitation.

Seismic survey
The use of high intensity sound waves to examine deep geological structures.

Sextant
A navigational instrument used to measure the angles between the Moon, the Sun, stars, and other objects such as the horizon.

Shear
The difference in speed of water movement in adjacent regions or layers creates friction and turbulence.

Shelf sea
The shallow but often highly productive seas over continental shelves.

Side-scan sonar
High resolution sound-imaging of the seabed.

Soft corals
Coral species that do not have a hard outer blanket of calcium carbonate. Soft corals do not form reefs.

Sonar
Sound Navigation and Ranging. The detection of objects in or on water using pulsed beams of sound waves and their reflected echoes.

Sponges
Invertebrates that consist of complex aggregations of cells, bound together by protein fibers and mineral spicules.

Spray zone
The area along a shore that is above the normal high-tide zone.

Spring tide
A tide that occurs at or near the time of a new or full moon with a large tidal rise and fall.

Strait
A narrow channel of water that connects two larger bodies of water, and thus lies between two landmasses.

Subduction zone
The area where one crustal plate is forced under another plate, giving rise to volcanic activity and earthquakes. These zones are usually marked by deep trench systems in the oceans.

Submersible
A small underwater vehicle designed for deep-sea research and other tasks.

Sunlight zone
The upper layer of the ocean where enough sunlight reaches to support the growth of phytoplankton.

Symbiosis
The close beneficial feeding relationship between two species.

Tethys Sea
The body of water partially enclosed by the C-shaped Pangean supercontinent. It was closed when Pangea split into Laurasia and Gondwana.

Thermohaline circulation
Water movement caused by differences in density produced by salinity and/or temperature changes.

Tide
The regular rising and falling of the sea that results from gravitational attraction of the Moon, the Sun, and other astronomical bodies acting upon rotating Earth.

Tide pool
A depression on a shore, usually rocky, that remains filled with seawater when exposed at low tide.

Tidewater glacier
A glacier that flows into the sea, producing icebergs as pieces break off.

Trade winds
The steady winds that blow from east to west, toward the equator to replace hot air rising from the equatorial region.

Transit time
The time it takes a water particle to travel through a described region. Also the time it takes to empty and replace all water in a described region.

Transport
The amount of water carried by a current in mass or volume per unit time.

Trench
A narrow deep depression in the ocean floor, often associated with the subduction of an oceanic plate at a continental margin.

Trophic web
The complex feeding relationships between plants and animals in a habitat.

Tropics
The zone between the Tropic of Cancer (23°27'N) and the Tropic of Capricorn (23°27'S) which approximates to the area of the ocean where water temperatures remain above 69°F (20°C).

Tsunami
A huge wave created by earthquake or volcanic explosion that can cause massive destruction in coastal areas. Mistakenly called a "tidal wave."

Typhoon
The name used for cyclones in the western Pacific Ocean, including the China Sea.

Upwelling
The rising of deep cold nutrient laden waters into the surface layers, close to continental coasts.

Water budget
The balance sheet of water entering and leaving a region; includes effect of currents, rainfall, evaporation, and rivers.

Water lens
A body of water wedged between two other layers of water and kept together in lentil-shaped form.

Wave
The disturbance in water caused by the movement of energy through the water.

Zooanthellae
Single-celled photosynthetic organisms that live in coral tissues in a symbiotic relationship.

Zooplankton
Small animals that spend all or part of their lifecycles floating in the surfaces layers of the ocean, either grazing on phytoplankton or preying on other zooplankton.

GAZETTEER

Glossary of foreign terms

Archipièlag....................archipelago
Bahía.....................................bay
Baja, Bajo.........................shoal
Boca.......................channel, river
Bocche, Bogazi.................strait
Cabo, Cap, Capo...............cape
Cayo..key
Dao.....................................island
Damagheh.........................cape
Dawhat..................bay, cove, inlet
Denizi..................................sea
Ensenada...................bay, cove
Golfe, Golfo.......................gulf
Île, Isla, Isola..................island
Jazirat, Jazireh...............islands
Kepulauan..........archipelago islands
Ko, Koh...........................island
Khawr, Khowr.....bay, channel, inlet
Kólpos, Körfezi................gulf
Laguna...........................lagoon
Mui............................cape, point
Mys..........................cape, point
Peñón.......................point, rock
Punta................................point
Ra's, Ras, Rås..................cape
Selat, Stretto.................strait
Tanjung.................cape, point
Teluk....................................bay

A

Hokkaidō–Kotzebue Sound

Hokkaidō, *Pac.* 179 X-7
Hollick-Kenyon Peninsula, *Sou.* 105 P-7
Holmes Reef, *Pac.* 199 S-6
Holy Island, *Atl.* 115 O-5
Home Bay, *Arc.* 101 T-10
Hon Khoai, *Pac.* 187 V-8
Hon Rai, *Pac.* 187 V-6
Honshū, *Pac.* 166 K-5
Honshū, *Pac.* 179 U-13
Hooker, *Arc.* 99 S-6
Hopen, *Arc.* 99 Q-9
Horizon Deep, *Pac.* 193 V-6
Horizon Ridge, *Ind.* 159 S-7
Hormoz, *Ind.* 153 Y-6
Horn Island, *Pac.* 195 X-10
Horseshoe Seamounts, *Atl.* 113 R-7
Hotspur Fracture Zone, *Atl.* 133 R-5
Hotspur Seamount, *Atl.* 133 O-5
Howland Island, *Pac.* 167 P-9
Hoy, *Atl.* 115 P-5
Huahine, *Pac.* 213 N-10
Hudson Bay, *Arc.* 96 K-8
Hudson Strait, *Arc.* 101 U-13

I

Iğneada Burnu, *Atl.* 131 O-6
Iberian Abyssal Plain, *Atl.* 113 R-7
Ibiza, *Atl.* 128 L-7
Iceland, *Atl.* 113 Q-2
Iceland Basin, *Atl.* 113 Q-3
Iceland-Faeroe Rise, *Atl.* 113 R-2
Icelandic Plateau, *Arc.* 98 K-10
Icy Bay, *Pac.* 173 T-2
Ie-jima, *Pac.* 181 U-10
Ifalik, *Pac.* 191 T-6
Ihavandhippolhu Atoll, *Ind.* 151 V-10
Iheya-jima, *Pac.* 181 U-10
IJsselmeer, *Atl.* 115 V-11
Iki, *Pac.* 181 V-6
Iki-suidō, *Pac.* 179 P-14
Île Brion, *Atl.* 119 S-5
Île d'Anticosti, *Atl.* 119 S-3
Île d'Oléron, *Atl.* 127 X-7
Île d'Ouessant, *Atl.* 127 S-4
Île d'Yeu, *Atl.* 127 W-6
Île de l'Est, *Atl.* 119 S-5
Île de Jerba, *Atl.* 129 P-9
Île de la Gonâve, *Atl.* 123 Q-4
Île de la Tortue, *Atl.* 123 R-3
Île de Noirmoutier, *Atl.* 127 W-6
Île de Ré, *Atl.* 127 X-7
Île des Pins, *Pac.* 197 X-7
Île du Harve Aubert, *Atl.* 119 R-6
Île Europa, *Ind.* 157 S-10
Île Juan de Nova, *Ind.* 157 U-7
Île Lamèque, *Atl.* 119 Q-5
Île Tromelin, *Ind.* 155 U-8
Îles Barren, *Ind.* 157 V-8
Îles Chausey, *Atl.* 127 X-3
Îles de la Madeleine, *Atl.* 119 R-5
Îles de Mingan, *Atl.* 119 R-3
Îles du Vent, *Pac.* 213 N-10
Îles Glorieuses, *Ind.* 157 X-3
Îles Kerguelen, *Sou.* 103 Z-5
Îles Kerkenah, *Atl.* 129 P-9
Îles Maria, *Pac.* 212 M-12
Îles Palliser, *Pac.* 213 P-9
Îles Sous le Vent, *Pac.* 212 M-10
Ilha Benguérua, *Ind.* 157 P-10
Ilha da Trindade, *Atl.* 133 P-6
Ilha do Bazaruto, *Ind.* 157 P-10
Ilha Puga Puga, *Ind.* 157 S-6
Ilhas Martin Vas, *Atl.* 133 P-5
Îls de Groix, *Atl.* 127 U-5
Imarssuak Channel, *Atl.* 113 O-3
Ince Burun, *Atl.* 131 T-5
Independence Fjord, *Arc.* 97 R-10
Indian-Antarctic Ridge, *Ind.* 159 X-13
Indispensable Reefs, *Pac.* 197 V-3
Indomed Fracture Zone, *Ind.* 155 S-13
Indus Cone, *Ind.* 151 S-4
Instituta Okeanologii Rise, *Pac.* 177 T-6
Interview Island, *Ind.* 147 V-9
Inubō-zaki, *Pac.* 179 W-12
Investigator Group, *Ind.* 161 W-3
Investigator Ridge, *Ind.* 163 S-6
Ionian Basin, *Atl.* 129 R-8
Ionian Islands, *Atl.* 129 S-8
Ionian Sea, *Atl.* 129 R-7
Irō-zaki, *Pac.* 179 V-13
Irabu-jima, *Pac.* 181 S-11
Irbe Strait, *Atl.* 117 U-9
Ireland, *Atl.* 113 S-4
Irian Jaya, *Pac.* 195 S-5
Iriomote-jima, *Pac.* 181 R-12
Irish Sea, *Atl.* 113 T-4
Irminger Basin, *Atl.* 113 O-3
Isakov Seamount, *Pac.* 168 L-8
Iselin Bank, *Sou.* 107 T-12
Iselin Seamount, *Sou.* 103 S-11
Ise-wan, *Pac.* 179 U-13
Ishigaki-jima, *Pac.* 181 S-11
Ishikari-wan, *Pac.* 179 W-7
Isla Ángel de la Guarda, *Pac.* 207 U-8
Isla Aracena, *Atl.* 139 P-3
Isla Baltra, *Pac.* 209 W-5
Isla Beata, *Atl.* 123 R-5
Isla Blanquilla, *Atl.* 123 W-8
Isla Carmen, *Pac.* 207 V-11
Isla Cedros, *Pac.* 207 S-9
Isla Cerralvo, *Pac.* 207 W-11
Isla Clarence, *Atl.* 139 O-3
Isla Clarion, *Pac.* 207 T-15
Isla Coiba, *Atl.* 122 L-10
Isla Dawson, *Atl.* 139 P-3
Isla de Altamura, *Pac.* 207 W-11
Isla de Bioco, *Atl.* 135 X-4
Isla de Cozumel, *Atl.* 121 U-8
Isla de Guanaja, *Atl.* 122 J-5
Isla de la Juventud, *Atl.* 121 W-7
Isla de los Estados, *Atl.* 139 U-4
Isla de Margarita, *Atl.* 123 W-8
Isla de Providencia, *Atl.* 122 L-7
Isla de Roatán, *Atl.* 122 J-5
Isla de San Andrés, *Atl.* 122 M-7
Isla de Utila, *Atl.* 122 I-5
Isla Española, *Pac.* 209 X-6
Isla Espíritu Santo, *Pac.* 207 W-11
Isla Fernandina, *Pac.* 209 U-5
Isla Genovesa, *Pac.* 209 X-4
Isla Gordon, *Atl.* 139 Q-4
Isla Grande de Tierra del Fuego, *Atl.* 139 Q-3
Isla Guadalupe, *Pac.* 207 Q-9
Isla Hoste, *Atl.* 139 Q-5
Isla Isabela, *Pac.* 209 U-5
Isla La Tortuga, *Atl.* 123 V-8
Isla Lennox, *Atl.* 139 S-5
Isla Londonderry, *Atl.* 139 O-4
Isla Marchena, *Pac.* 209 V-4
Isla Maria Cleofas, *Pac.* 207 X-13
Isla María Madre, *Pac.* 207 X-13
Isla María Magdalena, *Pac.* 207 X-13
Isla Mona, *Atl.* 123 U-4
Isla Navarino, *Atl.* 139 R-4
Isla Noir, *Atl.* 139 N-4
Isla Nueva, *Atl.* 139 S-5
Isla Orchila, *Atl.* 123 V-8
Isla Picton, *Atl.* 139 S-4
Isla Pinta, *Pac.* 209 V-4
Isla Riesco, *Atl.* 139 O-2
Isla Roca Partida, *Pac.* 207 U-14
Isla San Ambrosio, *Pac.* 211 X-5
Isla San Benedicto, *Pac.* 207 V-14
Isla San Cristóbal, *Pac.* 209 X-5
Isla San Esteban, *Pac.* 207 U-9
Isla San Felix, *Pac.* 211 W-5
Isla San José, *Pac.* 207 V-11
Isla San Juanito, *Pac.* 207 X-13
Isla San Lorenzo, *Pac.* 207 U-9
Isla San Salvador, *Pac.* 209 W-5
Isla Santa Catalina, *Pac.* 207 V-11
Isla Santa Cruz, *Pac.* 209 W-5
Isla Santa Fé, *Pac.* 209 W-5
Isla Santa Inés, *Atl.* 139 O-3
Isla Santa Margarita, *Pac.* 207 U-11
Isla Santa Maria, *Pac.* 209 V-6
Isla Saona, *Atl.* 123 T-4
Isla Socorro, *Pac.* 207 V-15
Isla Stewart, *Atl.* 139 O-4
Isla Tiburón, *Pac.* 207 U-9
Isla Wolf, *Pac.* 209 V-4
Islas de la Bahía, *Atl.* 122 J-5
Islas del Maíz, *Atl.* 122 L-8
Islas Diego Ramirez, *Atl.* 139 R-6
Islas Las Aves, *Atl.* 123 U-8
Islas Los Roques, *Atl.* 123 U-8
Islas Marías, *Pac.* 207 Y-13
Islas Orcadas Rise, *Atl.* 133 P-12
Islas Revillagigedo, *Pac.* 207 t-15
Islas Wollaston, *Atl.* 139 S-5
Isle of Man, *Atl.* 115 N-10
Isle of Portland, *Atl.* 127 W-1
Isle of Wight, *Atl.* 127 X-1
Isles Chesterfield, *Pac.* 197 T-6
Isles Loyaute, *Pac.* 197 W-5
Isles of Scilly, *Atl.* 127 R-1
Isola d'Elba, *Atl.* 129 O-5
Isola di Pantelleria, *Atl.* 129 P-8
Isole Lipari, *Atl.* 129 Q-7
Isole Pelagie, *Atl.* 129 P-8
Israelite Bay, *Ind.* 161 R-3
Isthmus of Kra, *Pac.* 187 O-7
Isthmus of Panama, *Atl.* 123 N-9
Itbayat, *Pac.* 185 W-3
Izena-jima, *Pac.* 181 U-10
Izu-Ogasawara Trench, *Pac.* 168 K-7
Izu-shotō, *Pac.* 179 V-14

J

Jabrīn, *Ind.* 153 S-5
Jackson, *Arc.* 99 S-6
Jamaica, *Atl.* 112 I-10
Jamaica Channel, *Atl.* 123 P-4
James Ross Island, *Sou.* 105 Q-5
Jan Mayen, *Arc.* 98 L-10
Jan Mayen Fracture Zone, *Arc.* 98 L-10
Jan Mayen Ridge, *Arc.* 98 L-10
Japan Basin, *Pac.* 179 R-9
Japan Rise, *Pac.* 179 Y-12
Japan Trench, *Pac.* 179 X-12
Jarvis Island, *Pac.* 167 Q-9
Jason Peninsula, *Sou.* 105 Q-6
Java, *Pac.* 185 Q-15
Java Ridge, *Pac.* 189 N-15
Java Sea, *Ind.* 159 T-5
Java Trench, *Ind.* 159 S-6
Jazā'ir az Zubayr, *Ind.* 149 T-11
Jazā'ir Farasān, *Ind.* 149 T-10
Jazīrat Ḩawār, *Ind.* 153 R-7
Jazīrat Abū Ẓaby, *Ind.* 153 V-9
Jazīrat Abū 'Alī, *Ind.* 153 Q-5
Jazīrat al 'Arabiyah, *Ind.* 153 Q-5
Jazīrat al Hanish al Kabīr, *Ind.* 149 V-12
Jazīrat al Jurayd, *Ind.* 153 R-6
Jazīrat al Muḩarraq, *Ind.* 153 R-7
Jazīrat Antufash, *Ind.* 149 U-11
Jazīrat Faylakah, *Ind.* 153 P-3
Jazīrat Harqūs, *Ind.* 153 Q-5
Jazīrat Jabal Zuqar, *Ind.* 149 U-12
Jazīrat Janā, *Ind.* 153 Q-5
Jazīrat Karān, *Ind.* 153 Q-5
Jazīrat Kubbar, *Ind.* 153 P-3
Jazīrat Kurayn, *Ind.* 153 Q-5
Jazīrat Maşīrah, *Ind.* 151 P-4
Jazīrat Marawwah, *Ind.* 153 U-9
Jazīrat Qārūh, *Ind.* 153 P-4
Jazīrat Qannah, *Ind.* 153 Q-5
Jazīrat Tārūt, *Ind.* 153 R-6
Jazīrat Umm al Marādim, *Ind.* 153 P-4
Jazīreh-ye Fārsī, *Ind.* 153 Q-5
Jazīreh-ye Khān, *Ind.* 153 R-5
Jazīreh-ye Khārk, *Ind.* 153 Q-3
Jazirah Doberai, *Pac.* 189 X-10
Jemaja, *Pac.* 185 P-11
Jersey, *Atl.* 127 W-2
Jūn al Kuwayt, *Ind.* 153 O-3
Jizō-zaki, *Pac.* 179 R-12
Johnston Atoll, *Pac.* 167 P-7
Joides Basin, *Sou.* 107 V-11
Joinville Island, *Sou.* 105 R-4
Jolo, *Pac.* 185 W-10
Jones Sound, *Arc.* 101 P-6
Joseph Bonaparte Gulf, *Pac.* 195 N-12
Juan Fernández Islands, *Pac.* 211 W-6
Jutland Bank, *Atl.* 115 W-7
Jylland, *Atl.* 115 Y-7

K

Kabaena, *Pac.* 189 Q-12
Kaburuang, *Pac.* 189 U-7
Kadan Kyun, *Pac.* 187 N-3
Kadmat, *Ind.* 151 W-8
Kahoolawe, *Pac.* 175 V-7
Kai Besar, *Pac.* 189 X-12
Kai Kecil, *Pac.* 189 X-12
Kaiwi Channel, *Pac.* 175 V-7
Kakabia, *Pac.* 189 R-13
Kalamyts'ka Zatoka, *Atl.* 131 S-3
Kalao, *Pac.* 189 Q-13
Kalaotoa, *Pac.* 189 R-13
Kaledupa, *Pac.* 189 S-12
Kalpeni, *Ind.* 151 W-9
Kamarān, *Ind.* 149 U-11
Kamcatskij Zaliv, *Pac.* 177 X-5
Kamchatka, *Pac.* 166 M-3
Kamchatka Basin, *Pac.* 171 O-6
Kamchatka Peninsula, *Pac.* 171 N-6
Kamchatskiy Zaliv, *Pac.* 171 N-6
Kami-Koshiki-jima, *Pac.* 179 P-15
Kammu Seamount, *Pac.* 169 O-7
Kamui-misaki, *Pac.* 177 O-11
Kanaga Island, *Pac.* 171 T-8
Kane Basin, *Arc.* 101 R-4
Kane Fracture Zone, *Atl.* 125 V-5
Kangaroo Island, *Ind.* 161 Y-5
Kanmaw Kyun, *Pac.* 187 O-4
Kanmon Kaikyō, *Pac.* 179 Q-13
Kaôh Kōng, *Pac.* 187 S-5
Kaôh Rŭng, *Pac.* 187 T-5
Kap Brewster, *Arc.* 98 J-9
Kap Farvel, *Arc.* 98 D-8
Kap Morris Jesup, *Arc.* 97 R-9
Kapingamarangi Rise, *Pac.* 183 T-7
Kara Sea, *Arc.* 99 V-6
Karaginskiy Zaliv, *Pac.* 177 Y-3
Karakelong, *Pac.* 189 T-7
Karamian, *Pac.* 185 T-14
Karimata, *Pac.* 185 Q-13
Karkinits'ka Zatok, *Atl.* 131 R-3
Kashima-nada, *Pac.* 179 W-12
Kaskūs, *Ind.* 153 R-6
Katchall, *Ind.* 147 W-12
Katiu, *Pac.* 213 Q-10
Kattegat, *Atl.* 117 N-9
Kauai Channel, *Pac.* 175 U-7
Kauai, *Pac.* 175 U-6
Kauehi, *Pac.* 213 P-10
Kaula Island, *Pac.* 175 T-6
Kau-ye Kyun, *Pac.* 187 N-5
Kavaratti, *Ind.* 151 W-8
Kayak Island, *Pac.* 173 S-2
Kebrit Deep, *Ind.* 149 R-6
Kefallinia Valley, *Atl.* 129 S-8
Kekeroma-jima, *Pac.* 181 U-9
Kelso Bank, *Pac.* 197 U-8
Kemp Peninsula, *Sou.* 105 R-9
Kenai Peninsula, *Pac.* 173 Q-2
Kene Plateau, *Atl.* 128 M-7
Kenn Reefs, *Pac.* 197 T-7
Kennedy Entrance, *Pac.* 173 P-3
Kepulauan Alor, *Pac.* 189 S-13
Kepulauan Anambas, *Pac.* 185 P-11
Kepulauan Aru, *Pac.* 195 S-6
Kepulauan Asia, *Pac.* 191 O-8
Kepulauan Ayu, *Pac.* 189 W-9
Kepulauan Babar, *Pac.* 189 V-13
Kepulauan Banda, *Pac.* 189 V-11
Kepulauan Banggai, *Pac.* 189 R-10
Kepulauan Barat Daya, *Pac.* 189 U-13
Kepulauan Bonerate, *Pac.* 189 Q-13
Kepulauan Gorong, *Pac.* 189 W-11
Kepulauan Kai, *Pac.* 189 X-12
Kepulauan Kangean, *Pac.* 189 N-13
Kepulauan Karimunjawa, *Pac.* 185 R-14
Kepulauan Laut Kecil, *Pac.* 189 N-12
Kepulauan Leti, *Pac.* 189 U-13
Kepulauan Lingga, *Pac.* 185 P-12
Kepulauan Mapia, *Pac.* 191 P-8
Kepulauan Nanusa, *Pac.* 189 U-6
Kepulauan Natuna, *Pac.* 185 Q-10
Kepulauan Obi, *Pac.* 189 U-10
Kepulauan Sabalana, *Pac.* 185 V-15
Kepulauan Sangir, *Pac.* 189 T-7
Kepulauan Solor, *Pac.* 189 S-13
Kepulauan Taka'Bonerate, *Pac.* 189 Q-13
Kepulauan Talaud, *Pac.* 189 U-7
Kepulauan Tambelan, *Pac.* 185 P-12
Kepulauan Tanimbar, *Pac.* 189 X-13
Kepulauan Tengah, *Pac.* 189 O-13
Kepulauan Togian, *Pac.* 189 R-9
Kepulauan Tukangbesi, *Pac.* 189 S-12
Kepulauan Watubela, *Pac.* 189 X-11
Kepuluan Solor, *Pac.* 185 X-15
Kerch Strait, *Atl.* 131 V-3
Kerempe Burun, *Atl.* 131 S-5
Kerguelen, *Sou.* 103 Z-5
Kerguelen Islands, *Ind.* 163 N-13
Kerguelen Plateau, *Ind.* 159 N-13
Kermadec Islands, *Pac.* 193 T-7
Kermadec Ridge, *Pac.* 203 T-2
Kermadec Trench, *Pac.* 203 T-3
Khalīj al Ḩalāniyāt, *Ind.* 151 O-5
Khalīj Bumbah, *Atl.* 129 T-10
Khalīj Maşīrah, *Ind.* 151 P-4
Khalīj Tārūt, *Ind.* 153 R-6
Khalīj-e Deylam, *Ind.* 153 Q-2
Khalīj-e Nāy Band, *Ind.* 153 T-5
Khalīj-e Nakhīlū, *Ind.* 153 U-6
Khalîg el 'Arab, *Atl.* 129 V-10
Khatangskiy Zaliv, *Arc.* 97 W-6
Khawr al 'Udayd, *Ind.* 153 S-9
Khawr az Zubayr, *Ind.* 153 P-2
Khawr Qirqishān, *Ind.* 153 W-9
Khowr-e Māsheh, *Ind.* 153 V-6
Khowr-e Mūsa, *Ind.* 153 P-2
Khowr-e Soltānī, *Ind.* 153 R-3
Kiel Canal, *Atl.* 117 N-11
Kieler Bucht, *Atl.* 115 Z-9
Kihnu, *Atl.* 117 V-8
Kii-suidō, *Pac.* 179 T-14
Kikai-jima, *Pac.* 181 V-9
Kikladhes Plateau, *Atl.* 129 U-8
Kilttan, *Ind.* 151 W-8
King George Bay, *Atl.* 139 W-1
King George Island, *Sou.* 105 P-3
King George Seamount, *Pac.* 175 N-3
King Island, *Ind.* 159 Y-11
King Peninsula, *Sou.* 104 K-13
King William Island, *Arc.* 101 N-10
Kingman Reef, *Pac.* 167 P-8
Kinka-san, *Pac.* 179 X-11
Kisar, *Pac.* 189 U-13
Kiska Island, *Pac.* 171 R-8
Kittery Island, *Pac.* 174 K-3
Kitty Hawk Seamount, *Pac.* 185 S-8
Kizilimak Canyon, *Atl.* 131 U-5
Knob Island, *Atl.* 121 W-4
Ko Ang Thong, *Pac.* 187 P-6
Ko Chang, *Pac.* 187 S-4
Ko Khram, *Pac.* 187 Q-3
Ko Kut, *Pac.* 187 S-4
Ko Lanta, *Pac.* 187 O-9
Ko Libong, *Pac.* 187 O-9
Ko Phangan, *Pac.* 187 Q-6
Ko Phra Thong, *Pac.* 187 N-7
Ko Phuket, *Pac.* 187 N-8
Ko Samet, *Pac.* 187 R-3
Ko Samui, *Pac.* 187 Q-7
Ko Tao, *Pac.* 187 P-6
Ko Yao Yai, *Pac.* 187 O-8
Kobroör, *Pac.* 195 S-6
Kodiak Island, *Pac.* 173 P-3
Kodiak Seamount, *Pac.* 173 Q-4
Kodori Canyon, *Atl.* 131 Y-5
Kohler Seamount, *Ind.* 155 W-14
Kōje-do, *Pac.* 181 U-5
Ko-jima, *Pac.* 179 V-9
Kola Peninsula, *Arc.* 99 S-12
Kolbeinsey Ridge, *Arc.* 98 J-10
Kolga laht, *Atl.* 117 W-7
Komandorskiye Ostrova, *Pac.* 171 P-7
Komodo, *Pac.* 189 P-14
Kongsøya, *Arc.* 99 R-7
Korea Bay, *Pac.* 181 R-3
Korea Strait, *Pac.* 179 P-14
Korfa Zaliv, *Pac.* 171 O-5
Korff Ice Rise, *Sou.* 105 Q-13
Kosa Biryuchyy Ostriv, *Atl.* 131 U-2
Koshikijima-rettō, *Pac.* 181 U-7
Kotzebue Sound, *Arc.* 97 Q-2

Arc. Arctic Ocean *Atl.* Atlantic Ocean *Ind.* Indian Ocean *Pac.* Pacific Ocean *Sou.* Southern Ocean

Kōzu-shima–Nazca Ridge

Kōzu-shima, *Pac.*	179	V-13
Krms'kyy Pivostriv, *Atl.*	131	S-2
Kronotskiy Zaliv, *Pac.*	177	X-6
Kuchino-Erabu-shima, *Pac.*	181	U-8
Kuchino-shima, *Pac.*	181	V-8
Kumani Canyon, *Atl.*	131	V-3
Kume- jima, *Pac.*	181	T-10
Kundur, *Pac.*	185	O-12
Kupreanof Island, *Pac.*	173	W-4
Kurchatov Fracture Zone, *Atl.*	113	P-6
Kure Atoll, *Pac.*	174	J-3
Kuria Muria, *Ind.*	151	O-5
Kuril Basin, *Pac.*	177	R-9
Kuril Islands, *Pac.*	177	S-9
Kuril-Kamchatka Trench, *Pac.*	177	T-10
Kuro-shima, *Pac.*	181	V-8
Kuskokwim Bay, *Pac.*	171	X-5
Kvichak Bay, *Pac.*	171	Z-5
Kvitøya, *Arc.*	99	R-7
Kyōga-misaki, *Pac.*	179	S-12
Kyūshū, *Pac.*	181	V-7
Kyusyu-Palau Ridge, *Pac.*	183	P-2

L

Lārak, *Ind.*	153	Y-6
La Pérouse Strait, *Pac.*	179	W-6
Labrador Basin, *Arc.*	96	L-13
Labrador Sea, *Arc.*	101	X-13
Laccadive Islands, *Ind.*	151	U-8
Ladd Seamount, *Pac.*	174	K-2
Laesø, *Atl.*	117	O-9
Laguna de Términos, *Atl.*	121	R-9
Laguna Madre, *Atl.*	121	O-4
Laizhou Wan, *Pac.*	181	P-3
Lakor, *Pac.*	189	V-14
Lamon Bay, *Pac.*	185	W-6
Lan Yü, *Pac.*	181	Q-13
Lanai, *Pac.*	175	V-7
Lancaster Sound, *Arc.*	101	Q-7
Land's End, *Atl.*	127	S-1
Landfall Island, *Ind.*	147	V-9
Lands End, *Arc.*	100	K-5
Lane Downe Bank, *Pac.*	197	U-6
Langkawi, *Pac.*	187	P-10
Laptev Sea, *Arc.*	97	V-6
Larat, *Pac.*	189	X-13
Larsen Ice Shelf, *Sou.*	105	P-6
Lassiter Coast, *Sou.*	105	Q-9
Lataday Island, *Sou.*	105	N-9
Latakia Basin, *Atl.*	129	Y-8
Laurentian Channel, *Atl.*	119	U-6
Laurie Island, *Sou.*	105	U-3
Laut, *Pac.*	189	O-11
Lavoisier Island, *Sou.*	105	N-6
Laysan Island, *Pac.*	175	N-4
Lazerov Ice Shelf, *Sou.*	103	U-4
Leeward Islands, *Atl.*	123	V-3
Lemieux Islands, *Arc.*	101	V-12
Lena Tablemount, *Ind.*	155	S-14
Lesbos, *Atl.*	131	N-8
Lesbos Basin, *Atl.*	130	M-8
Lesser Antilles, *Atl.*	123	T-7
Lesser Sunda Islands, *Pac.*	182	I-9
Lesser Tunb, *Ind.*	153	W-7
Leti, *Pac.*	189	U-14
Levantine Basin, *Atl.*	129	V-10
Leven Bank, *Ind.*	157	Y-3
Leyte, *Pac.*	189	S-3
Leyte Gulf, *Pac.*	189	T-3
Liaodong Bandao, *Pac.*	181	Q-2
Liaodong Wan, *Pac.*	181	Q-2
Lifou, *Pac.*	197	X-6
Ligurian Sea, *Atl.*	129	N-5
Lihir Group, *Pac.*	191	W-10
Lihou Reef, *Pac.*	197	R-5
Limmen Bight, *Pac.*	195	S-13
Limnos, *Atl.*	129	U-7
Linapacan, *Pac.*	185	W-7
Lincoln Sea, *Arc.*	101	R-2
Lindeman Island, *Pac.*	199	U-10
Line Islands, *Pac.*	210	J-2
Lingga, *Pac.*	185	P-12
Lisianski Island, *Pac.*	174	L-4
Little America Basin, *Sou.*	107	R-8
Little Andaman, *Ind.*	147	V-10
Little Cayman, *Atl.*	122	M-3
Little Coco Island, *Ind.*	147	V-9
Little Inagua Island, *Atl.*	123	Q-2
Little Nicobar, *Ind.*	147	W-12
Lituya Bay, *Pac.*	173	V-3
Livingston Island, *Sou.*	105	O-4
Lizard Island, *Pac.*	199	R-5
Lizard Point, *Atl.*	127	T-1
Loaita Bank, *Pac.*	185	T-7
Lohatanjona Angadoka, *Ind.*	157	X-4
Loihi Seamount, *Pac.*	175	X-8
Loks Land, *Arc.*	101	V-13
Lolland, *Atl.*	117	O-11
Lomblen, *Pac.*	189	S-14
Lombok, *Pac.*	189	N-14
Lombok Basin, *Pac.*	189	N-15
Lomonosov Ridge, *Arc.*	97	R-9
Long Bay, *Atl.*	124	K-2
Long Island, *Atl.*	119	O-8
Long Island, *Atl.*	123	P-1
Long Island, *Pac.*	199	V-11
Lontar, *Pac.*	189	W-11
Loper Channel, *Sou.*	105	Q-3
Lord Howe Island, *Pac.*	201	S-6
Lord Howe Rise, *Pac.*	201	U-7
Lord Howe Seamount Chain, *Pac.*	197	U-9
Losap, *Pac.*	191	W-6
Lost Dutchmen Ridge, *Ind.*	159	R-8
Loudoun Seamount, *Pac.*	174	L-2
Lougheed Island, *Arc.*	101	N-5
Louisiade Archipelago, *Pac.*	197	R-3
Louisville Ridge, *Pac.*	203	X-3
Low Island, *Sou.*	105	O-4
Lower Cook Islands, *Pac.*	167	Q-11
Lü Tao, *Pac.*	181	Q-12
Lucipara, *Pac.*	189	U-12
Lüderitz Bay, *Atl.*	137	V-7
Luitpold Coast, *Sou.*	105	U-12
Lützow-Holm Bay, *Sou.*	103	V-5
Luzon, *Pac.*	190	K-2
Luzon Strait, *Pac.*	185	W-3
Lyakhovskiye Ostrova, *Arc.*	97	U-4
Lyddan Island, *Sou.*	105	W-11

M

Mcbride Head, *Atl.*	139	Z-1
Macclesfield Bank, *Pac.*	185	S-5
McClintock, *Arc.*	99	T-6
McClintock Channel, *Arc.*	100	M-7
McClure Strait, *Arc.*	100	K-6
McDonald Islands, *Ind.*	163	N-15
McDonald Islands, *Sou.*	103	Y-6
Mackenzie King Island, *Arc.*	100	M-5
McMurdo Sound, *Sou.*	107	W-8
Macquarie Island, *Pac.*	193	P-13
Macquarie Ridge, *Pac.*	201	T-15
Madagascar, *Ind.*	155	S-8
Madagascar Basin, *Ind.*	155	U-9
Madagascar Plateau, *Ind.*	155	T-10
Madagascar Ridge, *Ind.*	155	T-11
Madeira, *Atl.*	113	R-8
Madeira Ridge, *Atl.*	113	R-8
Madingley Rise, *Ind.*	155	V-6
Madura, *Pac.*	185	S-15
Maéwo, *Pac.*	197	X-4
Magellan Rise, *Pac.*	183	Z-6
Magellan Seamounts, *Pac.*	183	T-4
Magnetic Island, *Pac.*	199	S-9
Mai, *Pac.*	189	U-12
Maiao, *Pac.*	213	N-10
Mainland, *Atl.*	115	P-5
Majorca, *Atl.*	128	L-7
Majuro, *Pac.*	183	X-6
Makarov Basin, *Arc.*	97	R-8
Makarov Seamount, *Pac.*	168	M-8
Makassar Basin, *Pac.*	189	P-9
Makassar Strait, *Pac.*	189	P-9
Makatea, *Pac.*	213	O-10
Makemo, *Pac.*	213	Q-10
Makunudhoo Atoll, *Ind.*	151	V-10
Malaita, *Pac.*	197	V-2
Malakula, *Pac.*	197	X-5
Malaspina Glacier, *Pac.*	173	U-2
Mali Kyun, *Pac.*	187	N-3
Malta, *Atl.*	129	Q-8
Malta Plateau, *Atl.*	129	Q-8
Malta Ridge, *Atl.*	129	R-9
Malta Trough, *Atl.*	129	P-8
Mangaia, *Pac.*	212	K-12
Manganari Canyon, *Atl.*	131	P-5
Mangareva, *Pac.*	213	T-12
Mangole, *Pac.*	189	T-10
Manihi, *Pac.*	213	P-9
Manihiki Plateau, *Pac.*	193	X-3
Manila Trench, *Pac.*	185	V-6
Manim, *Pac.*	191	P-9
Mannar Island, *Ind.*	147	O-11
Mansel Island, *Arc.*	96	K-9
Manuae, *Pac.*	212	K-11
Manuhangi, *Pac.*	213	Q-11
Manui, *Pac.*	189	S-11
Manus Basin, *Pac.*	197	Q-1
Manus Island, *Pac.*	191	T-9
Manus Trench, *Pac.*	191	T-8
Mapin, *Pac.*	189	P-5
Mapmakers Seamounts, *Pac.*	183	V-2
Maré, *Pac.*	197	X-7
Marguerite Bay, *Sou.*	105	O-7
Maria, *Pac.*	213	T-12
Mariana Islands, *Pac.*	191	U-1
Mariana Ridge, *Pac.*	191	T-3
Mariana Trench, *Pac.*	191	S-4
Mariana Trough, *Pac.*	191	T-1
Marie Byrd Canyon, *Sou.*	107	N-9
Marie Byrd Land, *Sou.*	103	O-9
Marie Byrd Seamount, *Sou.*	103	O-9
Marie-Galante, *Atl.*	123	Y-5
Marinduque, *Pac.*	189	R-2
Marion Dufresne Seamount, *Ind.*	162	K-15
Marion Reef, *Pac.*	199	X-9
Marmara, *Atl.*	131	O-7
Marmara Trough, *Atl.*	131	O-7
Maro Reef, *Pac.*	175	N-4
Marokau, *Pac.*	213	Q-11
Marotiri, *Pac.*	213	Q-14
Marquesas Fracture Zone, *Pac.*	213	R-8
Marquesas Islands, *Pac.*	213	R-6
Marquesas Keys, *Atl.*	121	X-5
Marsh Island, *Atl.*	121	R-3
Marshall Islands, *Pac.*	183	V-5
Marshall Seamounts, *Pac.*	183	W-5
Martin Vaz Fracture Zone, *Atl.*	133	R-6
Martinique Passage, *Atl.*	123	X-6
Marutea, *Pac.*	213	Q-10
Masalembu Besar, *Pac.*	185	T-15
Masalembu Kecil, *Pac.*	185	T-14
Masbate, *Pac.*	189	S-2
Mascarene Basin, *Ind.*	155	U-7
Mascarene Plain, *Ind.*	155	U-8
Mascarene Plateau, *Ind.*	155	U-6
Mashābih, *Ind.*	149	R-5
Massawa Channel, *Ind.*	149	T-11
Matagorda Bay, *Atl.*	121	P-3
Matagorda Island, *Atl.*	121	O-4
Mataiva, *Pac.*	213	N-9
Matak, *Pac.*	185	P-11
Mathematicians Seamounts, *Pac.*	205	S-4
Matsu Tao, *Pac.*	181	P-10
Matutuang, *Pac.*	189	T-6
Maud Rise, *Sou.*	103	S-3
Maug Islands, *Pac.*	191	T-1
Mauha Loa, *Pac.*	175	X-8
Maui, *Pac.*	175	W-7
Mauke, *Pac.*	212	L-11
Mauna Kea, *Pac.*	175	W-7
Maupihaa, *Pac.*	212	M-10
Maupiti, *Pac.*	212	M-10
Mauritius, *Ind.*	155	V-8
Mauritius Trench, *Ind.*	155	U-9
Maury Channel, *Atl.*	113	Q-5
Mawson Bank, *Sou.*	107	V-12
Mawson Sea, *Sou.*	103	X-11
Maya, *Pac.*	185	Q-13
Mayaguana Island, *Atl.*	123	R-2
Mayotte, *Ind.*	155	T-7
Mayu, *Pac.*	189	T-8
Mazarron Escarpment, *Atl.*	128	K-8
Medina Bank, *Atl.*	129	Q-9
Medina Escarpment, *Atl.*	129	Q-9
Mediterranean Sea, *Atl.*	129	R-8
Mehetia, *Pac.*	213	O-10
Melanesian Basin, *Pac.*	183	V-7
Melita Valley, *Atl.*	129	Q-9
Mellish Reef, *Pac.*	197	T-5
Melville Fracture Zone, *Ind.*	162	M-11
Melville Island, *Arc.*	100	M-6
Melville Island, *Pac.*	195	O-10
Melville Peninsula, *Arc.*	101	P-11
Menard Fracture Zone, *Pac.*	211	O-9
Mendana Fracture Zone, *Pac.*	205	W-10
Mendeleyev Ridge, *Arc.*	97	S-6
Mendelssohn Seamount, *Pac.*	175	S-4
Mer d'Iroise, *Atl.*	127	T-4
Mercury Seamount, *Pac.*	174	L-2
Mergui Archipelago, *Ind.*	147	Y-10
Merir, *Pac.*	191	O-7
Mernoo Bank, *Pac.*	203	S-5
Meta Incognita Peninsula, *Arc.*	101	T-12
Meteor Rise, *Atl.*	133	W-11
Miangas, *Pac.*	189	U-6
Miaodao Qundao, *Pac.*	181	P-3
Mid-Adriatic Basin, *Atl.*	129	Q-5
Midai, *Pac.*	185	Q-11
Mid-Atlantic Ridge, *Atl.*	111	F-16
Middle America Trench, *Pac.*	205	U-4
Middle Andaman, *Ind.*	147	V-9
Middle Bank, *Pac.*	175	T-6
Middle Brooks Bank, *Pac.*	175	Q-5
Middle Island, *Pac.*	199	V-11
Middle Mariana Ridge, *Pac.*	191	T-1
Middleton Reef, *Pac.*	201	T-5
Mid-Indian Basin, *Ind.*	163	O-7
Mid-Indian Ridge, *Ind.*	162	M-5
Mid-Pacific Mountains, *Pac.*	183	V-4
Midway Islands, *Pac.*	174	K-3
Mikura-jima, *Pac.*	179	V-14
Mill Island, *Arc.*	101	R-13
Millennium, *Pac.*	213	N-7
Miller Seamount, *Pac.*	173	S-6
Milwaukee Deep, *Atl.*	123	U-3
Minas Basin, *Atl.*	119	Q-7
Minas Channel, *Atl.*	119	P-7
Mindanao, *Pac.*	190	L-6
Mindoro, *Pac.*	185	W-6
Mindoro Strait, *Pac.*	185	V-6
Minicoy Island, *Ind.*	151	V-9
Minna Bluff, *Sou.*	107	V-7
Minorca, *Atl.*	128	M-7
Miquelon, *Atl.*	119	V-6
Miramichi Bay, *Atl.*	119	Q-6
Mirtoon Basin, *Atl.*	129	T-8
Miscou Island, *Atl.*	119	Q-5
Mi-shima, *Pac.*	179	Q-13
Misoöl, *Pac.*	189	W-10
Mississippi Fan, *Atl.*	121	T-4
Mississippi Sound, *Atl.*	121	T-2
Misteriosa Bank, *Atl.*	122	K-4
Misurata Valley, *Atl.*	129	Q-9
Mitiaro, *Pac.*	212	K-11
Miyake-jima, *Pac.*	179	V-13
Moa, *Pac.*	189	U-13
Moa Island, *Pac.*	195	X-9
Mobile Bay, *Atl.*	121	T-2
Mocha Fracture Zone, *Pac.*	211	V-8
Mohéli, *Ind.*	157	V-3
Mohns Ridge, *Arc.*	98	M-10
Molokai, *Pac.*	175	W-7
Molokai Fracture Zone, *Pac.*	175	X-7
Molu, *Pac.*	195	P-7
Molucca Sea, *Pac.*	189	T-9
Moluccas, *Pac.*	189	U-9
Møn, *Atl.*	117	O-11
Monaco Basin, *Atl.*	113	Q-8
Mono Rise, *Atl.*	123	N-8
Montague Island, *Pac.*	173	R-2
Monterey Bay, *Pac.*	207	O-4
Monterey Canyon, *Pac.*	207	O-4
Monterey Fan, *Pac.*	207	O-4
Moonless Mountains, *Pac.*	167	S-6
Moonless Seamounts, *Pac.*	169	V-8
Moore Embayment, *Sou.*	107	V-7
Moorea, *Pac.*	213	N-10
Morane, *Pac.*	213	S-12
Moray Firth, *Atl.*	115	P-6
Moresby Island, *Pac.*	173	X-6
Moreton Seamount, *Pac.*	197	T-8
Mornington Abyssal Plain, *Pac.*	211	V-10
Mornington Island, *Pac.*	195	U-14
Moro Gulf, *Pac.*	189	R-5
Moromaho, *Pac.*	189	S-12
Morotai, *Pac.*	189	V-8
Mortlock Islands, *Pac.*	191	W-6
Morton Seamount, *Pac.*	173	S-7
Mosquito Coast, *Atl.*	122	L-7
Motsuta-misaki, *Pac.*	179	V-8
Motu One, *Pac.*	212	M-10
Moubray Bay, *Sou.*	107	V-13
Mount's Bay, *Atl.*	127	T-1
Mouth of the Yangtze, *Pac.*	181	Q-7
Mouths of the Danube, *Atl.*	131	P-3
Mouths of the Mekong, *Pac.*	185	P-8
Moyo, *Pac.*	189	O-13
Mozambique Basin, *Ind.*	157	R-14
Mozambique Channel, *Ind.*	157	R-10
Mozambique Escarpment, *Ind.*	155	R-11
Mozambique Plateau, *Ind.*	157	P-15
Mozambique Ridge, *Ind.*	155	R-11
Muertos Trough, *Atl.*	123	S-5
Muhu, *Atl.*	117	V-8
Mui Ca Mau, *Pac.*	187	V-8
Mukawwar, *Ind.*	149	R-8
Muna, *Pac.*	189	R-12
Murilo Atoll, *Pac.*	191	W-5
Murman Rise, *Arc.*	97	U-12
Muroto-zaki, *Pac.*	179	S-14
Murray Fracture Zone, *Pac.*	169	T-8
Murray Ridge, *Ind.*	151	R-3
Mururoa, *Pac.*	213	S-12
Musandam Peninsula, *Ind.*	153	X-7
Musicians Seamounts, *Pac.*	175	T-4
Mussau Island, *Pac.*	191	U-9
Mussau Trough, *Pac.*	191	V-8
Mustique, *Atl.*	123	X-7
Mutsu-wan, *Pac.*	179	W-9
Mwokil, *Pac.*	191	Z-6
Mys Alevina, *Pac.*	177	T-3
Mys Aniva, *Pac.*	179	Y-6
Mys Ayya, *Atl.*	131	S-4
Mys Chauda, *Atl.*	131	U-3
Mys Chukotskiy, *Pac.*	171	U-3
Mys Dezhneva, *Pac.*	171	W-2
Mys Duga-Zapadnaya, *Pac.*	177	R-3
Mys Elizavety, *Pac.*	177	Q-5
Mys Govena, *Pac.*	171	O-5
Mys Kazantip, *Atl.*	131	U-3
Mys Khersones, *Atl.*	131	S-3
Mys Kril'on, *Pac.*	179	X-6
Mys Lopatka, *Pac.*	177	W-7
Mys Navarin, *Pac.*	171	S-4
Mys Olyutorskiy, *Pac.*	171	Q-5
Mys Tarkhankut, *Atl.*	131	R-3
Mys Terpeniya, *Pac.*	177	R-8
Mys Tolstoy, *Pac.*	177	V-3
Mys Yevpatoriys'kyy, *Atl.*	131	R-3
Mys Yuzhnyy, *Pac.*	177	V-4

N

Naifeh Seamount, *Pac.*	175	O-3
Nakadōri-shima, *Pac.*	181	U-6
Nakano-shima, *Pac.*	181	V-8
Namib Desert, *Atl.*	137	V-4
Namibia Abyssal Plain, *Atl.*	137	S-6
Namoluk, *Pac.*	191	V-6
Namonuito, *Pac.*	191	U-5
Nancowry, *Ind.*	147	W-12
Nankai Trough, *Pac.*	179	S-15
Nanri Dao, *Pac.*	181	P-11
Nansei-Shotō Ridge, *Pac.*	181	R-12
Nansei-Shotō Trench, *Pac.*	181	R-12
Nansen Basin, *Arc.*	99	R-5
Nansen Sound, *Arc.*	101	P-3
Napuka, *Pac.*	213	R-9
Narcondam Island, *Ind.*	147	X-9
Nares Abyssal Plain, *Atl.*	112	K-9
Nares Strait, *Arc.*	101	R-3
Narva Bay, *Atl.*	117	X-7
Natal Basin, *Ind.*	155	R-12
Natal Seamount, *Ind.*	155	P-11
Natal Valley, *Ind.*	155	Q-10
Natuna Besar, *Pac.*	185	Q-10
Natuna Sea, *Pac.*	185	P-12
Naturaliste Fracture Zone, *Ind.*	159	S-10
Naturaliste Plateau, *Ind.*	159	T-10
Nauru, *Pac.*	183	W-8
Navassa Island, *Atl.*	123	P-4
Nazareth Bank, *Ind.*	162	M-8
Nazca Ridge, *Pac.*	211	W-4

Arc. Arctic Ocean *Atl.* Atlantic Ocean *Ind.* Indian Ocean *Pac.* Pacific Ocean *Sou.* Southern Ocean

Arc. Arctic Ocean *Atl.* Atlantic Ocean *Ind.* Indian Ocean *Pac.* Pacific Ocean *Sou.* Southern Ocean